Geometry and Analysis of Projective Spaces

A Series of Books in Mathematics

R. A. Rosenbaum, EDITOR

Introduction to Matrices and Linear Transformations
  Daniel T. Finkbeiner, II

Introduction to Probability and Statistics (Third Edition)
  Henry L. Alder and Edward B. Roessler

The USSR Olympiad Problem Book: Selected Problems and Theorems of
  Elementary Mathematics
  D. O. Shklarsky, N. N. Chentzov, and I. M. Yaglom

Mathematics: The Man-made Universe
  Sherman K. Stein

Set Theory and Logic
  Robert R. Stoll

Problems in Differential Equations
  J. L. Brenner

Foundations of Linear Algebra
  A. I. Mal'cev

Computational Methods of Linear Algebra
  D. K. Faddeev and V. N. Faddeeva

Geometry and Analysis of Projective Spaces
  C. E. Springer

Golden Gate Editions

A Concrete Approach to Abstract Algebra
  W. W. Sawyer

A Modern View of Geometry
  Leonard M. Blumenthal

Sets, Logic, and Axiomatic Theories
  Robert R. Stoll

The Solution of Equations in Integers
  A. O. Gelfond

An Elementary Introduction to the Theory of Probability
  B. V. Gnedenko and A. Ya. Khinchin

The Real Number System in an Algebraic Setting
  J. B. Roberts

Elements of Astromechanics
  Peter van de Kamp

Geometry and Analysis of
Projective Spaces

C. E. SPRINGER

The University of Oklahoma

W. H. FREEMAN AND COMPANY

San Francisco and London

TO MY DAUGHTER *Susanne*

Preface

The purpose of this book is to provide an elementary introduction to many important and significant concepts from the elegant field of projective geometry, not only for the use of undergraduate and graduate students of mathematics but also for teachers of high school geometry. Teachers of euclidean geometry may also use the material offered here to augment their knowledge of and enthusiasm for their subject by becoming acquainted with the role of euclidean geometry as a specialized type of projective geometry. Accordingly, a distinguishing feature of the book is the unusual extent to which projective concepts are given metric interpretations in the euclidean plane. Projective concepts are introduced gradually by means of metric notions, but the projective significance appears at a later stage. This approach should be a meaningful one for the reader who has had no experience with projective geometry. An axiomatic development is not employed—partly because the novice is not ready to appreciate fully such a treatment, and partly because the harvest of interesting results is much reduced if the reader must always be concerned with the succession of theorems necessary to prove a given statement.

The plan of the book is to give first a rather thorough development of the geometry of points on a projective line, and then to extend the ideas, in turn, to two- and higher-dimensional projective spaces. Because of the leisurely pace and the explanation of new techniques from algebra and analysis as they are needed, much of the material can be read by one with only a knowledge of college algebra and trigonometry. However, for some sections of the book a knowledge of analytical geometry and the elementary calculus is assumed. The tensor notation is introduced gradually, for the purpose of abbreviation and to prepare the reader to comprehend the tensor concept used in Chapter 8, on the conic. The lists of exercises contain not only routine problems designed to test understanding of the text and of the illustrative examples but also problems to test the reader's ability to generalize certain parts of the textual material. In many cases, hints are offered for the solution of the latter type of exercises.

There is sufficient material for use in two three-hour courses, although topics for a one-semester course may be selected. The common practice of "starring" those sections which may be omitted without disturbing the continuity of the course is not followed here. Rather it is considered advisable to leave the selection of topics to the teacher according to the interests of himself and of his class. In recent lectures in a one-semester three-hour course on analytic projective geometry at the University of Oklahoma, I omitted the last two sections of Chapter 3, the last two sections of Chapter 5, and Chapter 10. Because Chapters 9 and 10 are independent of each other, some classes may prefer to omit Chapter 9.

I wish to express my deep appreciation to Mr. Donald Wayne Calvin for doing part of the proofreading and preparation of the index during my absence on vacation.

C. E. SPRINGER

Norman, Oklahoma
  January, 1964

Contents

Chapter 8. *The Conic*

Chapter 9. *Noneuclidean Geometries*

Chapter 10. *Higher-Dimensional Geometry*

CHAPTER 1

Homographies in One Dimension

1-1. Point set on a line

As in analytical geometry, it is often useful to establish a one-to-one correspondence between the real numbers and the points of a straight line. Select an origin point O (with abscissa zero) and a unit point U to the right of O on the horizontal line, so that U has abscissa 1. Then any point P with abscissa x is to the right of O if x is positive or left of O if x is negative. For any two points $P_1(x_1)$ and $P_2(x_2)$, the segment P_1P_2 is oriented in the positive direction if $x_2 > x_1$ and in the negative direction if $x_2 < x_1$. Note that for the directed segments P_1P_2 and P_2P_1 it is true that

$$P_1P_2 + P_2P_1 = (OP_2 - OP_1) + (OP_1 - OP_2) = 0,$$

from which $P_1P_2 = -P_2P_1$ for any two points P_1, P_2 on the line, and that $P_1P_2 + P_2P_3 + P_3P_1 = 0$ for any three points on the line. The numerical value of the length of the segment P_1P_2, regardless of its orientation, is denoted by $|P_1P_2|$ or by the absolute value $|x_2 - x_1|$. It is essential to distinguish between a directed line segment, say, P_1P_2, and the number (with the appropriate sign) that indicates its length and orientation. Two distinct directed line segments may have the same length and the same orientation.

EXAMPLE

If P_1, P_2, P_3 have abscissas -2, 3, 5, what number is associated with $P_1P_2 + P_3P_1$?

Solution: Here $P_1P_2 = x_2 - x_1 = 3 - (-2) = 5$, and $P_3P_1 = x_1 - x_3 = -2 - 5 = -7$. Hence, $P_1P_2 + P_3P_1 = 5 - 7 = -2$.

1-2. Mappings between two point sets

A few elementary examples will introduce some notions that will be helpful in the later study of projective geometry of a straight line. (Hereafter, *line* will mean straight line.) Consider two oriented lines l and $\bar{l}$—not necessarily coplanar. Employ an abscissa x with origin O on l and an abscissa $\bar{x}$ with origin $\bar{O}$ on $\bar{l}$. If the function $f(x)$ is defined (and single-valued) for every x, then $\bar{x} = f(x)$ assigns a point $\bar{P}$ on $\bar{l}$ for every point P on l. The equation $\bar{x} = f(x)$ is called a mapping of l onto $\bar{l}$. The function f determines the nature of the mapping. For instance, the mapping $\bar{x} = \sin x$ takes all points of line l into a segment of length two on $\bar{l}$. The points x, $x + 2\pi$, $x + 4\pi$, $\cdots$ on l map into a single point on $\bar{l}$ so the mapping is not one-to-one. For an instance of a one-to-one mapping consider

EXAMPLE 1

Discuss the mapping M: $\bar{x} = 2x + 3$ between two parallel lines.

Solution: To effect this mapping the abscissa x is doubled and then 3 is added to obtain $\bar{x}$. Thus, for instances, $x = -4 \to \bar{x} = -5$, $x = 0 \to \bar{x} = 3$, and $x = 2 \to \bar{x} = 7$. Figure 1 shows how the points on l are "spread" into the points

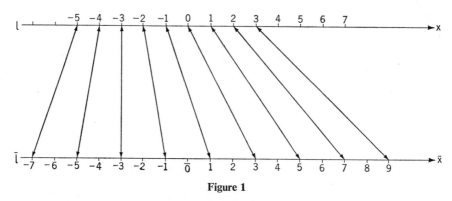

Figure 1

on $\bar{l}$. To every x a unique value of $\bar{x}$ is found, and therefore to every point P on l there corresponds a unique point $\bar{P}$ on $\bar{l}$.

The inverse of the mapping M, denoted by M^{-1}, is given by

$$M^{-1}:   \quad x = \frac{1}{2}\bar{x} - \frac{3}{2}.$$

It is evident that to every $\bar{x}$ there corresponds a unique x and therefore that each point $\bar{P}$ on $\bar{l}$ has a unique image P on l. Hence, one may write $x = -4 \leftrightarrow \bar{x} = -5$, $x = 0 \leftrightarrow \bar{x} = 3$, and $x = 2 \leftrightarrow \bar{x} = 7$. The mapping is clearly one-to-one. Furthermore, it is apparent in this example that the mapping is *continuous*, which means that nearby points on l map into nearby points on $\bar{l}$. More precisely, this means that for any arbitrarily small neighborhood $\bar{N}$ of points about $\bar{P}$, say, there is always a neighborhood N of points about the image point P such that the points of N map into the set $\bar{N}$. For instance, can a set on l be found which will map into the interval $2 - \epsilon < \bar{x} < 2 + \epsilon$ on $\bar{l}$? The desired set is given by $(-1 - \epsilon)/2 < x < (-1 + \epsilon)/2$, for arbitrarily small positive ϵ.

It will be seen later that the mapping $\bar{x} = f(x)$—with $f(x)$ a linear function of x, as in Example 1—is a special case of a more general mapping called a *projectivity* (or, equivalently, a *homography*). In turn, the projectivities (or homographies) are special cases of a more general type of mapping called a *topological mapping* (or, equivalently, a *homeomorphism*). In contrast to Ex-

ample 1, which is a continuous one-to-one mapping between two euclidean lines
l and $\bar{l}$, we will now consider an example that is not everywhere continuous.
Indeed, it will be seen to be undefined at one point.

EXAMPLE 2

Discuss the mapping M: $\bar{x} = 1/(x - 2)$.

Solution: The inverse M^{-1} is given by $x = (2\bar{x} + 1)/\bar{x}$. A glance at M and M^{-1}
will reveal that unusual behavior is expected for points near $x = 2$ on l and for

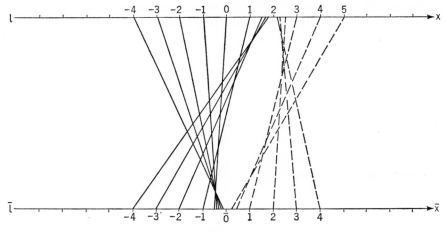

Figure 2

points near $\bar{x} = 0$ on $\bar{l}$. In Fig. 2 the solid lines join corresponding points for $x < 2$
on l.

Note that $x = 0 \leftrightarrow \bar{x} = -\frac{1}{2}$, $x = 1 \leftrightarrow \bar{x} = -1$, $x = \frac{3}{2} \leftrightarrow \bar{x} = -2$. Furthermore,
$x = 1.99 \leftrightarrow \bar{x} = -100$ and $x = 1.999 \leftrightarrow \bar{x} = -1000$. The point $\bar{P}(\bar{x})$ on $\bar{l}$ recedes
farther and farther to the left on $\bar{l}$ as $P(x)$ on l approaches $x = 2$ from the left on l.
There is no point on $\bar{l}$ corresponding to $x = 2$ on l. The dotted lines in Fig. 2 join
corresponding points for $x > 2$ on l. Note that $x = 5 \leftrightarrow \bar{x} = \frac{1}{3}$, $x = 4 \leftrightarrow \bar{x} = \frac{1}{2}$,
$x = 3 \leftrightarrow \bar{x} = 1$, and that $x = \frac{5}{2} \leftrightarrow \bar{x} = 2$, $x = 2.01 \leftrightarrow \bar{x} = 100$, $x = 2.001 \leftrightarrow \bar{x} =$
1000. As x approaches 2 from the right, $\bar{x}$ becomes greater in the positive direction.
As x approaches 2 from either side there is a unique point on $\bar{l}$ corresponding to
each point on l, but at $x = 2$ on l a corresponding point on $\bar{l}$ does not exist. From
M^{-1} a similar situation exists relative to the point where $\bar{x} = 0$. There is no point
on l corresponding to $\bar{x} = 0$ on $\bar{l}$. The mapping M from l to $\bar{l}$ is discontinuous at
$x = 2$, and M^{-1} is discontinuous at $\bar{x} = 0$.

Remark: In Fig. 2 the lines l and $\bar{l}$ were taken as parallel. This is not necessary. Note that lines joining corresponding points on l and $\bar{l}$ under the mapping
of Example 2 appear to outline a curve to which the lines are tangents. There
is actually such a curve, and it is called the *envelope* of the lines joining corresponding points under the mapping M. (It will be shown later that this curve
is a conic section. See Exercise 10.)

EXERCISES

1. Construct a figure for Example 2 with l and $\bar{l}$ coplanar but not parallel. Select arbitrarily an origin and a unit point on each line and then draw a sufficient number of lines joining corresponding points on l and $\bar{l}$ to observe that these lines are apparently tangent to a curve.

2. Now let l and $\bar{l}$ be noncoplanar in Example 2. What do you visualize as the locus of the lines joining corresponding points on l and $\bar{l}$?

3. In Example 1, let l and $\bar{l}$ be coplanar. What is the envelope of the lines joining corresponding points (a) in case l and $\bar{l}$ are parallel? (b) in case l and $\bar{l}$ are not parallel?

4. In Example 1, let lines l and $\bar{l}$ coincide, with O at $\bar{O}$, and let the unit point be the same for both lines. Are there points which map into themselves?

5. Let l and $\bar{l}$ coincide as in Exercise 4. Find the points that remain fixed under the mapping of Example 2.

6. At what point is the mapping $\bar{x} = (ax + b)/(cx + d)$ discontinuous? Find the inverse mapping. At what point is it discontinuous?

7. Consider a family of straight lines represented by $f(x, y, \sigma) = 0$, where f is a linear function of x and y, and σ is a parameter. For any σ, $f(x, y, \sigma) = 0$ and $f(x, y, \sigma + \Delta\sigma) = 0$ may be said to represent "neighboring" lines of the family. The linear combination

$$\frac{f(x, y, \sigma + \Delta\sigma) - f(x, y, \sigma)}{\Delta\sigma} = 0$$

of two neighboring lines contains the intersection of the lines. Let $\Delta\sigma \to 0$ to arrive at $\partial f/\partial\sigma = 0$. The intersection of the lines $f(x, y, \sigma) = 0$, $\partial f/\partial\sigma = 0$, is called the *characteristic* point of the line $f(x, y, \sigma) = 0$, and the locus of the characteristic points, as σ varies, is the *envelope* of the family $f(x, y, \sigma) = 0$. Show that the envelope of the family $f(x, y, \sigma) = 0$ is obtained by eliminating σ from the equations

$$f(x, y, \sigma) = 0, \quad \frac{\partial f(x, y, \sigma)}{\partial\sigma} = 0.$$

8. Use the type of development in Exercise 7 to show how to find the envelope of a family of curves $F(x, y, \sigma) = 0$, where $F(x, y, \sigma) = 0$ is not linear in x and y.

9. Find the envelope of the family of lines $x \cos\theta + y \sin\theta - a = 0$.

   Ans. $x^2 + y^2 = a^2$.

10. (a) Show that the envelope of lines joining corresponding points $P(\sigma)$ and $\bar{P}(\bar{\sigma})$ on two parallel lines under the mapping $\bar{\sigma} = 1/(\sigma - 2)$ is a conic. *Suggestion:* Let $P(\sigma)$ be the point with coordinates $(\sigma, 0)$ on the x axis, and $\bar{P}(\bar{\sigma})$ the point with coordinates $(1/(\sigma - 2), a)$ on the line $y = a$. The equation of $P\bar{P}$ is then

$$y = \frac{a(\sigma - 2)}{1 + 2\sigma - \sigma^2}(x - \sigma).$$

Eliminate σ from this equation and its derivative with respect to σ to obtain

$$a^2x^2 + 4axy + 8y^2 - 4a^2x - 12ay + 4a^2 = 0.$$

Verify that this is an ellipse, and that the tangents to it at $(2, 0)$ and $(0, a)$ are the lines $y = 0$ and $y = a$, respectively.

(b) Show analytically that if the distance between the parallel lines in Example 1 is a and the point $\overline{O}$ is taken as origin and the y axis is the line $\overline{O}O$, the envelope of the lines joining points $(\sigma, 0)$ and $((\sigma - 3)/2, a)$ is the point $(-3, 2a)$.

1-3. A model for the euclidean line

Draw a circle C and a tangent line $\bar{l}$ to it at point S (Fig. 3). Take point N on C diametrically opposite S. A mapping of points on C to points on $\bar{l}$ is effected by drawing rays through N. For instance, the correspondent of any point A is the point $\overline{A}$ on $\bar{l}$ where the ray NA intersects $\bar{l}$. Under this mapping the point S maps into itself. To every point on the circle there is a unique point on the line, *with one exception*. The tangent line l to C at N has no point in common with line $\bar{l}$ in euclidean geometry. If point N is

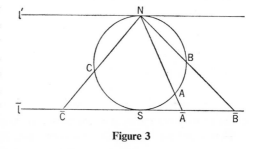

Figure 3

deleted from the circle, then a one-to-one correspondence exists between the remaining points of the circle and the points of line l. One may say that the circle with one point deleted is a *model* for the euclidean line. Note that a point cannot describe a continuous path from C to B by way of N. The only continuous path is by the route CAB on the circle, and therefore the continuous path for the corresponding point on $\bar{l}$ is $\overline{C}\overline{A}\overline{B}$.

It is desirable to have a point on $\bar{l}$ which is the correspondent of point N. Let such a point be postulated for line $\bar{l}$ and denote it by $\overline{N}$. (It may be called the *ideal* point on $\bar{l}$.) With the addition of point $\overline{N}$ to the euclidean line $\bar{l}$ every point on the closed (complete) circle C has a correspondent on $\bar{l}$. The closed circle may be styled a *model* for the point set composed of the euclidean line augmented by one point. The augmented euclidean line is called the *projective line*, or a projective space of one dimension. Because the points of the closed circle are in one-to-one correspondence with the points of the projective line, the latter is seen to be a closed space. The addition of the ideal point to the euclidean line may appear artificial at this stage; however, it will be seen in the next section that the name "ideal point" is merely used for a pair of numbers.

It should be noted here that the concept of "betweenness" is not the same for the euclidean and the projective line. Because the only path from $\overline{C}$ to $\overline{B}$ on the euclidean line $\bar{l}$ is by way of $\overline{A}$, the point $\overline{A}$ can be described as "between" $\overline{C}$ and $\overline{B}$. But for the projective line (or its model, the circle) C can go to B by way of A or by way of N, and therefore $\overline{C}$ can go to $\overline{B}$ by way of $\overline{A}$ or by way of $\overline{N}$. Hence we may say that $\overline{B}$ is not between $\overline{C}$ and $\overline{A}$ on the euclidean line, but that $\overline{B}$ is between $\overline{C}$ and $\overline{A}$ on the (closed) projective line. The concept of closing the euclidean line to obtain the projective line will be extended later by adding a line to the euclidean plane to obtain the projective plane. Indeed, euclidean n-space is enlarged to projective n-space by a similar device.

1-4. Homogeneous coordinates

On the euclidean line a coordinate system was effected by a one-to-one correspondence between the points of the line and the real numbers. To a point P corresponds its abscissa x, a real number. It is proposed next to assign a *number pair* to each point. (Although a number pair may represent a point in a two-dimensional coordinate system, the pair represents a point of a line here because only the ratio of the numbers of the pair is significant.) Replace x by the pair $(x_1 : x_2)$, where $x = x_1/x_2$, with the understanding that the pair $(kx_1 : kx_2)$ represents the same point as $(x_1 : x_2)$ with $k \neq 0$. The pair $(0 : 0)$ will be excluded. Note that the pair $(4 : 2)$ is equivalent to $(2 : 1)$, that $(0 : 4)$ is equivalent to $(0 : 1)$, and that $(4 : 0)$ is equivalent to $(1 : 0)$, in the sense that equivalent number pairs represent the same point. All abscissas on the euclidean line can be written as ratios of number pairs, $x = x_1/x_2 = kx_1/kx_2$, with $k \neq 0$. The pair $(x_1 : x_2)$ with $x_2 = 0$ is not a point of the euclidean line. The coordinates $(x_1 : 0) \equiv (1 : 0)$ may be assigned to the ideal point on the projective line, or it may be said that the ideal point is the point with allowable coordinates $(1 : 0)$. Indeed, the projective line may be defined as the set made up of the totality of ordered number pairs $(x_1 : x_2)$, with $(kx_1 : kx_2)$ equivalent to $(x_1 : x_2)$, and with $k \neq 0$.

It will be found *convenient* to use number pairs as coordinates in euclidean space and *necessary* in projective space. If x is replaced by x_1/x_2, then x_1 and x_2 are called homogeneous coordinates in one dimension. On replacing x and $\bar{x}$ by x_1/x_2 and $\bar{x}_1/\bar{x}_2$ in Example 1 of Section 1-2, one obtains the mapping

(1)
$$\frac{\bar{x}_1}{\bar{x}_2} = 2\frac{x_1}{x_2} + 3 = \frac{2x_1 + 3x_2}{x_2},$$

which can be expressed in equivalent form by the two equations

(2)
$$k\bar{x}_1 = 2x_1 + 3x_2,$$
$$k\bar{x}_2 = x_2.$$

Equations (2) are readily seen to be equivalent to equation (1) by dividing the first equation in (2) by the second. The point at $x = 1$ on l may now be given coordinates $x_1 = 1$, $x_2 = 1$, so that the corresponding point on $\bar{l}$ is given by

$$k\bar{x}_1 = 2(1) + 3(1) = 5,$$

$$k\bar{x}_2 = 1.$$

Thus, the corresponding value of $\bar{x}$ is $5/1$.

It is to be noticed here that under the mapping in (2), the point with coordinates (1:0) yields $k\bar{x}_1 = 2$, $k\bar{x}_2 = 0$, so the point corresponding to (1:0) is the point (2:0), i.e., the point (1:0). Thus, one property of the mapping in Example 1 of Section 1-2 is that the ideal point on l maps into the ideal point on $\bar{l}$. Any mapping of the type

(3)
$$k\bar{x}_1 = ax_1 + bx_2,$$
$$k\bar{x}_2 = x_2,$$

(or of the equivalent type $\bar{x} = ax + b$ in nonhomogeneous coordinates), where $a \neq 0$, takes the ideal point into the ideal point. It is called an *affine* mapping in one dimension. The inverse of the mapping in (3), given by

$$\sigma x_1 = \bar{x}_1 - b\bar{x}_2,$$
$$\sigma x_2 = \qquad a\bar{x}_2,$$

where $\sigma = a/k$ is an arbitrary nonzero number, is also an affine mapping.

It will be instructive to see the form of Example 2 in Section 1-2 in homogeneous coordinates. One finds

$$\frac{\bar{x}_1}{\bar{x}_2} = \frac{x_2}{x_1 - 2x_2},$$

or, equivalently,

(4)
$$k\bar{x}_1 = x_2,$$
$$k\bar{x}_2 = x_1 - 2x_2,$$

with the inverse

(5)
$$\sigma x_1 = 2\bar{x}_1 + \bar{x}_2,$$
$$\sigma x_2 = \bar{x}_1.$$

Note that from (4) the pair (1:1) on $l \leftrightarrow (-1:1)$ on $\bar{l}$, and that the point (2:1) on $l \leftrightarrow (1:0)$ on $\bar{l}$. Thus, the point with abscissa 2 on l maps into the ideal point on $\bar{l}$. Also note from (5) that the point (0:1) on $\bar{l} \leftrightarrow (1:0)$ on l. Thus, the point with abscissa zero on $\bar{l}$ maps into the ideal point on l.

The discussion of Example 2 showed that no point on the euclidean line $\bar{l}$ corresponds to $x = 2$ on l; but if $\bar{l}$ is a projective line, it is now seen that $x = 2$ on l has a correspondent in the ideal point on $\bar{l}$. Similarly, the point $\bar{x} = 0$ on $\bar{l}$ has the ideal point on the projective line l as its unique correspondent.

Whereas equations (2) are a particular instance of the general affine mapping (3) on a line, equations (4) exhibit a particular instance of the general mapping expressed by

(5')
$$k\bar{x}_1 = ax_1 + bx_2,$$
$$k\bar{x}_2 = cx_1 + dx_2,$$

where a, b, c, d are arbitrary real numbers. By division, equations (5) take the form of the single equation

$$\frac{\bar{x}_1}{\bar{x}_2} = \frac{ax_1 + bx_2}{cx_1 + dx_2} = \frac{a\dfrac{x_1}{x_2} + b}{c\dfrac{x_1}{x_2} + d},$$

or

(6) $M:$ $\bar{x} = \dfrac{ax + b}{cx + d}.$

The relation (6) between abscissas x and $\bar{x}$ determines a mapping M of points on l to points on $\bar{l}$. The inverse mapping M^{-1} is obtained by solving (6) to obtain

(7) $M^{-1}:$ $x = \dfrac{-d\bar{x} + b}{c\bar{x} - a}.$

Either M or M^{-1} is called a *homography* between lines l and $\bar{l}$. The term *projectivity* is also used for the mapping M (or M^{-1}). A geometrical meaning for the term projectivity will be seen later. Meanwhile, some fundamental facts relative to equation (6) will be set forth. This section will conclude with a homogeneous form of equation (6) which is equivalent to (5′) in a more convenient form. Write $a = a_{11}$, $b = a_{12}$, $c = a_{21}$, $d = a_{22}$ to have

(8)
$$k\bar{x}_1 = a_{11}x_1 + a_{12}x_2 = \sum_{j=1}^{2} a_{1j}x_j,$$

$$k\bar{x}_2 = a_{21}x_1 + a_{22}x_2 = \sum_{j=1}^{2} a_{2j}x_j.$$

The two equations (8) can be written as

(9) $k\bar{x}_i = \sum_{j=1}^{2} a_{ij}x_j,$ $i = 1, 2.$

Now the summation sign Σ will be discarded, and it will be understood that a repeated index, as j in equation (9), indicates a summation with j ranging over 1 and 2. Thus, the homography (9) takes the simpler form

(10) $M:$ $k\bar{x}_i = a_{ij}x_j,$

where $i = 1$ for the first equation in (8) and $i = 2$ for the second equation, and j sums over 1, 2. The index j is called an *umbral* index or a *dummy* index. Any other letter could be used to indicate the sum. For instance, equations (10) could be written equivalently as $\rho\bar{x}_k = a_{kr}x_r$, where ρ is any nonzero number, $k = 1$ and 2 in the respective equations, and r is the dummy index which indicates a summation. Each of the equivalent forms (6) and (10) for the mapping M will be found useful in the study of homographies. The particular form to be used will be dictated by the type of problem encountered.

1-5. The modulus; singular homography

The array of coefficients in the right member of equation (6), indicated by

$$\begin{pmatrix} a & b \\ c & d \end{pmatrix},$$

is called the *matrix* of the mapping. The determinant of this matrix, indicated by

$$\begin{vmatrix} a & b \\ c & d \end{vmatrix} \equiv ad - bc,$$

is called the modulus of the mapping. If (10) is used instead of (6), the matrix is (a_{ij}) and the determinant is $|a_{ij}| \equiv a_{11}a_{22} - a_{12}a_{21}$.

Although it was stated that a, b, c, d in (5) are arbitrary real numbers, the restriction $ad - bc \neq 0$ will now be made because of the following:

If the modulus $ad - bc$ is zero, all points on l map into a single point on $\bar{l}$.

To show this, note that from $ad = bc$ it follows that $a/b = c/d = \sigma$, or $a = b\sigma$, $c = d\sigma$, with $bd \neq 0$. Use of these expressions for a and c in (6) gives

$$\bar{x} = \frac{b\sigma x + b}{d\sigma x + d} = \frac{b(\sigma x + 1)}{d(\sigma x + 1)} = \frac{b}{d},$$

which means that every point on line l maps into the single point with abscissa b/d on $\bar{l}$. This mapping is said to be *singular*. Henceforth, nonsingular mappings will be considered, so the restriction $|a_{ij}| \neq 0$ will be enforced.

1-6. Homography determined by three pairs of points

The nonsingular mapping described in equations (6) may be written in the form

(11) $$c\bar{x}x + d\bar{x} - ax - b = 0, \qquad ad - bc \neq 0.$$

Although there are four coefficients here, they are not all essential because the equation may be divided by any one of the coefficients which is not zero. Observe that if $c = 0$ and $ad \neq 0$, equation (11) takes the form (3) of an affine mapping. In this case the equation $d\bar{x} = ax + b$ can be divided by d to obtain an equation of the type

(12) $$\bar{x} = \alpha x + \beta,$$

which shows that an affine mapping from one line to another has only two essential coefficients. Observe that α could be assigned any one of a single infinity of values and that, for each of these, β could take on any one of a single infinity of values. For this reason equation (12) is said to represent a doubly infinite set of affine mappings. In equation (12) the variables x and $\bar{x}$ are coordinates of points on lines l and $\bar{l}$, respectively, and the variables α and β (called *parameters*) may be assigned at will to obtain a particular affine mapping. It is of interest that the condition $ad - bc \neq 0$, with $c = 0$, becomes $ad \neq 0$, which restricts a and therefore α to be nonzero. If $\alpha = 1$, (12) gives a single infinity of mappings called *translations*. From the form of equation (12) it should be evident that the assignment of two pairs of corresponding points on l and $\bar{l}$ determines an affine mapping (see Exercise 5).

It will be shown next that

three pairs of corresponding points determine a nonaffine mapping of the form of equation (11).

In order to do this, divide equation (11) by the nonzero parameter c to obtain an equation of the form

$$(13) \qquad \bar{x}x + \alpha\bar{x} + \beta x + \gamma = 0.$$

Let the three points on l have abscissas x_i, with $i = 1, 2, 3$, and their correspondents on $\bar{l}$ the abscissas $\bar{x}_i$, with $i = 1, 2, 3$. Now, on demanding that each pair $(\bar{x}_i, x_i)$ satisfy (13), one obtains the three equations

$$(14) \qquad \bar{x}_i x_i + \alpha\bar{x}_i + \beta x_i + \gamma = 0, \qquad\qquad i = 1, 2, 3.$$

If the determinant

$$(15) \qquad \begin{vmatrix} \bar{x}_1 & x_1 & 1 \\ \bar{x}_2 & x_2 & 1 \\ \bar{x}_3 & x_3 & 1 \end{vmatrix}$$

is not equal to zero (see Exercise 6), equations (14) can be solved for α, β, γ, and these values can then be placed in (13) to obtain the unique homography determined by the three given pairs of points on l and $\bar{l}$.

Remark: The determination of the homography by three pairs of corresponding points can be done more elegantly by use of the following theorem from algebra.

THEOREM: *The four homogeneous equations*

$$a_{i1}y_1 + a_{i2}y_2 + a_{i3}y_3 + a_{i4}y_4 = 0, \qquad\qquad i = 1, 2, 3, 4,$$

have a nontrivial solution—a solution for which the y's are not all zero—if and only if the determinant of the coefficients vanishes, that is, if and only if

$$\begin{vmatrix} a_{11} & a_{12} & a_{13} & a_{14} \\ a_{21} & a_{22} & a_{23} & a_{24} \\ a_{31} & a_{32} & a_{33} & a_{34} \\ a_{41} & a_{42} & a_{43} & a_{44} \end{vmatrix} = 0.$$

(The condition can be indicated more briefly by $|a_{ij}| = 0$.)

In order to use this theorem, identify the quantities $1, \alpha, \beta, \gamma$ in the four equations in (13) and (14) with y_1, y_2, y_3, y_4, respectively. Thus, the equation of the desired homography takes the determinantal form

$$(16) \qquad \begin{vmatrix} \bar{x}x & \bar{x} & x & 1 \\ \bar{x}_1x_1 & \bar{x}_1 & x_1 & 1 \\ \bar{x}_2x_2 & \bar{x}_2 & x_2 & 1 \\ \bar{x}_3x_3 & \bar{x}_3 & x_3 & 1 \end{vmatrix} = 0.$$

EXAMPLE

Determine the homography for which three pairs of corresponding points $(\bar{x}_i, x_i)$ are $(-8, 1)$, $(-3, 0)$, $(7, 4)$.

First solution: Place the pairs in the second, third, and fourth rows of (16) to obtain

$$\begin{vmatrix} \bar{x}x & \bar{x} & x & 1 \\ -8 & -8 & 1 & 1 \\ 0 & -3 & 0 & 1 \\ 28 & 7 & 4 & 1 \end{vmatrix} = 0,$$

which, on expanding, gives the desired homography in the form

$$\bar{x}x - 2\bar{x} - 2x - 6 = 0.$$

Second solution: Use (11) in the form

$$\bar{x} = \frac{ax + b}{cx + d} = \frac{\alpha x + \beta}{x + \gamma}.$$

Use of the pairs $(-8, 1)$, $(-3, 0)$, $(7, 4)$ successively gives the three equations

$$-8 = \frac{\alpha + \beta}{1 + \gamma}, \quad -3 = \frac{\beta}{\gamma}, \quad 7 = \frac{4\alpha + \beta}{4 + \gamma},$$

which have the solution $\alpha = 2$, $\beta = 6$, $\gamma = -2$, so the desired homography is

$$\bar{x} = \frac{2x + 6}{x - 2}.$$

Remark: The second form of solution may be the more expedient in many cases.

EXERCISES

1. Show that the inverse of equations (10) does not exist if the mapping is singular.

2. Write equations (10) with $i = 1, 2, 3$, and j ranging over 1, 2, 3. What is $|a_{ij}|$?

3. Write equations (10) with $i = 1, \cdots, n + 1$, and j ranging over 1, $\cdots$, $n + 1$. Indicate what $|a_{ij}|$ means in this case. (For $n = 1$, equations (10) are recovered as a homography from a line to a line; for $n = 2$, one obtains a homography from a plane to a plane, etc. In general, the equations represent a homography from a linear n-space to a linear n-space.)

4. Under what condition would the mapping in Exercise 2 be expected to be singular? What would be the corresponding condition in Exercise 3?

5. Show that an affine mapping between two lines is determined by two pairs of corresponding points.

6. Suppose the determinant in (15) is zero. Show in this case that the three pairs of corresponding points determine an affine mapping.

7. Prove the theorem of the last section concerning a set of homogeneous equations.

8. Let the l and $\bar{l}$ lines be coplanar and perpendicular. Show that the homography $\bar{x} = (ax + b)/(cx + d)$ is a rectangular hyperbola in the $x\bar{x}$-plane if $c \neq 0$, and $ad - bc \neq 0$. Make the translations $x = x' - (d/c)$, $\bar{x} = \bar{x}' + (a/c)$ to obtain the

form $c^2x'\bar{x}' = bc - ad$. (In euclidean geometry the hyperbola is regarded as having two branches. The euclidean plane is an open plane, just as the euclidean line was seen to be an open line. There are no points corresponding to $x = -d/c$ or to $\bar{x} = a/c$ on the hyperbola. But in projective geometry this defect is erased by adding two points to the euclidean plane and therefore all points on the line determined by these two points. This line may be styled the *ideal* line. In the projective plane, the hyperbola is a closed curve which intersects the ideal line in two distinct points.) (See Theorem 4 in Section 6-5.)

9. Determine the homography which maps the abscissas 1, 2, 3 on line l into the abscissas 2, -1, 1, respectively, on line $\bar{l}$. Are there any real abscissas on l which have the same value as their correspondents on $\bar{l}$ under this particular homography?
   Ans. $5x\bar{x} - 9\bar{x} - 7x + 15 = 0$.

10. If x goes into $\bar{x}$ by the homography M_1: $a_1\bar{x}x + b_1\bar{x} + c_1x + d_1 = 0$ and $\bar{x}$ goes into $\bar{\bar{x}}$ by the homography M_2: $a_2\bar{\bar{x}}\bar{x} + b_2\bar{\bar{x}} + c_2\bar{x} + d_2 = 0$, show that x goes directly into $\bar{\bar{x}}$ by a homography M_3. Here M_3, called the *product* of M_1 and M_2, is written as $M_3 = M_2M_1$. Is M_2M_1 the same as M_1M_2? Show that the modulus of the product of M_1 and M_2 is equal to the product of the moduli of M_1 and M_2.

11. Choose abscissas $x_1 = 0$, $x_2 = 1$ on line l, and find the correspondents $\bar{x}_1$ and $\bar{x}_2$ under $\bar{x} = (ax + b)/(cx + d)$. Show that, in general, $x_2 - x_1 \neq \bar{x}_2 - \bar{x}_1$. This means that the length of a segment on line l is not invariant under a homography. Is length invariant under an affine mapping from l to $\bar{l}$?

12. Determine the homography which maps the number pairs $P_1(1:1)$, $P_2(2:1)$, $P_3(3:1)$ on line l into the number pairs $\bar{P}_1(1:0)$, $\bar{P}_2(0:1)$, $\bar{P}_3(1:1)$ on $\bar{l}$. (*Suggestion:* Begin with equation (10).)
   Ans. $k\bar{x}_1 = 2x_1 - 4x_2$, $k\bar{x}_2 = x_1 - x_2$.

1-7. Cross ratio

Consider three distinct points A, B, X on a euclidean line l. The *simple ratio* into which the point X divides the segment from A to B is defined by the quotient AX/XB, regardless of the relative positions of the three points on l. Select an origin point O and a unit point 1 on l and let A, B, X have abscissas a, b, x, respectively. Suppose $a < x < b$. Then $AX = x - a > 0$, and $XB = b - x > 0$. Hence, if point X is between A and B, then the simple ratio $AX:XB$ is always positive. (The same result is readily seen to hold if AB is oriented in the negative direction, i.e., if $b < a$.) Next suppose $a < b < x$, so that X is outside the segment AB. In this case, $AX = x - a > 0$ and $XB = b - x < 0$, so that the ratio $AX:XB$ is negative. In the final case, with $x < a < b$, $AX:XB$ is also negative. Hence, if the point X is *outside* the segment AB on the euclidean line l, the simple ratio into which X divides the segment AB is negative, whereas if X is between A and B, the ratio is positive.

As point X moves along the line l, the simple ratio into which X divides the fixed segment AB varies, and is a function of the abscissa x of X. If the simple ratio is denoted by λ/μ, one has

$$\frac{\lambda}{\mu} = \frac{AX}{XB} = \frac{x - a}{b - x},$$

or, on writing $\lambda/\mu = \sigma$ and solving for x,

(17) $$x = \frac{a + \sigma b}{1 + \sigma}.$$

Observe that x, the abscissa of X, is one parameter, which defines the position of point X, and that σ is another parameter, related to x by equation (17). The sum of the coefficients of a and b in (17) is unity, so the parametric expression for x relative to the two *base points* A and B, may be written

$$x = \alpha a + \beta b, \qquad\qquad \alpha + \beta = 1,$$

or

$$x = \alpha a + (1 - \alpha)b.$$

There is a one-to-one correspondence between the values of α and the points on the euclidean line. As α ranges from 1 to 0, the point X ranges from A to B. As α goes from 0 to $-\infty$, X moves from B toward the right along the horizontal line, and as α ranges from 1 to $+\infty$, X moves from A toward the left.

The points A and B were called *base points* above. But there are actually three base points. The unit point (call it C) must be specified before abscissas can be determined. It is interesting now to observe that the relation between the abscissa x on line l (equation (17)) and the parameter σ is a homography. Three pairs of corresponding "points" or values may be taken as $\sigma = 0 \leftrightarrow x = a$, $\sigma = 1 \leftrightarrow x = (a + b)/2$, $\sigma = \infty \leftrightarrow x = b$. The strategy for obtaining the correspondent for $x = b$ is to divide both numerator and denominator of $(a + \sigma b)/(1 + \sigma)$ by σ and then to take the limit as $\sigma \to \infty$. An alternative procedure is to use the homogeneous form $x = (\mu a + \lambda b)/(\mu + \lambda)$, and let $\mu = 0$, $\lambda \neq 0$ correspond to $x = b$. The use of the homogeneous parameter λ/μ for σ is convenient here, but note that the homography assigns the value $\sigma = -1$ (or $\lambda = -\mu$) to the ideal point that is used to augment the euclidean line to obtain the projective line. Apparently, then, σ may be considered a projective coordinate on line l, and the homographic relation between σ and the abscissa x is given by equation (17).

Next consider a point Y with abscissa y on line l. The simple ratio into which Y divides the segment AB is AY/YB. The ratio of the simple ratios into which points X and Y divide the segment AB is called the *cross ratio* of the four points A, B, X, Y and is usually denoted by the symbol (AB, XY). One has then

(18) $$(AB, XY) = \frac{AX}{XB} \div \frac{AY}{YB} = \frac{x - a}{b - x} \div \frac{y - a}{b - y}.$$

(The cross ratio is also called the *anharmonic* ratio, the *bi-ratio*, or the *double ratio*; *Doppelverhältnis*, in German; and *rapport anharmonique*, in French.)

The sign of the cross ratio should be investigated. On the euclidean line, if X and Y are both between A and B, then both simple ratios into which X and Y separately divide the segment AB are positive and, consequently, the cross ratio is positive. If both X and Y are outside AB, each simple ratio is negative, so the cross ratio is again positive. But if X, say, is inside AB and Y is outside AB, then one simple ratio is positive and the other is negative, so the cross ratio is negative.

Remark: Recall that on the projective line the segment AB divides the line into two parts, and that any point P may be regarded as between A and B. Hence, the two cases on the euclidean line, first with X, Y both inside AB and, second, with X, Y both outside AB, become only one case on the projective line. On the projective line, if the segment AB does not contain the ideal point, then the segment BA does contain it.

If the cross ratio of four points P_i, with $i = 1, 2, 3, 4$, has the value -1, the points are said to be *harmonic* or to form a *harmonic set*. Many instances of harmonic sets will appear in the sequel.

Equation (18) reveals that if the value of the cross ratio is assigned, and if three points are assigned, then the fourth point is determined uniquely. In particular, if the set is harmonic and three points P_1, P_2, P_3 are assigned, then the fourth point P_4 of the set is uniquely determined. A geometrical construction of P_4 by straightedge only will be shown later (Section 5-6). Meanwhile, the abscissa of P_4 can be found by use of equation (18).

EXAMPLE

Given the three points P_1, P_2, P_3 with respective abscissas 2, 3, 1 on a line l, find the abscissa of point P_4 such that P_1, P_2, P_3, P_4 form a harmonic set.

Solution: Let x denote the abscissa of P_4. The cross ratio $(2, 3, 1, x)$ must equal -1. Hence,

$$\frac{1-2}{1-3} \div \frac{x-2}{x-3} = -1,$$

which yields $x = 7/3$.

Remark: In this example, P_1 and P_2 may be regarded as the base points, and P_3 and P_4 as the points which divide the pair P_1P_2 into simple ratios. Here the pair P_3, P_4 are said to *separate* P_1, P_2 harmonically. The reader may verify that P_1, P_2 also separate P_3, P_4 harmonically.

1-8. Permutation effect on cross ratio

Four points A, B, C, D on a line can be ordered in 4! (or 24) different ways. Write them out. Some of them are $ABCD$, $ABDC$, $ADBC$, $DABC$, $CABD$, $CADB$. The following discussion will show that no more than six distinct values of the cross ratio of the four points can be obtained, regardless of the permutations of them.

Remark: Later the cross ratio of four lines and the cross ratio of four planes will be considered. For this reason the term "element" instead of "point" will be used. A parameterization of four elements will be effected. The cross ratio of four elements will be seen to be the cross ratio of their four respective parameters.

Note first that there are four possible orders obtainable by changing the order of elements in pairs. For instance, on starting with the pairs *AB, CD* one has the orders

$$AB, CD; \ BA, DC; \ CD, AB; \ DC, BA.$$

On using equation (18) with abscissas *a, b, c, d* of the points *A, B, C, D*, and on letting $r \equiv (abcd)$, one has

(19) $$r \equiv (abcd) \equiv \frac{c-a}{c-b} \div \frac{d-a}{d-b},$$

and

$$(badc) \equiv \frac{d-b}{d-a} \div \frac{c-b}{c-a} = r.$$

Similarly, it is readily shown that

$$(cdab) = (dcba) = r.$$

Hence, interchanging pairs or the order of elements of both pairs has no effect on the cross ratio.

It will be shown next that if *r* is the cross ratio of four elements in any one order, say $r = (ABCD)$, then all possible values of the cross ratio under permutation of the elements are in the set

(20) $$r, \ \frac{1}{r}, \ 1-r, \ \frac{1}{1-r}, \ \frac{r-1}{r}, \ \frac{r}{r-1}.$$

First, interchanging the elements of the first pair only (or of the second pair only) changes the cross ratio *r* to its reciprocal. If *a* and *b* are interchanged in equation (19), the result is the reciprocal of the fraction denoted by *r*. Hence,

$$(bacd) = \frac{1}{(abcd)} = \frac{1}{r}.$$

Similarly,

$$(abdc) = \frac{1}{(abcd)} = \frac{1}{r}.$$

Next, interchanging the outside elements only (*A* and *D*) or the inside elements only (*B* and *C*) effects a change in the cross ratio to its arithmetic complement, that is, to $1 - r$. To show this, note that from (19)

$$(dbca) = \frac{c-d}{c-b} \div \frac{a-d}{a-b},$$

and verify that this is $1 - r$. Similarly,

$$(acbd) = \frac{b-a}{b-c} \div \frac{d-a}{d-c} = 1 - r.$$

On interchanging b and d in $(acbd)$ one has

$$(acdb) = \frac{1}{(acbd)} = \frac{1}{1 - r},$$

and, on interchanging b and d in $(abdc) = \frac{1}{r}$, there results

$$(adbc) = 1 - \frac{1}{r} = \frac{r - 1}{r},$$

and, finally, interchanging b and c in $(adbc)$ yields

$$(adcb) = \frac{1}{(adbc)} = \frac{r}{r - 1}.$$

The set of values in (20) is *closed* under the two operations: dividing into 1, and subtracting from one. That is, the reciprocal of any member of the set is a member of the set, and the arithmetical complement of any member of the set is a member of the set.

Exceptional cases, obtained by equating two members of the set, are determined by the equations

$$r = \frac{1}{r}, \quad r = 1 - r, \quad r = \frac{1}{1 - r}, \quad r = \frac{r - 1}{r}, \quad r = \frac{r}{r - 1}.$$

From the first of these, $r^2 = 1$, so $r = 1$ and $r = -1$. Consider first $r = 1$. From (19), this means that

$$\frac{c - a}{c - b} \frac{d - b}{d - a} = 1,$$

which implies $(a - b)(c - d) = 0$; this requires that $a = b$ or $c = d$, so that the elements are not distinct. For distinct elements then, the value $r = 1$ is discarded. If $r = -1$, the six members in (20) reduce to the three members $(-1, 2, \frac{1}{2})$ which may be called the *harmonic* subset. If the four elements A, B, C, D are harmonic, the cross ratio is -1 for one ordering but may be 2 or $\frac{1}{2}$ for different orderings of the elements. For the case $(ABCD) = -1$, the elements C, D separate the elements A, B harmonically. Also, C and D are described as *harmonic conjugates* of each other with respect to A and B. The harmonic subset is the only exceptional case for real elements.

From $r = r/(r - 1)$, $r = 0$ and $r = 2$. The latter has been considered, and $r = 0$ is discarded because it cannot arise from distinct elements.

The only remaining exceptional cases come from $r = 1/(1 - r)$; that is, $r^2 - r + 1 = 0$, so that

$$r = \frac{1 \pm i\sqrt{3}}{2}.$$

Write $r = -\omega$, where ω is a cube root of unity ($\omega^3 = 1$), and note that all six values in the set (20) reduce to $-\omega$ or $-\omega^2$. These two values constitute what is styled the *equi-anharmonic* subset.

It is of interest to observe the variation of the cross ratio of four points on a line as the fourth point varies. Let A, B, C be fixed on l (Fig. 4) with abscissas a, b, c, and let the variable point P have abscissa x. With the ordering of points

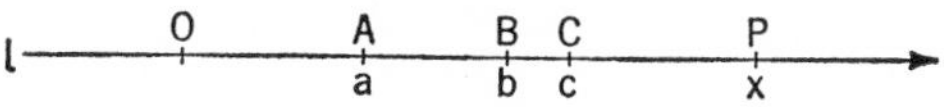

Figure 4

shown in Fig. 4, the cross ratio $r = (ABCP) = (abcx)$ is positive. As P moves toward the right, r remains positive, and

$$\lim_{x \to \infty} (ABCP) = \lim_{x \to \infty} \frac{c - a}{c - b} \div \frac{x - a}{x - b} = \frac{c - a}{c - b} = -\frac{AC}{CB},$$

which is merely the negative of the simple ratio into which C divides AB. (Note that if C is the midpoint of the segment AB, then C and the ideal point P are harmonic conjugates relative to A and B.)

Next, observe that as P moves toward A from the left, r is still positive, but

$$\lim_{x \to a} \frac{c - a}{c - b} \frac{x - b}{x - a}$$

does not exist. Equivalently, the situation may be described by saying that r becomes infinite. When P is between A and B, r is negative; as P approaches B, r becomes zero. As P moves from B to C, r is positive and goes to 1 as P goes to C.

The foregoing discussion indicates that the parameter r in $r = (abcx)$ is seen to be a projective coordinate, in the following sense. If the pair $r_1 : r_2$ is used for r, then the pair $(r_1 : 0)$, that is $(1 : 0)$, corresponds to the point A, the pair $(0 : 1)$ corresponds to point B, and the pair $(1 : 1)$ corresponds to C. There is a one-to-one correspondence between the pairs $(kr_1 : kr_2)$, with $k \neq 0$, and the points of the projective line. From

(21)
$$r = (abcx) = \frac{c - a}{c - b} \frac{x - b}{x - a} = \frac{\alpha x + \beta}{\gamma x + \delta},$$

where $\alpha = c - a$, $\beta = -b(c - a)$, $\gamma = c - b$, $\delta = -a(c - b)$, it is seen that the projective coordinate r is in homographic correspondence with the abscissa coordinate x of any point P on the line l. Note that here the lines l and $\bar{l}$ coincide, so instead of effecting a mapping of points from l to $\bar{l}$, as in Section 1-2, the homography gives a change of coordinate system.

The modulus of the transformation of (21) is $\alpha\delta - \beta\gamma = (b - c)(c - a)(a - b)$, which cannot vanish if a, b, c are distinct. It will be shown in the next section that the cross ratio of any four abscissas on l is equal to the cross ratio of the four corresponding projective coordinates.

The abscissa system of coordinates of points on a line is a special type of projective coordinate system. In order to realize this, start with the projective coordinate r of point P, as given by (21), relative to the three base points A, B, C

in Fig. 4. The first specialization is to require a to become infinite, which causes (21) to reduce to

$$r = \frac{x - b}{c - b}.$$

Next, select point B as the origin, so $b = 0$. The projective coordinate now becomes

$$r = \frac{x}{c}.$$

Finally, let C be the unit point, ($c = 1$), to have $r = x$. Thus, with proper choice of the three base points the projective coordinate becomes identical with the abscissa coordinate. (It will be seen later, in a similar way, that the familiar rectangular cartesian coordinate system for points in a plane is a special case of a more general *projective coordinate* system.)

1-9. Invariance of the cross ratio

In Exercise 11 on page 12 it was seen that the length of a segment on a line l is not the same after the mapping by a homography onto line $\bar{l}$; that is, distance is not invariant in projective or affine geometry. But if the homography is specialized to the special affine mapping $\bar{x} = x + h$, then distance is invariant. The segment from x_1 to x_2 has length $|x_2 - x_1|$; therefore $\bar{x}_1 = x_1 + h$ and $\bar{x}_2 = x_2 + h$ give $|\bar{x}_2 - \bar{x}_1| = |x_2 - x_1|$. This special affine mapping is the euclidean translation. As the mapping becomes more general, the number of invariants decreases. One may ask if there are any geometric entities which remain invariant under a general homography. An affirmative answer is afforded by the following

THEOREM: *The cross ratio of four numbers is invariant under a general homography.*

Proof: Carry out the homography on the four numbers x_i, with $i = 1, \cdots, 4$, by

$$\bar{x}_i = \frac{ax_i + b}{cx_i + d}, \qquad\qquad ad - bc \neq 0,$$

to obtain the four corresponding numbers $\bar{x}_i$, with $i = 1, \cdots, 4$. It is desired to show that $(\bar{x}_1\bar{x}_2\bar{x}_3\bar{x}_4) = (x_1x_2x_3x_4)$; that is,

$$\frac{\bar{x}_3 - \bar{x}_1}{\bar{x}_3 - \bar{x}_2} \div \frac{\bar{x}_4 - \bar{x}_1}{\bar{x}_4 - \bar{x}_2} = \frac{x_3 - x_1}{x_3 - x_2} \div \frac{x_4 - x_1}{x_4 - x_2}.$$

Calculate

$$\bar{x}_3 - \bar{x}_1 = \frac{ax_3 + b}{cx_3 + d} - \frac{ax_1 + b}{cx_1 + d} = \frac{(ad - bc)(x_3 - x_1)}{(cx_3 + d)(cx_1 + d)}.$$

Replace the subscript 1 by 2 to obtain

$$\bar{x}_3 - \bar{x}_2 = \frac{(ad - bc)(x_3 - x_2)}{(cx_3 + d)(cx_2 + d)}.$$

Then

$$\frac{\bar{x}_3 - \bar{x}_1}{\bar{x}_3 - \bar{x}_2} = \frac{x_3 - x_1}{x_3 - x_2} \frac{cx_2 + d}{cx_1 + d}.$$

Replace 3 by 4 to obtain

$$\frac{\bar{x}_4 - \bar{x}_1}{\bar{x}_4 - \bar{x}_2} = \frac{x_4 - x_1}{x_4 - x_2} \frac{cx_2 + d}{cx_1 + d}.$$

Division of the last two equations shows that

$$(\bar{x}_1\bar{x}_2\bar{x}_3\bar{x}_4) = (x_1x_2x_3x_4),$$

which completes the proof.

This theorem will be employed frequently to show that if the parameters of the elements of a first set are related to the parameters of a second set by a homography, then any four elements of the first set have the same cross ratio as the corresponding elements in the second set.

EXERCISES

1. Show that the inverse of a homography is a homography.

2. Write the cross ratio of the points P_i with abscissas x_i, with $i = 1, \cdots, 4$, respectively, and show that the points P_1, P_2 separate P_3, P_4 harmonically only if

$$(x_1 + x_2)(x_3 + x_4) = 2(x_1x_2 + x_3x_4).$$

3. Show that

$$\lim_{m \to \infty} (m, 0, 1, x) = x, \quad \lim_{m \to \infty} (0, m, r, -r) = -1, \quad \lim_{m \to \infty} (a, b, c, m) = \frac{c - a}{c - b}.$$

(These three limiting values of the cross ratio are of frequent occurrence.)

4. Prove that the cross ratio of four distinct elements cannot result in 1, 0, or ∞.

5. Show that the harmonic conjugate of a given point P with respect to two other given points A and B is unique, but that for three given points A, B, C it is possible to select P in three ways such that the set of four points A, B, C, P is harmonic.

6. Determine a value of m for which the lines

$$l_1: \quad y - 2 = 2(x - 1), \qquad l_2: \quad y - 2 = 3(x - 1),$$

$$l_3: \quad y - 2 = 4(x - 1), \qquad l_4: \quad y - 2 = m(x - 1)$$

meet the x-axis in four harmonic points. Use this value of m in the fourth line and find the cross ratio of the slopes of the four lines. Why should one expect this result? (See Exercise 7.)

7. Show that the cross ratio of the four points where the lines

$$y - b = \lambda_i(x - a), \qquad\qquad i = 1, \cdots, 4,$$

intersect the x-axis is equal to the cross ratio of the slopes of the four lines. *Suggestion:* This should be done with very little labor by use of the theorem in Section 1-9. Note that for $y = 0$, the x_i are related to the λ_i by

$$x_i = \frac{a\lambda_i - b}{\lambda_i}, \qquad\qquad i = 1, \cdots, 4.$$

What is the cross ratio of the ordinates of the points in which the four lines meet the y-axis? Find the cross ratio of the four points in which the lines meet the line $x = t$, $y = 1 - t$, where t is a parameter.

8. (a) If $(x_1x_2x_3x_4) = k$, show that

$$\frac{1 - k}{x_2 - x_1} = \frac{1}{x_4 - x_1} - \frac{k}{x_3 - x_1}.$$

(b) Now let $k = -1$ and interpret the result geometrically.
    Ans. The segment $x_2 - x_1$ is the harmonic mean of $x_3 - x_1$ and $x_4 - x_1$.

9. Prove that the points A, B separate C, D harmonically if and only if $\overline{MC}\,\overline{MD} = \overline{MA}^2$, where M is the midpoint of AB.

10. Take A and B as two base points on a line l, and take three more points P, Q, R on l. Define $\delta(PQ) \equiv c \log (AB, PQ)$, where c is an arbitrary nonzero constant. Show that the three requirements for distance on l are satisfied:
   (a) $\delta(PQ) + \delta(QR) = \delta(PR)$,
   (b) $\delta(PQ) + \delta(QP) = 0$,
   (c) $\delta(PP) = 0$.
   Further, show that
   (d) $(ABPQ)(ABQR)(ABRP) = 1$.
   Hint: Take the logarithm of the equation.

CHAPTER 2

Geometry of Points on a Line

2-1. Perspectivity between two point ranges

In Chapter 1 some attention was given to a homographic correspondence between the points of two arbitrary lines l and $\bar{l}$. This type of correspondence is considered further in this chapter. Here the two lines l and $\bar{l}$ are taken as coplanar, as was the case for Examples 1 and 2 in Section 1-2. An important distinction between two kinds of homography is illustrated by these two examples. In Example 1 the ideal point of line l corresponds to the ideal point of line $\bar{l}$. In other words, the intersection of the two lines l and $\bar{l}$ is a self-corresponding point. In contrast to this, the ideal point on l in Example 2 does not map into the ideal point on $\bar{l}$. If the lines are parallel they have the ideal point in common, but this intersection point is not self-corresponding. The homography illustrated by Example 1 is called a *perspectivity*, and that illustrated by Example 2 is called a *projectivity*. A perspectivity is a specialized projectivity. Another way to say this is that the set of all projectivities contains the set of all perspectivities as a subset.

Some synthetic geometry (that is, geometry without the use of a coordinate system) will now be employed to exhibit a characteristic property of the perspective correspondence between l and $\bar{l}$ in the plane which l and $\bar{l}$ determine. The points on a line are referred to as a *range* of points or a *point range*.

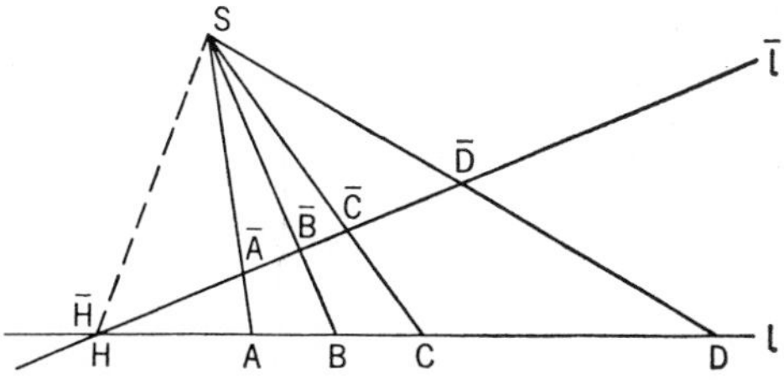

Figure 5

DEFINITION: *A perspectivity is a correspondence between two point ranges (l and $\bar{l}$) such that lines joining corresponding points are concurrent. The point of concurrence is called the* center *of the perspectivity.*

Note in Fig. 5 that only two pairs of corresponding points A, $\bar{A}$ and B, $\bar{B}$ are sufficient to determine the perspectivity, because lines $A\bar{A}$ and $B\bar{B}$ intersect in S, the center of perspectivity, and then any line through S intersects l and $\bar{l}$

in two corresponding points, say C and $\overline{C}$, of the perspectivity. In particular, if l and $\overline{l}$ intersect in H, then line SH intersects $\overline{l}$ at $\overline{H}$, which coincides with H. The intersection space of two one-dimensional spaces is self-corresponding if, and only if, the correspondence is a perspectivity.

It is necessary at this point to correlate the synthetic and analytic definitions of a perspectivity. First, note that if an x-abscissa system on l and an $\overline{x}$-abscissa system on $\overline{l}$ are established such that the intersection H of l and $\overline{l}$ is the common origin of the two systems, then $x = 0 \leftrightarrow \overline{x} = 0$, so that the general homography $\overline{x} = (ax + b)/(cx + d)$ must have $b = 0$. That is, the perspectivity would apparently be represented by $\overline{x} = x/(\alpha x + \beta)$. Then the two remaining essential parameters can be determined by assigning arbitrarily a pair of abscissas for A and $\overline{A}$, and a pair for B and $\overline{B}$. Hence, a homography of the type $\overline{x} = x/(\alpha x + \beta)$, with $\beta \neq 0$, may be regarded as a perspectivity with the origin points corresponding. Note that the point V with abscissa $x = -\beta/\alpha$ on l maps into the ideal point $\overline{I}$ on $\overline{l}$. Hence, the line SV must be parallel to $\overline{l}$. The point V is called the *vanishing point* on l. By finding the inverse $x = \beta\overline{x}/(1 - \alpha\overline{x})$, it is seen that the vanishing point $\overline{V}$ on l has abscissa $\overline{x} = 1/\alpha$.

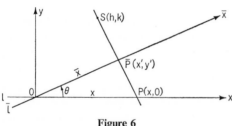

Figure 6

It is instructive now to use ordinary plane analytical geometry to develop the form for the perspectivity between lines l and $\overline{l}$. Let l and $\overline{l}$ intersect at the origin, with l along the x-axis, and let $\overline{x}$ be an abscissa measured from the origin along $\overline{l}$. With the y-axis taken as indicated in Fig. 6, take the point $S(h, k)$ as the center of the perspectivity. An arbitrary line through S intersects $\overline{l}$ and l in the corresponding points $\overline{P}$ and P. Point P has coordinates $(x, 0)$. Let $\overline{P}$ have coordinates (x', y') referred to the x- and y-axes. The equation of $\overline{l}$ is $y = mx$, where $m = \tan \theta$. But $\overline{P}$ is on $\overline{l}$, so $y' = mx'$. The line $S\overline{P}P$ has the equation

$$Y = \frac{k}{h - x}(X - x),$$

where (X, Y) are used for running coordinates on the line. Point $\overline{P}$ is on this line, so

$$y' = \frac{k(x' - x)}{h - x}.$$

On solving this equation with $y' = mx'$, one obtains

$$x' = \frac{kx}{mx + k - mh}, \quad y' = \frac{mkx}{mx + k - mh}.$$

From Fig. 6 it is seen that

$$\overline{x}^2 = x'^2 + y'^2,$$

which gives

(1)
$$\bar{x} = \frac{k\sqrt{1 + m^2}\,x}{mx + (k - mh)},$$

a homography for which $x = 0 \leftrightarrow \bar{x} = 0$. Observe that if θ is fixed, then m is fixed, and two parameters remain to be determined in equation (1). The choice of the center $S(h, k)$ determines the mapping. There is a doubly infinite set of choices for (h, k), so one may say that there are ∞^2 perspectivities between two given lines. Suppose next that with fixed point O of intersection of l and $\bar{l}$, the angle θ between l and $\bar{l}$ is allowed to vary. With the introduction of θ as a new parameter, there are ∞^3 perspectivities to consider.

2-2. Projectivity between two point ranges

The perspectivity in equation (1) does not take the general form of a general homography

$$\bar{x} = \frac{ax + b}{cx + d}$$

because it was required that $x = 0 \leftrightarrow \bar{x} = 0$. If a translation on the x-axis is made according to $x = x^* + p$, with x^* a new variable, the mapping (1) becomes

$$\bar{x} = \frac{ax^* + (ap + b)}{cx^* + (cp + d)}$$

(where $a = k\sqrt{1 + m^2}$, $c = m$, $d = k - mh$), which is now a general homography for which $x^* \leftrightarrow \bar{x}$. Because the translation itself is a special kind of perspectivity, it appears that a perspectivity followed by a perspectivity is a mapping of a more general type than a perspectivity. Indeed, the more general type is called a *projectivity*.

DEFINITION: *A* projectivity *is the product of two or more perspectivities.*

(The concept of the "product" of two mappings was introduced in Exercise 10 on page 12. Here, a perspectivity p_1 followed by perspectivity p_2 is the product mapping $p_2 p_1$, which is, in general, a projectivity.)

The product of two or more perspectivities is sometimes called a *chain* or a *sequence* of perspectivities. Hence, a projectivity may be defined as a sequence of perspectivities. Because a projectivity is described, in general, by a linear fractional function,

$$\bar{x} = \frac{ax + b}{cx + d},$$

and because this is the form for a homography, hereafter the terms homography and projectivity will be considered as synonymous.

An analytic proof was given in Section 1-6 (p. 10) for the theorem that a unique homography between two point ranges is determined by three pairs of corresponding points.

A synthetic proof is presented next for the

THEOREM: *A projectivity between two coplanar point ranges is determined by three pairs of corresponding points.*

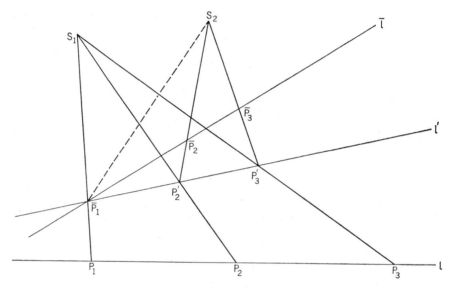

Figure 7

Proof: Take three arbitrary points P_1, P_2, P_3 on l (Fig. 7), and three arbitrary points $\overline{P}_1$, $\overline{P}_2$, $\overline{P}_3$ on $\overline{l}$. Take S_1 on the join of $P_1\overline{P}_1$ and project P_2, P_3 from S_1 on any line l' through $\overline{P}_1$ to obtain the points P_2', P_3' on l'. Then the intersection S_2 of the joins of P_2', $\overline{P}_2$ and P_3', $\overline{P}_3$ is a center from which $\overline{P}_1$, $\overline{P}_2$, $\overline{P}_3$ are projected into $\overline{P}_1$, P_2', P_3'. Further, S_1 is a center of perspectivity from which $\overline{P}_1$, P_2', P_3' are projected into P_1, P_2, P_3. Thus, the three arbitrary points P_1, P_2, P_3 on l are mapped by the product of two perspectivities with centers S_1 and S_2 into the three arbitrary points $\overline{P}_1$, $\overline{P}_2$, $\overline{P}_3$ on $\overline{l}$. If a fourth point P_4 is chosen on l it is mapped into P_4' on l' through S_1, and P_4' is, in turn, mapped into a unique point $\overline{P}_4$ on $\overline{l}$ through S_2. It remains, however, to show that the projectivity determined is unique. This may be accomplished as follows. Suppose a different construction is used, say, by selecting S_1^* on the join of $P_1\overline{P}_2$, from which P_2, P_3 project into P_2', P_3' on any line l' through $\overline{P}_2$. The joins of $\overline{P}_1$, P_2' and P_3', $\overline{P}_3$ determine S_2^*, from which $\overline{P}_2$, P_2', P_3' project into $\overline{P}_2$, $\overline{P}_1$, $\overline{P}_3$ on $\overline{l}$. Let P_4 on l project into $\overline{P}_4^*$ on $\overline{l}$. Then $(P_1P_2P_3P_4) = (\overline{P}_1\overline{P}_2\overline{P}_3\overline{P}_4) = (\overline{P}_1\overline{P}_2\overline{P}_3\overline{P}_4^*)$. From the equality of the latter two cross ratios it follows that the points $\overline{P}_4$ and $\overline{P}_4^*$ must coincide. Hence, the projectivity is uniquely determined.

Notation: The symbol $\underset{\wedge}{=}$ is generally used to denote a perspective correspondence. For instance, in Fig. 7 one may write

$$l(P_1P_2P_3\cdots) \overset{S_1}{\underset{\wedge}{=}} l'(P_1'P_2'P_3'\cdots) \overset{S_2}{\underset{\wedge}{=}} \bar{l}(\bar{P}_1\bar{P}_2\bar{P}_3\cdots).$$

This indicates that S_1 is the center of the first perspectivity and that certain ranges of points on lines l and l' are perspective, and, further, that a range on l' is perspective through S_2 with a range on l.

The symbol $\underset{\wedge}{-}$ may be used to denote a projective correspondence. Again in Fig. 7, one has

$$l(P_1P_2P_3\cdots) \underset{\wedge}{-} \bar{l}(\bar{P}_1\bar{P}_2\bar{P}_3\cdots).$$

As stated before, a perspectivity is seen to be a special case of a projectivity.

2-3. Vanishing points

In Section 2-1 the vanishing points for a perspectivity were defined. Similarly, for a projectivity between two ranges l and $\bar{l}$, the vanishing point on l is the point V which corresponds to the ideal point on $\bar{l}$, and the vanishing point on $\bar{l}$ is the point $\bar{V}$ which corresponds to the ideal point on l. To find V, observe that as $x \to -d/c$ in $\bar{x} = (ax + b)/(cx + d)$, $\bar{x} \to \infty$, so the abscissa of V on l is $-d/c$. From the inverse $x = (-d\bar{x} + b)/(c\bar{x} - a)$ as $\bar{x} \to a/c$, $x \to \infty$. Hence the abscissa of $\bar{V}$ on $\bar{l}$ is a/c.

A theorem concerning a metric property of a projectivity will be demonstrated next. The proof of the theorem indicates how the analysis can be simplified by special choice of the origin on each line.

THEOREM: *For every projectivity, the product of the distances of pairs of corresponding points from the vanishing points is constant.*

(This constant is called the *power* of the projectivity. It is the distance VP times the distance $\bar{V}\bar{P}$ in Fig. 8.)

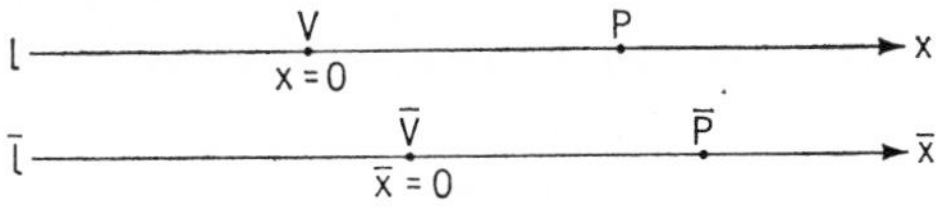

Figure 8

Proof: For simplicity, and without loss of generality, choose V, where $x = -d/c$, as the origin on l, so that $d = 0$. Likewise, choose $\bar{V}$, where $\bar{x} = a/c$, as the origin on $\bar{l}$, so that $a = 0$. The simplified form for the equation of the projectivity is now $x\bar{x} = b/c$. Since x and $\bar{x}$ are abscissas and b and c are constants for a given projectivity, the theorem is proved. (See Exercise 2.)

EXERCISES

1. What is the power of the projectivity $\bar{x} = ax + b$?

2. Calculate the power of the projectivity $c\bar{x}x + d\bar{x} - ax - b = 0$ without the special choice of origin used in the proof of the above theorem.

3. Use rectangular cartesian coordinates and project the points A_i, with coordinates $(a, m_i a)$ on the line $x = a$, from the origin into the points A_i' on the line $y = mx + b$. Next, project the points A_i' from the center $S(c, d)$ into the points A_i'' on the line $y = kx$. If μ is a parameter giving the distance from the origin to any point A_i'' and if λ $(= m_i a)$ is the parameter for the corresponding point A_i, show that

$$\mu = \frac{\alpha\lambda + \beta}{\gamma\lambda + \delta},$$

where

$$\alpha = -bc\sqrt{1 + k^2}, \quad \beta = abd\sqrt{1 + k^2},$$

$$\gamma = d - b - kc, \quad \delta = ak(b + cm) - adm.$$

4. Why is it true that the cross ratio of any four points A_i, with $i = 1, \cdots, 4$, of Exercise 3 is equal to the cross ratio of the four corresponding points A_i'', with $i = 1, \cdots, 4$?

5. Consider the mapping M: $\bar{x} = (2x + 1)/(x - 2)$, followed by the same mapping M: $\bar{\bar{x}} = (2\bar{x} + 1)/(\bar{x} - 2)$. The product mapping by which x goes directly into $\bar{\bar{x}}$ may be called the "square" (M^2) of the given mapping. Show that $M^2 = \mathcal{I}$, where $\mathcal{I}$ is the *identity* mapping ($\bar{x} = x$) for all x. (The mapping M here is an instance of a mapping of *period two*. It is also called an *involution*.)

6. Prove that the mapping $\bar{x} = (ax + b)/(cx + d)$ is of period two if and only if $a + d = 0$.

2-4. Projectivity on a line

Thus far, the lines l and $\bar{l}$ have been considered as being distinct. Now, let l and $\bar{l}$ coincide. Moreover, let the origins O and $\bar{O}$ coincide and use the same unit point for each range. All the results obtained for a homography continue to hold for this case, which can be described as a projective mapping of the line l into itself. Point P with abscissa x maps, in general, into another point $\bar{P}$ with abscissa $\bar{x}$. The question naturally arises, "Is there any point which maps into itself?" If it be demanded that $\bar{x} = x$ in

$$(2) \qquad\qquad\qquad \bar{x} = \frac{ax + b}{cx + d},$$

one obtains the quadratic equation

$$(3) \qquad\qquad\qquad cx^2 + (d - a)x - b = 0$$

with the roots

$$(4) \qquad\qquad x_1 = \frac{a - d + \sigma}{2c}, \quad x_2 = \frac{a - d - \sigma}{2c},$$

where $\sigma^2 \equiv (d - a)^2 + 4bc \equiv (a + d)^2 - 4(ad - bc)$. Hence, in general, there are *two* points which remain fixed under the mapping (2). These two points are variously referred to as *invariant* points, *double* points, *self-corresponding* points, or *fixed* points.

For one special case, observe that if $b = c = 0$ and $a = d$ in (2), then $\bar{x} = x$ for all x. This is the *identity* mapping I.

For another special case, let the mapping in (2) be affine; that is, let $c = 0$. If $d \neq a$, the fixed point with abscissa x_2 in (4) becomes the ideal point, which agrees with the previous definition of an affine mapping as one for which the ideal points correspond. The other fixed point is obtained by putting $\bar{x} = x$ in (2), with $c = 0$, to obtain

$$x = \frac{b}{d-a}.$$

Finally, if $c = 0$ and $a = d$ in (2), the mapping becomes a mere translation, $\bar{x} = x + (b/a)$, for which the fixed points coincide at the ideal point.

Three cases arise relative to the roots of equation (3), according as the discriminant $\sigma^2 \equiv (d-a)^2 + 4bc$ is positive, zero, or negative. As is usual in mathematics, the three respective cases are referred to as hyperbolic, parabolic, and elliptic.

Case 1. The roots of (3) are real and distinct, so there are two real fixed points. The mapping (2) is called a *hyperbolic* projectivity.

Case 2. The roots of (3) are real and coincident, so there is only one fixed point under the *parabolic* projectivity (2).

Case 3. The roots of (3) are complex and distinct, so there are no real fixed points under the *elliptic* projectivity (2).

Consider the hyperbolic case with the two real abscissas x_1 and x_2 of the invariant points I_1 and I_2 (Fig. 9). It will be shown next that the cross ratio $(x_1 x_2 x \bar{x})$

Figure 9

is the same for every pair of corresponding points P and $\bar{P}$. This will be done in two ways. The first is by direct calculation of

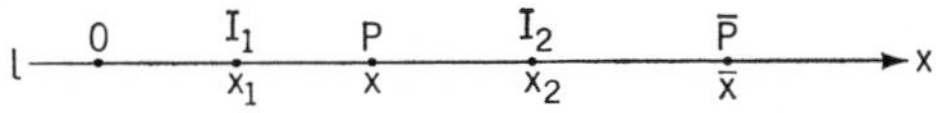

$$(I_1 I_2 P \bar{P}) = (x_1 x_2 x \bar{x}) = \frac{x - x_1}{x - x_2} \div \frac{\bar{x} - x_1}{\bar{x} - x_2} = \frac{x\bar{x} + x_1 x_2 - \bar{x}x_1 - x x_2}{x\bar{x} + x_1 x_2 - \bar{x}x_2 - x x_1}.$$

Use of (2) and (4) in the last expression gives

$$\frac{\frac{1}{c}(ax - d\bar{x} + b) - \frac{b}{c} - \frac{\bar{x}}{2c}(a - d + \sigma) - \frac{x}{2c}(a - d - \sigma)}{\frac{1}{c}(ax - d\bar{x} + b) - \frac{b}{c} - \frac{\bar{x}}{2c}(a - d - \sigma) - \frac{x}{2c}(a - d + \sigma)},$$

which simplifies to

$$\frac{(x - \bar{x})(a + d + \sigma)}{(x - \bar{x})(a + d - \sigma)} = \frac{a + d + \sigma}{a + d - \sigma}.$$

Hence, the result is independent of x and $\bar{x}$. Let the constant value obtained for the cross ratio be denoted by K. It is called the *characteristic* invariant of the projectivity (2). The result just obtained is stated in the

THEOREM: *The cross ratio of the two invariant points of a hyperbolic projectivity and any pair of corresponding points is a real constant.*

The second proof of this theorem follows from the fact that the cross ratio of any four points on l is invariant under a projectivity. Take the four points as I_1, I_2, P_1, P_2, which map into $I_1, I_2, \overline{P}_1, \overline{P}_2$. Hence,

$$(I_1 I_2 P_1 P_2) = (I_1 I_2 \overline{P}_1 \overline{P}_2).$$

Let f_1, f_2 be the abscissas of the fixed points I_1, I_2; x_1, x_2, those of P_1, P_2; and $\overline{x}_1, \overline{x}_2$, those of $\overline{P}_1, \overline{P}_2$. It follows that

$$(f_1 f_2 x_1 x_2) = (f_1 f_2 \overline{x}_1 \overline{x}_2),$$

or

$$\frac{x_1 - f_1}{x_1 - f_2} \div \frac{x_2 - f_1}{x_2 - f_2} = \frac{\overline{x}_1 - f_1}{\overline{x}_1 - f_2} \div \frac{\overline{x}_2 - f_1}{\overline{x}_2 - f_2},$$

which equation can be cast into the form

$$\frac{x_1 - f_1}{\overline{x}_1 - f_1} \div \frac{x_1 - f_2}{\overline{x}_1 - f_2} = \frac{x_2 - f_1}{\overline{x}_2 - f_1} \div \frac{x_2 - f_2}{\overline{x}_2 - f_2} = K.$$

This last equation is to be interpreted to mean that the abscissas x, $\overline{x}$ of any pair of corresponding points P, $\overline{P}$ make the expression

$$\frac{x - f_1}{\overline{x} - f_1} \div \frac{x - f_2}{\overline{x} - f_2}$$

a constant. This completes the second proof of the theorem.

Remark: The power of a projectivity as defined in Section 2-3 is a metric invariant, but the characteristic invariant K is a projective invariant. The latter does not involve distance.

It follows from the foregoing proof that a hyperbolic projectivity can be written in the form

$$\frac{x - f_1}{\overline{x} - f_1} \div \frac{x - f_2}{\overline{x} - f_2} = K$$

or

(5)
$$\frac{\overline{x} - f_2}{\overline{x} - f_1} = K \frac{x - f_2}{x - f_1},$$

where f_1, f_2, K are constants. Hence, a hyperbolic projectivity is determined by the invariant points and the characteristic invariant. An elliptic projectivity can also be written in the form (5), but in this case the constants are complex numbers.

Just as the hyperbolic projectivity can be written in the form (5), given a characteristic constant and the invariant points, the parabolic projectivity can be exhibited similarly in terms of its single invariant point and a characteristic constant.

Because $(d - a)^2 + 4bc = 0$, if $c = 0$, then $a = d$ and (2) is a translation, for which the fixed points coincide at the ideal point.

Suppose next that $c \neq 0$. Write equation (2) in the form

(6)
$$\bar{x} = \frac{\dfrac{a}{c}x + \dfrac{b}{c}}{x + \dfrac{d}{c}}.$$

Let f be the abscissa of the double fixed point. Then $a - d = 2cf$ and from $\sigma = 0$ it follows that $b = -cf^2$. If a/c is written as α, equation (6) becomes

$$\bar{x} = \frac{\alpha x - f^2}{x + \alpha - 2f},$$

which can be rearranged to obtain

$$\frac{\bar{x} - x}{(\bar{x} - f)(x - f)} = \frac{1}{f - \alpha},$$

or

$$\frac{1}{\bar{x} - f} - \frac{1}{x - f} = -\frac{1}{f - \alpha}.$$

Besides the fixed abscissa f, only one parameter remains. The parabolic projectivity may therefore be expressed in the form

$$\frac{1}{\bar{x} - f} = \frac{1}{x - f} + p,$$

where $x = f$ at the double fixed point, and p is a parameter.

2-5. Quadratic involution on a line

The mapping $\bar{x} = -x$ is called a *reflection* about the origin. It is of period two because—if the mapping is repeated—one obtains $\bar{\bar{x}} = -\bar{x} = x$, the identity mapping. The reflection is a special kind of projectivity of period two.

DEFINITION: *A* quadratic involution (*or more simply, an* involution) *is a projectivity of period two.*

If the projective mapping is denoted by M, then $MM = M^2 = I$, the identity mapping. By following each of M^2 and I by the inverse mapping M^{-1}, one has

$$M^{-1}(MM) = M^{-1}I.$$

The associative property holds for mappings, so $M^{-1}(MM) = (M^{-1}M)M = IM = M$ for the left member and $M^{-1}I = M^{-1}$ for the right member. Hence, it appears that for a mapping M of period two, the inverse mapping M^{-1} is the same as M. An involution may be defined as a mapping which is identical with its inverse

If p is the smallest integer for which $M^p = I$, then M is called a mapping of period p.* (See Exercise 10 below.)

In order to find the equation for an involution, require that point $P(x)$ map into $\bar{P}(\bar{x})$ by

$$\bar{x} = \frac{ax + b}{cx + d}$$

and that $\bar{P}(\bar{x})$ map into $P(x)$ by

$$x = \frac{a\bar{x} + b}{c\bar{x} + d}.$$

The last two equations may be written in the forms

$$cx\bar{x} - ax + d\bar{x} - b = 0,$$

$$cx\bar{x} - a\bar{x} + dx - b = 0.$$

On subtracting, one finds $(a + d)(x - \bar{x}) = 0$. Because the mapping is not the identity, $\bar{x} - x \neq 0$, so $d = -a$. Therefore, the equation of the involution is

$$\bar{x} = \frac{ax + b}{cx - a}$$

or

(7)
$$cx\bar{x} - a(x + \bar{x}) - b = 0.$$

Observe that equation (7) is symmetric in x and $\bar{x}$. An involution is therefore determined by a symmetric bilinear form, and is consequently a symmetric projectivity. Because equation (7) contains only two essential constants, an involution is determined by two pairs of corresponding points.

The modulus of equation (7) is $-a^2 - bc \equiv -(a^2 + bc)$ which is assumed to be nonzero. Because of this and because $d = -a$, the two roots x_1 and x_2 in equations (4) of Section 2-4 are distinct. Thus, an involution always has two distinct invariant points. If d is replaced by $-a$ in the formula of Section 2-4 for the characteristic invariant K, it is seen that $K = -1$. Hence, every pair of corresponding points separate the invariant points harmonically. An involution is determined by its invariant points and may therefore be given the equivalent

DEFINITION: *An involution is a projective correspondence between pairs of elements which separate two fixed elements harmonically.*

If x_1 and x_2 are, as before, the abscissas of the fixed points, then the equation of the involution is

(8)
$$(x_1 x_2 x \bar{x}) = -1.$$

(See equation (5) of Section 2-4.) Equation (8) can be put into the convenient form

---

* For such mappings with $p > 2$, see R. F. A. Clebsch, *Vorlesungen über Geometrie*, Teubner, 1906, Vol. 1, p. 398.

(9)
$$x\bar{x} - \frac{x_1 + x_2}{2}(x + \bar{x}) + x_1 x_2 = 0,$$

for which the modulus is $-\frac{1}{4}(x_1 - x_2)^2 \neq 0$.

From equation (7), it is seen that $x = a/c$ is the correspondent of the ideal point. Also from equation (7) the fixed points of the involution are given by $cx^2 - 2ax - b = 0$, from which $(x_1 + x_2)/2 = a/c$. Hence, the point $x = a/c$ is the midpoint of the segment joining the fixed points. It is, therefore, called the *center* of the involution.

It will be shown next that

THEOREM: *The product of the distances of every pair of corresponding points from the center of an involution is a constant.*

This constant is called the *power* of the involution. The power is given by

$$\left(x - \frac{a}{c}\right)\left(\bar{x} - \frac{a}{c}\right) = \left(\frac{cx - a}{c}\right)\left(\frac{ax + b}{cx - a} - \frac{a}{c}\right),$$

which reduces to $(a^2 + bc)/c^2$, independent of x. Note that an involution is determined by its center and its power. If the origin of abscissas is taken at the center, then $a = 0$, and the involution has the equation $x\bar{x} = b/c$.

Finally, observe that if $c = 0$ in equation (7), the involution is given by $x + \bar{x} = -b/a$, from which $(x + \bar{x})/2 = -b/2a$, so that the midpoint of the segment joining every pair of corresponding points is the same point with abscissa $-b/2a$. The mapping is seen to be a reflection followed by a translation. If the midpoint is the origin, then $b = 0$ and the mapping is merely the reflection $\bar{x} = -x$ about the origin.

EXERCISES

1. Show that if the characteristic invariant K has the value -1, the projectivity (2) is an involution.

2. Find the characteristic invariant of the affine mapping $\bar{x} = ax + b$ when $a \neq 1$.

3. Find the fixed points under the projectivity

$$\bar{x}x + 4\bar{x} - 5x - 6 = 0$$

and verify that the cross ratio of these points and any pair of corresponding points is a constant.

Ans. 7/2.

4. Find the value of k for which the points represented by $x^2 - x - 6 = 0$ separate harmonically the points given by $3x^2 - 5x + k = 0$.

Ans. $k = 41/2$.

5. Write the equation of the involution for which the invariant points have abscissas -2 and 6.

Ans. $\bar{x} = (2x + 12)/(x - 2)$.

6. Find the involution which takes the points $x = 2$, $x = 3$, into the points $x = -1$, $x = 0$, respectively.

$$\text{Ans. } \bar{x}x - (x + \bar{x}) + 3 = 0.$$

7. Prove that the characteristic invariant of the product of two projectivities having the same fixed points is the product of their characteristic invariants. (*Hint:* This can be done very simply by use of equation (5) in Section 2-4.)

8. Show that the product of two parabolic projectivities with the same double fixed point $x = f$, but with parameters p_1 and p_2, respectively, is a parabolic projectivity with parameter $p_1 + p_2$.

9. If x_1 and x_2 are the abscissas of the fixed points of a hyperbolic projectivity, show that the characteristic invariant is given by $(cx_1 + d)/(cx_2 + d)$.

10. Show that the projectivity M: $\bar{x} = \dfrac{ax + b}{cx + d}$ is of period 3, that is, $M^3 = I$, if and only if

$$a^2 + bc + ad + d^2 = 0.$$

11. Show that an involution has only one vanishing point, which is the center of the involution.

12. Show that (a) if the fixed points are chosen to be $x = \pm 1$, the hyperbolic projectivity takes the form

$$\bar{x} = \frac{x + \alpha}{\alpha x + 1},$$

(b) if the single fixed point is $x = 0$, the parabolic projectivity has the form

$$\bar{x} = \frac{x}{\alpha x + 1},$$

and (c) if the fixed points are $x = \pm i$, the elliptic projectivity is expressed by

$$\bar{x} = \frac{x - \alpha}{\alpha x + 1}.$$

13. Verify that the projectivity $x \to \bar{x}$ given by $\bar{x} = (ax + b)/(cx + d)$ can be effected by the sequence of mappings $x_1 = cx$, $x_2 = x_1 + d$, $x_3 = 1/x_2$, $x_4 = [(bc - ad)/c]x_3$, $\bar{x} = x_4 + (a/c)$. These mappings are, in turn, a stretching, a translation, an inversion, a stretching, and a translation.

2-6. Projectivity in homogeneous coordinates

Although homogeneous coordinates for points were introduced in Section 1-4, most of the intervening geometry of point ranges was developed by use of non-homogeneous coordinates. This procedure was due, in part, to a desire for simplicity in the analysis, and also, in part, to a natural tendency to employ metric notions in the development. When an abscissa x was used to locate a point, a distance was involved. Henceforth, projective notions will be considered primarily, and homogeneous projective coordinates will be found most convenient. It will be recalled, from Section 1-4, that the device of using number pairs to represent points allowed the addition of the point with the pair (1:0) to the euclidean line to obtain the projective line. There will be no need for the symbol ∞ in the homogeneous coordinates to be employed. Another advantage of homogeneous coordinates is that all equations are homogeneous.

Homogeneous projective coordinates of a point are defined as follows. Consider the three fixed points A, B, C on a line l with respective number pairs $(1:0)$, $(0:1)$, $(1:1)$ assigned to them. Then the number pair $(x_1:x_2)$ for any other point P on l is defined by

$$\frac{x_1}{x_2} = (ABCP).$$

If the cross ratio $(ABCP)$ is evaluated by replacing A by $(a_1:a_2)$, B by $(b_1:b_2)$, C by $(c_1:c_2)$, and P by $(p_1:p_2)$, the result is

$$\frac{c_1a_2 - a_1c_2}{c_1b_2 - c_2b_1} \frac{b_2p_1 - b_1p_2}{a_2p_1 - a_1p_2}.$$

Now put $a_1 = 1$, $a_2 = 0$, $b_1 = 0$, $b_2 = 1$, $c_1 = 1$, $c_2 = 1$ to obtain p_1/p_2, which will be written as $(x_1:x_2)$. Only the ratios of the coordinates are defined, that is, the points $(x_1:x_2)$ and $(kx_1:kx_2)$, with $k \neq 0$, are identical. And if two points coincide their homogeneous coordinates are proportional. There is no point with coordinates $(0:0)$.

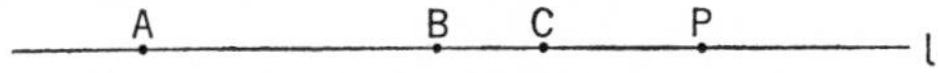

Figure 10

A geometrical interpretation of homogeneous coordinates can be seen as follows. From Fig. 10,

(10) $$(ABCP) = (PCBA) = \frac{BP/BC}{AP/AC} = \frac{x_1}{x_2}.$$

Note that BP/BC is the length of BP with BC as unit length, and that AP/AC is the length of AP with AC as unit length. The homogeneous coordinates of P are then any two numbers which are proportional to the distances from P to two base points B and A, the distances being measured in their respective units (BC and AC) and given the proper sign.

Remarks: The term "distance" continues to appear. The distance between two points is not invariant under a general projective mapping but the ratio of two distances, as in equation (10), is invariant because $(ABCP) = (\overline{A}\,\overline{B}\,\overline{C}\,\overline{P})$, where A maps into $\overline{A}$, B into $\overline{B}$, etc., under the projectivity. The set of all translations and rotations under which the distance between two points is invariant will be seen (Section 7-5) to be a subset of the set of projectivities in the plane. Although it is possible to develop projective geometry entirely independently of metric ideas, the present approach (using distance) has some merit in being simpler for the reader who approaches the subject for the first time.

2-7. Fixed points

In order to introduce gradually the use of homogeneous coordinates, the problem of finding the fixed points under a projectivity will be undertaken, although it was solved in Section 2-4 by use of nonhomogeneous coordinates. The general homography (projectivity) between two lines l and $\bar{l}$ (which are now taken as coinciding) is given by equation (10) in Section 1-5 as

$$(11) \qquad\qquad M: \qquad k\bar{x}_i = a_{ij}x_j, \qquad\qquad i, j = 1, 2,$$

where j is a dummy index indicating a sum. It is desired to find the fixed points under the mapping M. For a point with coordinates x_i to map into itself, the new coordinates $\bar{x}_i$ must be proportional to the x_i. Hence, equations* (11) read as

$$\lambda x_i = a_{ij}x_j$$

or

$$(12) \qquad\qquad a_{ij}x_j - \lambda x_i = 0,$$

where, at this point, λ is an arbitrary nonzero proportionality factor. In order to see the meaning of equations (12), write them in full to obtain

$$a_{11}x_1 + a_{12}x_2 - \lambda x_1 = 0,$$
$$a_{21}x_1 + a_{22}x_2 - \lambda x_2 = 0,$$

or

$$(13) \qquad\qquad \begin{aligned} (a_{11} - \lambda)x_1 + a_{12}x_2 &= 0, \\ a_{21}x_1 + (a_{22} - \lambda)x_2 &= 0. \end{aligned}$$

Now employ the theorem of Section 1-6 on homogeneous equations to show that a nontrivial solution for equations (13) exists if and only if

$$(14) \qquad\qquad \begin{vmatrix} a_{11} - \lambda & a_{12} \\ a_{21} & a_{22} - \lambda \end{vmatrix} = 0,$$

which puts the condition on λ that it satisfy a quadratic equation. Let the roots of (14) be denoted by λ_1 and λ_2. For $\lambda = \lambda_1$ the first equation of (13) gives

$$\frac{x_1}{x_2} = -\frac{a_{12}}{a_{11} - \lambda_1}.$$

Use of $\lambda = \lambda_1$ in the second of equations (13) gives

$$\frac{x_1}{x_2} = -\frac{a_{22} - \lambda_1}{a_{21}},$$

so that

$$\frac{a_{12}}{a_{11} - \lambda_1} = \frac{a_{22} - \lambda_1}{a_{21}},$$

which is seen to be a consequence of equation (14). Hence, the coordinates of one fixed point may be taken as $(-a_{12}, a_{11} - \lambda_1)$, or equivalently as $(a_{22} - \lambda_1, -a_{21})$.

---

* Although there is apparently only one equation in (11), the free index i assumes both of the values 1 and 2, so that there are actually two equations in (11). Use of the plural in referring to an equation with one or more free indices will occur frequently.

Use $\lambda = \lambda_2$ in the first of (13) to find the second fixed point $(-a_{12}, a_{11} - \lambda_2)$.

In preparation for generalization to spaces of higher dimension, the analysis from equation (12) will be written in more concise form as follows. First, note that equations (12) are identically,

$$(15) \qquad\qquad a_{ij}x_j - \lambda\delta_{ij}x_j = 0,$$

where δ_{ij}, called the Kronecker delta, is defined to have the value 1 if $i = j$, and 0 if $i \neq j$. Thus, $\delta_{11} = \delta_{22} = 1$, while $\delta_{12} = \delta_{21} = 0$. When $i = 1$ and j is allowed to sum over 1, 2 in (15), the result is the first of equations (13). In turn, where $i = 2$, equation (15) gives the second of (13). Equations (15) may be expressed in the form

$$(16) \qquad\qquad (a_{ij} - \lambda\delta_{ij})x_j = 0,$$

which are recognized as homogeneous equations that have a nontrivial solution if and only if

$$(17) \qquad\qquad |a_{ij} - \lambda\delta_{ij}| = 0,$$

which is merely another way of writing the determinantal equation (14).

As in Section 1-5, the matrix of the mapping in (11) is

$$(18) \qquad\qquad \begin{pmatrix} a_{11} & a_{12} \\ a_{21} & a_{22} \end{pmatrix},$$

or, more concisely, (a_{ij}). The modulus of the mapping, written $|a_{ij}|$, is nonzero for a nonsingular mapping. This is described by saying that the *rank* of the matrix (a_{ij}) is two. Observe that the matrix is not a number, but that the determinant of the matrix is a number obtained by expanding the determinant. In case $|a_{ij}| = 0$, then

$$a_{11}a_{22} - a_{12}a_{21} = 0$$

or

$$\frac{a_{11}}{a_{21}} = \frac{a_{12}}{a_{22}},$$

which shows that the two rows of the matrix are proportional.

If the matrix of the coefficients in equations (16), that is, the matrix $(a_{ij} - \lambda\delta_{ij})$, is written in full, one has

$$\begin{pmatrix} a_{11} - \lambda & a_{12} \\ a_{21} & a_{22} - \lambda \end{pmatrix}.$$

This is called the *characteristic matrix* of the matrix (a_{ij}). The determinant of the characteristic matrix is called the *characteristic polynomial*, and if the latter is equated to zero, as in equation (17), the result is called the *characteristic equation* of the matrix (a_{ij}). The *zeros* of the characteristic polynomial, which are the *roots* of the characteristic equation, are called the *characteristic numbers* for the matrix (a_{ij}). Note that the rank of the characteristic matrix is less than two if λ takes the value of a characteristic number. The German word eigenwerte may be translated as *proper values* or *characteristic values*, so the term eigenvalues is often used in English as synonymous with characteristic values.

All of the definitions in this section can be extended readily to apply to concepts in projective spaces of two and higher dimensions. For instance, equations (11) describe a projectivity of a plane into itself if i and j are allowed the range 1, 2, 3. (See Section 7-2.)

EXAMPLE

Find the characteristic values of the matrix

$$\begin{pmatrix} -4 & 12 \\ 1 & -5 \end{pmatrix}$$

and interpret the results relative to a projectivity on a line.

Solution: By definition, the characteristic values are the roots of

$$\begin{vmatrix} -4 - \lambda & 12 \\ 1 & -5 - \lambda \end{vmatrix} = 0$$

or of

$$\lambda^2 + 9\lambda + 8 = 0.$$

The characteristic values are therefore -1 and -8. An interpretation is that the projectivity

$$k\bar{x}_1 = -4x_1 + 12x_2,$$

$$k\bar{x}_2 = \quad x_1 - 5x_2,$$

has fixed points which are solutions of

$$(-4 - \lambda)x_1 + \quad 12 \quad x_2 = 0,$$

$$x_1 + (-5 - \lambda)x_2 = 0,$$

for $\lambda = -1$, and for $\lambda = -8$. With $\lambda = -1$, the first (or second) of the last two equations gives the fixed point $(4:1)$, and $\lambda = -8$ yields the fixed point $(-3:1)$.

Remark: The projectivity of this Example is

$$\bar{x} = \frac{-4x + 12}{x - 5}$$

in nonhomogeneous coordinates. The fixed points, obtained from the roots of $x^2 - x - 12 = 0$, are 4 and -3. Apparently, for the projectivity on a line, the λ matrix (that is, the characteristic matrix) is not necessary. The more general type of analysis was introduced here for the one-dimensional space to facilitate understanding, in a subsequent study, of projectivities in spaces of higher dimension.

EXERCISES

1. Determine the characteristic values of the matrix

$$\begin{pmatrix} -5 & 12 \\ 1 & -6 \end{pmatrix},$$

and interpret the results relative to a projective mapping on a line.

2. As an extension of the theory of Section 2-7, write the characteristic matrix of the three-by-three matrix

$$\begin{pmatrix} 1 & 1 & 1 \\ 6 & 0 & -2 \\ 0 & 0 & 1 \end{pmatrix}.$$

Write the characteristic polynomial. Find the characteristic values of the matrix. Attempt a generalization to the plane of the geometric interpretation presented in the text for the one-dimensional space.

3. Find the fixed points of the mapping $p\bar{x}_1 = x_1 + 12x_2$, $p\bar{x}_2 = 2x_1 - x_2$.

Ans. $(3, 1), (-2, 1)$.

CHAPTER 3

Geometry and Invariants

3-1. Binary forms

A homogeneous polynomial in any number of variables is called a *form*. (The term *quantic*, used formerly, is synonymous with form.) A form is called *binary*, *ternary, quaternary*, $\cdots$, *q-ary* according as it has two variables x_1, x_2; three variables x_1, x_2, x_3; four variables x_1, $\cdots$, x_4; $\cdots$; q variables x_1, $\cdots$, x_q. The *order* of a form is the algebraic degree of any one of its terms. A form is referred to as *linear, quadratic, cubic, quartic*, $\cdots$, *n-ic*, according as the degree is 1, 2, 3, 4, $\cdots$, n. Thus, a form of degree (or order) n and with q variables may be styled a *q-ary n*-ic. For instance,

$$a_1 x_1^3 + 3a_2 x_1^2 x_2 + 3a_3 x_1 x_2^2 + a_4 x_2^3$$

is a binary form (two variables). Its order is three. Therefore, it is described as a binary cubic form. Only binary forms will be considered.

A binary *n*-ic f can be expressed as

$$f \equiv a_0 x_1^n + {}_nC_1 a_1 x_1^{n-1} x_2 + {}_nC_2 a_2 x_1^{n-2} x_2^2 + \cdots + {}_nC_{n-1} a_{n-1} x_1 x_2^{n-1} + a_n x_2^n,$$

or, in the more compact form,

$$f \equiv \sum_{i=0}^{n} {}_nC_i a_i x_1^{n-i} x_2^i,$$

where the ${}_nC_i$ (the number of combinations of n objects taken i at a time) are the binomial coefficients; that is, ${}_nC_i$ is the coefficient of the $(i + 1)$th term in the expansion of $(x_1 + x_2)^n$. The coefficients in the binary *n*-ic could be written as A_0, A_1, $\cdots$, A_n, but the binomial coefficients are often convenient in working with forms. A binary quadratic form f may be written as

$$f \equiv a_{ij} x_i x_j \equiv a_{11} x_1 x_1 + a_{12} x_1 x_2$$

$$+ a_{21} x_2 x_1 + a_{22} x_2 x_2.$$

The matrix of its coefficients is

$$(a_{ij}) \equiv \begin{pmatrix} a_{11} & a_{12} \\ a_{21} & a_{22} \end{pmatrix}.$$

If it is true for a second-order matrix that $a_{12} = a_{21}$, the matrix is said to be *symmetric*. In the form f the product $x_1 x_2$ is the same as $x_2 x_1$, so the coefficient of each of these cross-product terms can be taken as $\frac{1}{2}(a_{12} + a_{21})$, and this would yield a symmetric matrix. Hence, there is no loss in generality in assuming that the matrix of the form is symmetric—that is, $a_{12} = a_{21}$.

EXAMPLE

Write the matrix of the form $2x_1^2 + 3x_1 x_2 + 4x_2^2$.

Solution: The symmetric matrix is

$$\begin{pmatrix} 2 & \frac{3}{2} \\ \frac{3}{2} & 4 \end{pmatrix}$$

although other matrices could be written. For instance, if the term $3x_1 x_2$ is written as $x_1 x_2 + 2x_2 x_1$, the matrix would be

$$\begin{pmatrix} 2 & 1 \\ 2 & 4 \end{pmatrix}.$$

3-2. Simultaneous invariant of two linear forms

Geometrically, a binary linear form represents one point in the following sense. On equating the binary linear form $a_i x_i \equiv a_1 x_1 + a_2 x_2$ to zero, it is seen that the equation is satisfied only by the point $(x_1 : x_2) \equiv (-a_2 : a_1)$. There is not much of geometrical interest in one point. However, consider a second binary linear form $b_i x_i \equiv b_1 x_1 + b_2 x_2$, which represents the point $(x_1 : x_2) \equiv (-b_2 : b_1)$. Now, with two points at hand, one may ask for a condition under which the two points coincide. An answer can be found from

$$-\frac{a_2}{a_1} = -\frac{b_2}{b_1},$$

in the form

$$a_1 b_2 - a_2 b_1 = 0.$$

Also, it may be required that the equations

(1)
$$\begin{aligned} a_1 x_1 + a_2 x_2 &= 0, \\ b_1 x_1 + b_2 x_2 &= 0 \end{aligned}$$

have a common nontrivial solution, the condition for which is that the determinant of the coefficients in (1) be zero; that is,

$$\begin{vmatrix} a_1 & a_2 \\ b_1 & b_2 \end{vmatrix} = 0$$

or, as before,

(2)
$$a_1 b_2 - a_2 b_1 = 0.$$

It is important to note that equation (2) contains a function of the coefficients of the pair of forms $a_i x_i$ and $b_i x_i$, the vanishing of which function has the geometric interpretation that the points represented by the two forms coincide.

The plan is now to transform $a_i x_i$ and $b_i x_i$ by $k x_i = c_{ij} \bar{x}_j$ to two new forms in the new variables $\bar{x}_i$. Two interpretations can be given for this process. First, the points x_i on l are mapped into points $\bar{x}_i$ on $\bar{l}$ (l and $\bar{l}$ do not necessarily coincide). It is to be expected that if the points represented by $a_i x_i$ and $b_i x_i$ on l coincide, then the points on $\bar{l}$ which are represented by the new forms should also coincide. The algebra to be developed will reveal this to be true. This first aspect of $k x_i = c_{ij} \bar{x}_j$ as a mapping of points has been called the "alibi" aspect. The second interpretation of $k x_i = c_{ij} \bar{x}_j$ is that a change of coordinates on line l is effected; the points on l remain fixed but their coordinates change. This is called the "alias" aspect. For instance, the translation $x = \bar{x} + h$ on a line moves every point a distance $|h|$ under the alibi aspect, whereas under the alias aspect the points are unchanged but the origin is shifted by a distance $|h|$. A simple illustration from plane analytical geometry is $x = \bar{x} + h$, $y = \bar{y} + k$, a translation in the plane. Under the alibi aspect, the axes are fixed but every point $(\bar{x}, \bar{y})$ is translated to a new position. Under the alias aspect there are two sets of axes (two coordinate systems) and a point has coordinates (x, y) in one system and different coordinates $(\bar{x}, \bar{y})$ in the other system. Either interpretation can be used in what follows.

The expression which $a_i x_i$ takes when transformed by $k x_i = c_{ij} \bar{x}_j$ is given by

$$a_i \left(\frac{1}{k} c_{ij} \bar{x}_j \right) = \frac{1}{k} a_i c_{ij} \bar{x}_j = \bar{a}_j \bar{x}_j,$$

from which the new coefficients $\bar{a}_j$ are given by

$$(3) \qquad \bar{a}_j = \frac{1}{k} a_i c_{ij}.$$

Similarly, the new coefficients $\bar{b}_j$ are given by

$$(4) \qquad \bar{b}_j = \frac{1}{k'} b_i c_{ij}.$$

The condition that the new forms $\bar{a}_j \bar{x}_j$ and $\bar{b}_j \bar{x}_j$ represent coincident points is $\bar{a}_1 \bar{b}_2 - \bar{a}_2 \bar{b}_1 = 0$. But how is $\bar{a}_1 \bar{b}_2 - \bar{a}_2 \bar{b}_1$ related to $a_1 b_2 - a_2 b_1$? Does the vanishing of one require the vanishing of the other? To calculate $\bar{a}_1 \bar{b}_2 - \bar{a}_2 \bar{b}_1$, note from (3) and (4) that

$$\bar{a}_1 \bar{b}_2 - \bar{a}_2 \bar{b}_1 = \frac{1}{kk'} (a_i c_{i1} b_h c_{h2} - a_i c_{i2} b_h c_{h1})$$

$$= \frac{1}{kk'} a_i b_h (c_{i1} c_{h2} - c_{i2} c_{h1}).$$

Note that a dummy index i was changed to h because an index indicating a summation must occur just twice. Observe also that when the double sum on i and h is carried out, the terms $a_1 b_1$ and $a_2 b_2$ are both multiplied by zero. The surviving terms yield the interesting result

$$\bar{a}_1 \bar{b}_2 - \bar{a}_2 \bar{b}_1 = \frac{1}{kk'} (a_1 b_2 -- a_2 b_1)(c_{11} c_{22} - c_{12} c_{21})$$

or

(5)
$$\begin{vmatrix} \bar{a}_1 & \bar{a}_2 \\ \bar{b}_1 & \bar{b}_2 \end{vmatrix} = \frac{1}{kk'} \begin{vmatrix} a_1 & a_2 \\ b_1 & b_2 \end{vmatrix} \begin{vmatrix} c_{11} & c_{12} \\ c_{21} & c_{22} \end{vmatrix},$$

which states that the function $\bar{a}_1\bar{b}_2 - \bar{a}_2\bar{b}_1$ is (up to the factor $1/kk'$) the same function in the original coefficients of the forms multiplied by the modulus $|c_{ij}|$ of the linear transformation $kx_i = c_{ij}\bar{x}_j$. Hence, if $a_1b_2 - a_2b_1 = 0$, then, since $|c_{ij}| \neq 0$, the function $\bar{a}_1\bar{b}_2 - \bar{a}_2\bar{b}_1$ must also be zero. Geometrically, if the two given forms a_ix_i and b_ix_i represent coincident points, then the transformed forms $\bar{a}_i\bar{x}_i$ and $\bar{b}_i\bar{x}_i$ also represent coincident points.

Because of the relation between $a_1b_2 - a_2b_1$ and $\bar{a}_1\bar{b}_2 - \bar{a}_2\bar{b}_1$ exhibited in (5), the function $a_1b_2 - a_2b_1$ of coefficients of the two given forms is called an *invariant* under the substitution $kx_i = c_{ij}\bar{x}_j$. Other instances of invariants and their geometrical meaning will be met later.

Remark: The vanishing or nonvanishing of an invariant is of significance. Note that the factor $1/kk'$ in (5) does not affect the vanishing of the invariant. Indeed, no loss of generality would have been incurred if the constants k and k' had each been taken as unity. Henceforth, a nonzero constant factor in an invariant will be neglected.

Equation (5) exhibits an instance of the following more general situation. Let a set of forms be given in the variables x_i. Transform the set by $x_i = c_{ij}\bar{x}_j$, with modulus $J \equiv |c_{ij}| \neq 0$, to a new set of forms in the variables $\bar{x}_i$.

DEFINITION: *If a function $\bar{I}$ of the coefficients of the new set of forms is equal to a power of the modulus times the same function I of the corresponding coefficients of the given set of forms, then the function $\bar{I}$ is called an* invariant *of the new set of forms.*

In symbols, this means that
$$\bar{I} = IJ^w.$$

The exponent w of the power to which the modulus J is raised is called the *weight* of the invariant. If $w = 0$, so that $I = \bar{I}$, the function I is called an *absolute* invariant. If $w \neq 0$, the function I is sometimes called a *relative* invariant. Note that the *set* of forms may consist of a single form.

The result in equation (5) shows that for the given set of forms a_ix_i and b_ix_i, an invariant I is the function $a_1b_2 - a_2b_1$, so (5) may be written as
$$\bar{I} = IJ,$$

which shows that $a_1b_2 - a_2b_1$ is an invariant of weight one. This invariant may be styled a *simultaneous* invariant of two binary linear forms.

3-3. Binary quadratic form

A single binary quadratic form $f \equiv a_{ij}x_ix_j$, when equated to zero, represents two points. This is seen as follows. Write the equation, assuming $a_{12} = a_{21}$, as

$$a_{11}x_1^2 + 2a_{12}x_1x_2 + a_{22}x_2^2 = 0.$$

For convenience, one may divide by x_2^2 and write x for the ratio $x_1 : x_2$, to obtain

(6) $$a_{11}x^2 + 2a_{12}x + a_{22} = 0.$$

The nature of the points determined by (6) is revealed by the *discriminant* $D \equiv (a_{12}^2 - a_{11}a_{22})$. (A factor 4 has been discarded here.) The *determinant* of the matrix of the form f is

$$d \equiv \begin{vmatrix} a_{11} & a_{12} \\ a_{21} & a_{22} \end{vmatrix},$$

which is the negative of the *discriminant* of the form f.

THEOREM: *The determinant of a binary quadratic form is an invariant of weight two.*

Proof: Algebraically, one carries out the linear substitution $x_i = c_{ij}\bar{x}_j$ on the form $f \equiv a_{ij}x_ix_j$ to obtain the transformed form $\bar{f} \equiv \bar{a}_{ij}\bar{x}_i\bar{x}_j$. Geometrically, one performs a projectivity on the points x_i of line l to obtain points $\bar{x}_i$ on line $\bar{l}$. In particular, the points determined by $f = 0$ on line l map into points determined by $\bar{f} = 0$ on line $\bar{l}$. By the substitution $x_i = c_{ij}\bar{x}_j$, one obtains

$$f \equiv a_{ij}x_ix_j = a_{ij}c_{ik}\bar{x}_kc_{jl}\bar{x}_l = a_{ij}c_{ik}c_{jl}\bar{x}_k\bar{x}_l = \bar{a}_{kl}\bar{x}_k\bar{x}_l \equiv \bar{f},$$

from which the new coefficients $\bar{a}_{kl}$ are given by

$$\bar{a}_{kl} = a_{ij}c_{ik}c_{jl}.$$

Note that the free indices on both sides are k and l. The determinant of the left member must equal the determinant of the right member of the last equation; that is,

(7) $$|\bar{a}_{kl}| = |a_{ij}c_{ik}c_{jl}|.$$

The right member can readily be verified to be the product of the three determinants $|a_{ij}|$, $|c_{ik}|$, $|c_{jl}|$. If d, $\bar{d}$ are the determinants of the forms f, $\bar{f}$, and, as before, J is the modulus of the mapping, then it is seen that

(8) $$\bar{d} = dJ^2,$$

so that d is an invariant of weight two. This completes the proof of the theorem.

Remark: Since $J \neq 0$, by hypothesis, the vanishing of d implies $\bar{d} = 0$; thus if the points determined by $f = 0$ coincide, then the points determined by $\bar{f} = 0$ also coincide. This instance shows again that the vanishing of an invariant implies a geometric property.

Although equation (7) can be shown by tedious algebra to lead to equation (8) for the simple case in which the subscripts vary over the range 1, 2, it will be seen in the following section that the step from equation (7) to (8) can be made immediately even for the range $1, \cdots, n$ of the subscripts.

3-4. Multiplication of matrices and of determinants

The product of the two square matrices

$$A \equiv (a_{ij}) \equiv \begin{pmatrix} a_{11} & a_{12} \\ a_{21} & a_{22} \end{pmatrix}, \quad B \equiv (b_{ij}) \equiv \begin{pmatrix} b_{11} & b_{12} \\ b_{21} & b_{22} \end{pmatrix}$$

is defined by

$$AB = (a_{ij})(b_{kl}) = \begin{pmatrix} a_{11}b_{11} + a_{12}b_{21} & a_{11}b_{12} + a_{12}b_{22} \\ a_{21}b_{11} + a_{22}b_{21} & a_{21}b_{12} + a_{22}b_{22} \end{pmatrix}.$$

Observe that the element in the upper left corner of the product matrix AB is $a_{1i}b_{i1}$, which is called the *inner* product of the first row of matrix A with the first column of matrix B. The element in the upper right corner of the matrix AB is $a_{1i}b_{i2}$. The elements in the second row of AB are $a_{2i}b_{i1}$ and $a_{2i}b_{i2}$. The product AB may therefore be expressed as the matrix

$$AB \equiv \begin{pmatrix} a_{1i}b_{i1} & a_{1i}b_{i2} \\ a_{2i}b_{i1} & a_{2i}b_{i2} \end{pmatrix}.$$

This, in turn, may be shortened to

$$(9) \qquad\qquad AB \equiv (a_{ki}b_{il}),$$

in which the repeated index i indicates that a sum takes place in each element, and the k and l take the value pairs 1, 1 and 1, 2 for the elements in the first row of AB, and 2, 1 and 2, 2 for the second row.

EXAMPLE 1

Multiply the matrices

$$A \equiv \begin{pmatrix} 1 & 2 \\ 3 & 4 \end{pmatrix}, \quad B \equiv \begin{pmatrix} -1 & 2 \\ 2 & -3 \end{pmatrix}.$$

Solution: By the rule stated above, the product AB is given by

$$AB = \begin{pmatrix} 1 & 2 \\ 3 & 4 \end{pmatrix}\begin{pmatrix} -1 & 2 \\ 2 & -3 \end{pmatrix} = \begin{pmatrix} -1+4 & 2-6 \\ -3+8 & 6-12 \end{pmatrix} = \begin{pmatrix} 3 & -4 \\ 5 & -6 \end{pmatrix}.$$

In order to show that multiplication of matrices is not commutative (that is, $AB \neq BA$), observe that

$$BA = \begin{pmatrix} -1 & 2 \\ 2 & -3 \end{pmatrix}\begin{pmatrix} 1 & 2 \\ 3 & 4 \end{pmatrix} = \begin{pmatrix} -1+6 & -2+8 \\ 2-9 & 4-12 \end{pmatrix} = \begin{pmatrix} 5 & 6 \\ -7 & -8 \end{pmatrix}.$$

The matrix AB is not the same as matrix BA. One must therefore be careful not to change the order in multiplying matrices. (See Exercises 3 and 5 below.)

If i and j in the matrices $A \equiv (a_{ij})$ and $B \equiv (b_{ij})$ range over $1, \cdots, n$ instead of 1, 2, the product AB is again defined by (9), in which k and l range also over $1, \cdots, n$. Further, if $A \equiv (a_{kr})$ is an $m \times n$ matrix—that is, if k ranges over

1, $\cdots$, m and r ranges over 1, $\cdots$, n so that A has m rows and n columns—and if $B \equiv (b_{sl})$ is an $n \times p$ matrix (n rows and p columns), then the product AB is defined again by (9), in which i is summed from 1, $\cdots$, n in each element, k ranges over 1, $\cdots$, m, and l over 1, $\cdots$, p. The product matrix $AB = (a_{ki}b_{il}) = (c_{kl})$, is then an $m \times p$ matrix (m rows and p columns). The following example exhibits the product of a 2×3 matrix and a 3×2 matrix.

EXAMPLE 2

If

$$A \equiv \begin{pmatrix} 2 & 1 \\ -1 & 2 \\ 0 & 1 \end{pmatrix}, \quad B \equiv \begin{pmatrix} 1 & 2 & 3 \\ 2 & -1 & 1 \end{pmatrix},$$

find the product AB.

Solution:

$$AB = \begin{pmatrix} 2 & 1 \\ -1 & 2 \\ 0 & 1 \end{pmatrix} \begin{pmatrix} 1 & 2 & 3 \\ 2 & -1 & 1 \end{pmatrix}$$

$$= \begin{pmatrix} (2)(1)+(1)(2) & (2)(2)+(1)(-1) & (2)(3)+(1)(1) \\ (-1)(1)+(2)(2) & (-1)(2)+(2)(-1) & (-1)(3)+(2)(1) \\ (0)(1)+(1)(2) & (0)(2)+(1)(-1) & (0)(3)+(1)(1) \end{pmatrix}$$

$$= \begin{pmatrix} 4 & 3 & 7 \\ 3 & -4 & -1 \\ 2 & -1 & 1 \end{pmatrix}.$$

If $A \equiv (a_{ij})$ and $B \equiv (b_{ij})$ are square matrices, the determinant of A, denoted by $|A|$, is $|a_{ij}|$, and the determinant of B is $|b_{ij}|$. The determinant of the product matrix AB, denoted by $|AB|$, is given by $|a_{ij}| |b_{kl}| = |a_{ij}b_{jl}|$. That is, the determinant of the product of two square matrices is the product of the determinants of the two matrices. Note that, since rows and columns of a determinant may be interchanged without altering the value of the determinant, it follows that $|A| = |a_{ij}| = |a_{ji}|$, and that $|AB| = |A| \, |B| = |B| \, |A|$.

EXAMPLE 3

If

$$A = \begin{pmatrix} 1 & 2 \\ 3 & 4 \end{pmatrix}, \quad B = \begin{pmatrix} -1 & 2 \\ 2 & -3 \end{pmatrix},$$

find the determinant of the product AB.

Solution: From Example 1, the product AB is given by

$$AB = \begin{pmatrix} 3 & -4 \\ 5 & -6 \end{pmatrix}.$$

Hence,

$$|AB| = \begin{vmatrix} 3 & -4 \\ 5 & -6 \end{vmatrix} = -18 + 20 = 2.$$

The same result is obtained from

$$|AB| = |A||B| = \begin{vmatrix} 1 & 2 \\ 3 & 4 \end{vmatrix} \begin{vmatrix} -1 & 2 \\ 2 & -3 \end{vmatrix} = (-2)(-1) = 2.$$

In general, for the determinant of the product of two square matrices of the same order,

$$|(a_{ij})(b_{kl})| = |a_{ij}| \, |b_{kl}| = |a_{ij}b_{jl}| = |b_{kr}a_{rl}|.$$

The product of three square matrices of the same order is given by

$$|(a_{ij})(b_{kl})(c_{rs})| = |a_{ij}b_{jl}| \, |c_{rs}| = |a_{ij}| \, |b_{kl}| \, |c_{rs}|.$$

In the theorem of the preceding section the new coefficients were found to be $\bar{a}_{kl} = a_{ij}c_{ik}c_{jl}$. The determinant of the matrix $(\bar{a}_{kl})$ can be written as

$$|\bar{a}_{kl}| = |a_{ij}| \, |c_{rs}| \, |c_{pq}|$$

or

$$\bar{d} = dJ^2,$$

as in (8). This result holds for the transformation $x_i = c_{ij}\bar{x}_j$ on the form $a_{ij}x_ix_j$, for the range $1, \cdots, n + 1$ of all subscripts. In this general case, the n-ary quadratic form $a_{ij}x_ix_j$ is transformed by an n-dimensional projectivity $x_i = c_{ij}\bar{x}_j$ to obtain the form $\bar{a}_{ij}\bar{x}_i\bar{x}_j$ in the new variables.

The concept of a *group* of projectivities will now be explained. Let S be the set of all nonsingular projectivities in one dimension. This is represented by $\bar{x}_i = c_{ij}x_j$, where the c_{ij} range over all real numbers for which $|c_{ij}| \neq 0$. The following attributes of the set S will be demonstrated:

1. *The product of any two members of S is a member of S.*
2. *The inverse of each member of S is a member of S.*

The set S is an instance of a *group*.* In order to show that attribute 1 holds, take any projectivity given by, say,

$$\bar{x}_i = \alpha_{ij}x_j, \qquad\qquad |\alpha_{ij}| \neq 0,$$

and any second projectivity

$$\bar{\bar{x}}_k = \beta_{ki}\bar{x}_i, \qquad\qquad |\beta_{ki}| \neq 0.$$

The product of the two projectivities is the projectivity given by

$$\bar{\bar{x}}_k = \beta_{ki}\alpha_{ij}x_j = c_{kj}x_j.$$

Hence, the product of any two projectivities is a projectivity. Note that if $A \equiv (\alpha_{ij})$ and $B \equiv (\beta_{ki})$, then the matrix $C \equiv (c_{kj})$ of the product projectivity is given by $C = BA$.

To show that attribute 2 holds, one may solve any projectivity $\bar{x}_i = \alpha_{ij}x_j$ in the set for x_j to obtain $x_j = \gamma_{jk}\bar{x}_k$, by virtue of the fact that $|\alpha_{ij}| \neq 0$. Note that $\bar{x}_i = \alpha_{ij}x_j$ and $\bar{\bar{x}}_k = \gamma_{ki}\bar{x}_i = \gamma_{ki}\alpha_{ij}x_j$, with $\bar{\bar{x}}_k \equiv x_k$. Hence, $\gamma_{ki}\alpha_{ij} = \delta_{kj}$. If Γ is the matrix (γ_{ki}), then $\Gamma A = I$, where I is the identity matrix (δ_{kj}). By

---

* For more information concerning the theory of groups and matrices the reader is referred to R. V. Andree, *Selections from Modern Abstract Algebra*, Holt, Rinehart & Winston, New York, 1958.

multiplying by A^{-1} (the inverse of the matrix A), one finds $\Gamma A A^{-1} = I A^{-1}$, or, since $A A^{-1} = I$, one has $\Gamma = A^{-1}$. The inverse of A may be defined as the matrix A^{-1} for which $A A^{-1} = A^{-1} A = I$. (See Exercise 9.)

Remark: In the group of projectivities the elements of the set are projectivities, and the *"product"* of two elements of the set means that one projectivity of the set is *followed by* another of the set to produce a projectivity of the set. The *group operation* here is that of taking the product of projectivities of the set. In any group, the group operation must be defined. For instance, for the operation of addition, the set of all positive and negative integers (including zero) form a group, because the sum of any two elements in the set is an integer, and the negative of each element is in the set. The sum of any element and its inverse (i.e., its negative) is zero, which is the (additive) identity element in the set. If the group operation is changed from addition to ordinary multiplication, the set of integers is no longer a group, because the quotient of two integers may not be in the set. Moreover, the element zero has no inverse.

EXERCISES

1. Use the invariant in equation (2) to determine the value of k for which the forms $2x_1 + 3x_2$ and $x_1 + kx_2$ represent the same point.

2. Carry out the transformation $x_1 = 2\bar{x}_1 + 3\bar{x}_2$, $x_2 = \bar{x}_1 + \bar{x}_2$ on the form $f \equiv x_1^2 + 4x_1x_2 + 2x_2^2$ to obtain the transformed form $\bar{f}$. Verify equation (8). Show that since f represents two distinct real points, $\bar{f}$ must also represent two distinct real points.

3. If M_1 is the mapping $\bar{x}_i = a_{ij}x_j$ with matrix $A \equiv (a_{ij})$, and M_2 is the mapping $\bar{\bar{x}}_j = b_{jk}\bar{x}_k$ with matrix $B \equiv (b_{jk})$, the product mapping (M_1 followed by M_2) is indicated by $M_3 = M_2M_1$. Show that the matrix of the mapping M_3 is the product matrix BA.

4. Use the result in Exercise 3 to find the product M_2M_1 of the projectivities

$$M_1: \qquad \bar{x}_1 = 2x_1 + 3x_2, \qquad M_2: \qquad \bar{x}_1 = x_1 - x_2,$$
$$\bar{x}_2 = x_1 + x_2, \qquad\qquad \bar{x}_2 = x_1 + 2x_2.$$

Ans. $\bar{x}_1 = x_1 + 2x_2$, $\bar{x}_2 = 4x_1 + 5x_2$.

5. Verify associativity in the product of three matrices; that is, show that $A(BC) = (AB)C$, where

$$A = \begin{pmatrix} 1 & 2 \\ 3 & 4 \end{pmatrix}, \quad B = \begin{pmatrix} 0 & 1 \\ -1 & 2 \end{pmatrix}, \quad C = \begin{pmatrix} 2 & -1 \\ 1 & 2 \end{pmatrix},$$

by calculating first the product of A and BC, and second, the product of AB and C.

Ans. The common result is $ABC = \begin{pmatrix} 1 & 12 \\ 3 & 26 \end{pmatrix}$.

6. Use matrices to show that the projectivity

$$\bar{x}_1 = 2x_1 - x_2,$$
$$\bar{x}_2 = 7x_1 - 3x_2$$

is of period 3. That is, verify that if A is the matrix of the transformation, then $A^3 = I$, where I is the identity matrix $\begin{pmatrix} 1 & 0 \\ 0 & 1 \end{pmatrix}$. (See Exercise 11 on p. 32.)

7. Show that

$$\Delta \equiv \begin{vmatrix} a & h & g \\ h & b & f \\ g & f & c \end{vmatrix}$$

is an invariant of the ternary quadratic form

$$f \equiv ax^2 + by^2 + cz^2 + 2fyz + 2gzx + 2hxy$$

under the linear substitution

$$x = \lambda_1 \bar{x} + \lambda_2 \bar{y} + \lambda_3 \bar{z},$$
$$L: \quad y = \mu_1 \bar{x} + \mu_2 \bar{y} + \mu_3 \bar{z},$$
$$z = \nu_1 \bar{x} + \nu_2 \bar{y} + \nu_3 \bar{z}.$$

Suggestion: The algebra is extremely tedious if the given notation is employed. Write the form as $f \equiv a_{ij} x_i x_j$, with x_1, x_2, x_3 identified with x, y, z, respectively. Then $\Delta \equiv |a_{ij}|$. Write L as $x_i = \lambda_{ij} \bar{x}_j$, with $i, j = 1, 2, 3$, and let $J \equiv |\lambda_{ij}|$. Now

$$f \equiv a_{ij} x_i x_j = a_{ij} \lambda_{ik} \bar{x}_k \lambda_{jl} \bar{x}_l = a_{ij} \lambda_{ik} \lambda_{jl} \bar{x}_k \bar{x}_l = \bar{a}_{kl} \bar{x}_k \bar{x}_l \equiv \bar{f},$$

where

$$\bar{a}_{kl} = a_{ij} \lambda_{ik} \lambda_{jl},$$

from which

$$\bar{\Delta} \equiv |\bar{a}_{kl}| = |a_{ij} \lambda_{ik} \lambda_{jl}| = |a_{ij}||\lambda_{rs}||\lambda_{pq}|,$$

so that

$$\bar{\Delta} = \Delta J^2.$$

8. Show that $\Delta = 0$ in Exercise 7, if and only if the form f is *reducible*, that is, f is the product of two linear factors. Hence, give a geometrical interpretation of the result in Exercise 7. (It may be noted that if z is set equal to 1 in f, then $f = 0$ gives the usual form of a conic in elementary analytical geometry. Take $\bar{z} = 1$ also, $\nu_1 = \nu_2 = 0$ and $\nu_3 = 1$, so that L becomes an affine mapping in the euclidean plane.)

9. Write out the four equations expressed by $\gamma_{ki} \alpha_{ij} = \delta_{kj}$, where all subscripts range over 1, 2. Assume $|\alpha_{ij}| \neq 0$ and solve for the elements γ_{ki} of the matrix $\Gamma \equiv (\gamma_{ki})$. Then verify that if $A \equiv (\alpha_{ij})$, then $\Gamma A = I$.

10. Show that if the two group properties 1 and 2 in Section 3-4 (p. 45) are satisfied, then the identity mapping must be in the set S.

11. In the theory of groups, associativity is usually a requirement. Show from the associativity of a product of matrices that the associativity requirement is always satisfied for projectivities.

3-5. Simultaneous invariant of two quadratic forms

It was seen in Section 3-3 that the points P_1, P_2 on line l represented by the binary quadratic form $f \equiv a_{ij} x_i x_j$ coincide if and only if the determinant $d \equiv |a_{ij}|$ vanishes. A second form $g \equiv b_{ij} x_i x_j$ represents two points Q_1, Q_2 on l. Suppose both $|a_{ij}|$ and $|b_{ij}|$ are not zero. Then four distinct points P_1, P_2, Q_1, Q_2 are given by $f = 0$ and $g = 0$. The question naturally arises: Under what condition(s) do Q_1, Q_2 separate P_1, P_2 harmonically? The answer is given in the following

THEOREM: *The points represented by*

$$f \equiv a_{ij}x_ix_j \equiv a_{11}x_1^2 + 2a_{12}x_1x_2 + a_{22}x_2^2 = 0$$

are separated harmonically by the points given by

$$g \equiv b_{ij}x_ix_j \equiv b_{11}x_1^2 + 2b_{12}x_1x_2 + b_{22}x_2^2 = 0$$

if, and only if,

(10) $$h_{fg} \equiv a_{11}b_{22} - 2a_{12}b_{12} + a_{22}b_{11} = 0.$$

Proof: Let the abscissas of the points P_1, P_2 given by $f \equiv a_{11}x^2 + 2a_{12}x + a_{22} = 0$ be x', x'', and those of Q_1, Q_2 given by $g \equiv b_{11}y^2 + 2b_{12}y + b_{22} = 0$ be y', y''. It is assumed that $(P_1P_2Q_1Q_2) = -1$, which is true if, and only if, $(x'x''y'y'') = -1$; that is,

$$\frac{y' - x'}{x' - x''} \div \frac{y'' - x'}{y'' - x''} = -1,$$

which takes the form

$$2(x'x'' + y'y'') - (x' + x'')(y' + y'') = 0.$$

The product $x'x''$ of the roots of $f = 0$ is a_{22}/a_{11} and the sum $x' + x''$ is $-2a_{12}/a_{11}$. Similar formulas obtain for $y'y''$ and $y' + y''$. Hence, the last equation becomes

$$2\left(\frac{a_{22}}{a_{11}} + \frac{b_{22}}{b_{11}}\right) - \left(-2\frac{a_{12}}{a_{11}}\right)\left(-2\frac{b_{12}}{b_{11}}\right) = 0,$$

which gives

$$h_{fg} \equiv a_{11}b_{22} - 2a_{12}b_{12} + a_{22}b_{11} = 0$$

to complete the proof of the theorem. (Observe that the steps of this algebraic development are reversible, so that $h_{fg} = 0$ implies that the four points are harmonic.)

Two binary quadratic forms f and g are said to be *apolar* in case $h_{f_g} = 0$.

EXAMPLE 1

Determine the value(s) of k for which the points given by

$$f \equiv 2x_1^2 - kx_1x_2 - 12x_2^2 = 0, \quad$$
$$g \equiv x_1^2 + kx_1x_2 - 15x_2^2 = 0$$

constitute a harmonic set.

Solution: Here $a_{11} = 2$, $a_{12} = -k/2$, $a_{22} = -12$, $b_{11} = 1$, $b_{12} = k/2$, $b_{22} = -15$. Hence, the condition in equation (10) requires that

$$(2)(-15) - 2\left(-\frac{k}{2}\right)\left(\frac{k}{2}\right) + (-12)(1) = 0,$$

which gives $k = \pm 2\sqrt{21}$.

EXAMPLE 2

Find the form which separates both $f \equiv x_1^2 + 4x_1x_2 + x_2^2 = 0$ and $g \equiv 2x_1^2 - 4x_1x_2 + x_2^2 = 0$ harmonically.

Solution: Let the desired form be $q \equiv q_{11}x_1^2 + 2q_{12}x_1x_2 + q_{22}x_2^2$. Because q is apolar to $f (h_{qf} = 0)$ and also to $g (h_{qg} = 0)$, then q_{11}, q_{12}, q_{22} must satisfy

$$(1)q_{11} - 2(2)q_{12} + (1)q_{22} = 0,$$
$$(1)q_{11} - 2(-2)q_{12} + (2)q_{22} = 0,$$

or

$$q_{11} - 4q_{12} + q_{22} = 0,$$
$$q_{11} + 4q_{12} + 2q_{22} = 0,$$

whose solutions are given by

$$q_{11}:q_{12}:q_{22} = \begin{vmatrix} -4 & 1 \\ 4 & 2 \end{vmatrix} : \begin{vmatrix} 1 & 1 \\ 2 & 1 \end{vmatrix} : \begin{vmatrix} 1 & -4 \\ 1 & 4 \end{vmatrix} = -12:-1:8.$$

Hence, the required form may be written as

$$q \equiv 6x_1^2 + x_1x_2 - 4x_2^2.$$

The type of solution here shows that the result is unique, for if it is supposed that some other form $l_{11}x_1^2 + 2l_{12}x_1x_2 + l_{22}x_2^2$ is harmonic to both f and g, then the l_{ij} are found to be proportional to the q_{ij} already obtained.

It has been seen that the cross ratio of four points on a line is invariant under a projectivity (Section 1-9). If f and g are subjected to the projectivity $x_i = c_{ij}\bar{x}_j$ to obtain $\bar{f}$ and $\bar{g}$, then $\bar{f} = 0$ and $\bar{g} = 0$ represent the points $\bar{P}_1$, $\bar{P}_2$, and $\bar{Q}_1$, $\bar{Q}_2$. The cross ratio $(\bar{P}_1\bar{P}_2\bar{Q}_1\bar{Q}_2) = (P_1P_2Q_1Q_2)$, so if the points P_1, P_2, Q_1, Q_2 constitute a harmonic set, then so do the points $\bar{P}_1$, $\bar{P}_2$, $\bar{Q}_1$, $\bar{Q}_2$; that is, if equation (10) holds for the unbarred coefficients, it must hold also for the barred coefficients of the transformed forms $\bar{f}$ and $\bar{g}$. This gives a geometric proof of the invariance of the polynomial in (10), which involves the coefficients of two forms. It is therefore called a *simultaneous invariant* of two binary quadratic forms. It is also called the *harmonic invariant* of f and g because of the geometric meaning of the vanishing of the invariant. An algebraic proof of invariance follows.

THEOREM: *The expression*

$$h_{fg} \equiv a_{11}b_{22} - 2a_{12}b_{12} + a_{22}b_{11}$$

is an invariant of the forms $f \equiv a_{ij}x_ix_j$ and $g \equiv b_{ij}x_ix_j$ under the substitution $x_i = c_{ij}\bar{x}_j$.

Proof: In order to simplify the writing, define the symbol ϵ_{ij} as follows: $\epsilon_{11} = \epsilon_{22} = 0$, $\epsilon_{12} = 1$, $\epsilon_{21} = -1$. If J is used again to denote the value $c_{11}c_{22} - c_{12}c_{21}$, then by use of the symbol ϵ_{ij}, one has, for instance,

$$\begin{vmatrix} c_{j1} & c_{j2} \\ c_{k1} & c_{k2} \end{vmatrix} = \epsilon_{jk} \begin{vmatrix} c_{11} & c_{12} \\ c_{21} & c_{22} \end{vmatrix} = \epsilon_{jk} J.$$

Note also that

$$\bar{h}_{\bar{f}\bar{g}} \equiv \bar{a}_{11}\bar{b}_{22} - 2\bar{a}_{12}\bar{b}_{12} + \bar{a}_{22}\bar{b}_{11} \equiv \begin{vmatrix} \bar{a}_{11} & \bar{a}_{12} \\ \bar{b}_{21} & \bar{b}_{22} \end{vmatrix} + \begin{vmatrix} \bar{b}_{11} & \bar{b}_{12} \\ \bar{a}_{21} & \bar{a}_{22} \end{vmatrix}$$

$$= \epsilon_{pq}\epsilon_{rs}\bar{a}_{pr}\bar{b}_{qs}.$$

In Section 3-3 it was seen that $\bar{a}_{pr} = a_{ij}c_{ip}c_{jr}$. Similarly, $\bar{b}_{qs} = b_{kl}c_{kq}c_{ls}$. Hence,

$$\bar{h}_{\bar{f}\bar{g}} \equiv \epsilon_{pq}\epsilon_{rs}\bar{a}_{pr}\bar{b}_{qs} = \epsilon_{pq}\epsilon_{rs}a_{ij}c_{ip}c_{jr}b_{kl}c_{kq}c_{ls}$$

$$= a_{ij}b_{kl}(\epsilon_{pq}c_{ip}c_{kq})(\epsilon_{rs}c_{jr}c_{ls}).$$

But

$$\epsilon_{pq}c_{ip}c_{kq} = c_{i1}c_{k2} - c_{i2}c_{k1} = \epsilon_{ik}J,$$

and $\epsilon_{rs}c_{jr}c_{ls} = \epsilon_{jl}J$, so that

$$\bar{h}_{\bar{f}\bar{g}} = \epsilon_{ik}\epsilon_{jl}a_{ij}b_{kl}J^2 = h_{fg}J^2,$$

which proves the theorem.

3-6. Resultant of two binary quadratic forms

The *resultant* (sometimes called the *eliminant*) of two binary forms f and g is a polynomial in the coefficients of the two forms which vanishes if and only if the two equations $f = 0$ and $g = 0$ have a root in common. The resultant R_{fg} of two binary quadratic forms $f \equiv a_{ij}x_ix_j$ and $g \equiv b_{ij}x_ix_j$ will be calculated by means of Sylvester's method of elimination. Divide each of the forms by x_2^2 and write $x = x_1/x_2$. The four equations

$$0x^3 + a_{11}x^2 + 2a_{12}x + a_{22} = 0,$$

$$a_{11}x^3 + 2a_{12}x^2 + a_{22}x + 0 = 0,$$

$$0x^3 + b_{11}x^2 + 2b_{12}x + b_{22} = 0,$$

$$b_{11}x^3 + 2b_{12}x^2 + b_{22}x + 0 = 0$$

are required to have a common solution. Because the equations are homogeneous in x^3, x^2, x, 1, a solution exists if and only if

$$R_{fg} \equiv \begin{vmatrix} 0 & a_{11} & 2a_{12} & a_{22} \\ a_{11} & 2a_{12} & a_{22} & 0 \\ 0 & b_{11} & 2b_{12} & b_{22} \\ b_{11} & 2b_{12} & b_{22} & 0 \end{vmatrix} = 0.$$

It can be verified that expansion of the determinant leads to the form

$$R_{fg} \equiv (a_{11}b_{22} - 2a_{12}b_{12} + a_{22}b_{11})^2 - 4(a_{11}a_{22} - a_{12}^2)(b_{11}b_{22} - b_{12}^2)$$

or

$$R_{fg} \equiv h_{fg}^2 - 4d_fd_g,$$

where d_f and d_g are the determinants of f and g.

The invariance of R_{fg} under a projectivity $x_i = c_{ij}\bar{x}_j$ is readily seen, as follows. It has been shown that h_{fg}, d_f, d_g are invariants of weight two. Hence,

$$\bar{R}_{\bar{f}\bar{g}} = \bar{h}_{\bar{f}\bar{g}}^2 - 4\bar{d}_{\bar{f}}\bar{d}_{\bar{g}} = h_{fg}^2 J^4 - 4d_f J^2 d_g J^2,$$

so that

$$\bar{R}_{\bar{f}\bar{g}} = R_{fg} J^4,$$

which means that R_{fg} is an invariant of weight four. The geometrical interpretation is that if two binary quadratic forms f and g have a point in common, this property is not disturbed by a projectivity on the forms. Also, the fact that coincident points project into coincident points is seen from the fact that d_f is invariant.

EXERCISES

1. Determine the value(s) of k for which the points given by $x_1^2 - 2x_1x_2 - 3x_2^2 = 0$ separate the pair $x_1^2 - 8x_1x_2 + kx_2^2 = 0$ harmonically.

2. Find the form which is apolar to both $f \equiv a_{ij}x_ix_j$ and $g \equiv b_{ij}x_ix_j$.

3. Show that if f is a binary quadratic form the resultant of the forms $\partial f/\partial x_1$ and $\partial f/\partial x_2$ is d_f, the determinant of f, and deduce that $f = 0$ has coincident roots if and only if the first partial derivatives of f have a common zero.

4. Use $R_{fg} \equiv h_{fg}^2 - 4d_f d_g$ to show that the forms $x_1^2 - 2x_1x_2 + 3x_2^2$ and $2x_1^2 + 3x_1x_2 + 2x_2^2$ do not have a common zero.

5. From the relative invariants

$$\bar{d}_f = d_f J^2, \quad \bar{d}_g = d_g J^2$$

deduce that d_f/d_g is an absolute invariant.

6. Find a condition on the coefficients of the cubic equation

$$ax^3 + 3bx^2 + 3cx + d = 0$$

under which two roots coincide. (*Hint:* If $f(x) = 0$ has a double root at $x = \alpha$, then $f'(\alpha) = 0$. Hence, write the eliminant of the cubic form and its derivative.

> *Ans.* $6abcd - 4ac^3 - a^2d^2 + 3b^2c^2 - 4b^3d = 0$, or, equivalently, $(ad - bc)^2 - 4(ac - b^2)(bd - c^2) = 0$.

7. Show that a form $k \equiv d_{ij}x_ix_j$ exists for which its points separate harmonically the points $f \equiv a_{ij}x_ix_j = 0$, $g \equiv b_{ij}x_ix_j = 0$, $h \equiv c_{ij}x_ix_j = 0$, if and only if

$$\begin{vmatrix} a_{11} & a_{12} & a_{22} \\ b_{11} & b_{12} & b_{22} \\ c_{11} & c_{12} & c_{22} \end{vmatrix} = 0.$$

Show that this determinant is a simultaneous invariant of the forms f, g, h, and that the vanishing of the determinant implies that the three pairs of points given by f, g, h are in involution.

3-7. Covariants, jacobians and hessians

An invariant I of a form or a set of forms was given in Section 3-2 as a function of the *coefficients* of the forms, which transforms by a projectivity $x_i = c_{ij}\bar{x}_j$ into $\bar{I}$ such that $\bar{I} = IJ^\omega$, where $J \equiv |c_{ij}|$.

DEFINITION: *A covariant of a set of forms is a function F of the coefficients and variables of the forms, which transforms by a projectivity* $x_i = c_{ij}\bar{x}_j$ *into a function $\bar{F}$ for which $\bar{F} = FJ^\omega$.*

The Jacobian

In order to exhibit the *jacobian* (after C. G. J. Jacobi, 1804–1851) of two binary quadratic forms f and g as an instance of a covariant, the meaning of the jacobian of any two functions of two variables x_1 and x_2 will be explained next. The *jacobian J* of two functions $\phi(x_1, x_2)$ and $\psi(x_1, x_2)$ is the functional determinant

$$J_{\phi\psi} \equiv \begin{vmatrix} \dfrac{\partial \phi}{\partial x_1} & \dfrac{\partial \phi}{\partial x_2} \\ \dfrac{\partial \psi}{\partial x_1} & \dfrac{\partial \psi}{\partial x_2} \end{vmatrix} = \begin{vmatrix} \phi_1 & \phi_2 \\ \psi_1 & \psi_2 \end{vmatrix}.$$

In particular, the jacobian of $f \equiv a_{ij}x_ix_j$ and $g \equiv b_{ij}x_ix_j$ is given by

$$J_{fg} \equiv \begin{vmatrix} f_1 & f_2 \\ g_1 & g_2 \end{vmatrix} = \begin{vmatrix} 2a_{11}x_1 + 2a_{12}x_2 & 2a_{12}x_1 + 2a_{22}x_2 \\ 2b_{11}x_1 + 2b_{12}x_2 & 2b_{12}x_1 + 2b_{22}x_2 \end{vmatrix}.$$

On expanding the determinant (and neglecting the factor 4), one finds

$$(11) \quad J_{fg} \equiv (a_{11}b_{12} - a_{12}b_{11})x_1^2 + (a_{11}b_{22} - a_{22}b_{11})x_1x_2 + (a_{12}b_{22} - a_{22}b_{12})x_2^2,$$

which is again a binary quadratic form.

Remark: Note that the jacobian of the projectivity $x_i = c_{ij}\bar{x}_j$ is

$$\begin{vmatrix} \dfrac{\partial x_1}{\partial \bar{x}_1} & \dfrac{\partial x_1}{\partial \bar{x}_2} \\ \dfrac{\partial x_2}{\partial \bar{x}_1} & \dfrac{\partial x_2}{\partial \bar{x}_2} \end{vmatrix} = \begin{vmatrix} c_{11} & c_{12} \\ c_{21} & c_{22} \end{vmatrix} = |c_{ij}|,$$

which explains the choice of the notation J for the modulus of the projectivity used heretofore.

It is desirable to write equation (11) in a more compact form. For this purpose use the symbol ϵ_{ij} introduced in Section 3-5. Also, it should be seen that if $f \equiv a_{ij}x_ix_j$ then $\frac{1}{2}(\partial f/\partial x_i) = a_{ik}x_k$. On neglecting the factor 4, one obtains equation (11) as follows:

$$(11') \qquad J_{fg} \equiv \begin{vmatrix} \dfrac{\partial f}{\partial x_1} & \dfrac{\partial f}{\partial x_2} \\ \dfrac{\partial g}{\partial x_1} & \dfrac{\partial g}{\partial x_2} \end{vmatrix} = \epsilon_{ij} \dfrac{\partial f}{\partial x_i} \dfrac{\partial g}{\partial x_j}$$

$$= \epsilon_{ij}a_{ik}x_kb_{jl}x_l = (\epsilon_{ij}a_{ik}b_{jl})x_kx_l.$$

The covariance of J_{fg} will be demonstrated in the proof of the following

THEOREM: *The jacobian J_{fg} of two binary quadratic forms f and g is a covariant of weight one.*

Proof: Observe that because $f \equiv a_{ij}x_i x_j$ transforms to $\bar{f} \equiv \bar{a}_{ij}\bar{x}_i \bar{x}_j$ by $x_i = c_{ij}\bar{x}_j$, it follows by the chain rule of the calculus that, for instance,

$$\frac{\partial \bar{f}}{\partial \bar{x}_1} = \frac{\partial f}{\partial x_1}\frac{\partial x_1}{\partial \bar{x}_1} + \frac{\partial f}{\partial x_2}\frac{\partial x_2}{\partial \bar{x}_1} = \frac{\partial f}{\partial x_i}\frac{\partial x_i}{\partial \bar{x}_1}$$

and that

(12)
$$\frac{\partial \bar{f}}{\partial \bar{x}_k} = \frac{\partial f}{\partial x_i}\frac{\partial x_i}{\partial \bar{x}_k}.$$

Now use (11') and (12) to calculate J_{fg} in the barred variables:

$$\bar{J}_{\bar{f}\bar{g}} = \epsilon_{kl}\frac{\partial \bar{f}}{\partial \bar{x}_k}\frac{\partial \bar{g}}{\partial \bar{x}_l} = \epsilon_{kl}\frac{\partial f}{\partial x_i}\frac{\partial x_i}{\partial \bar{x}_k}\frac{\partial g}{\partial x_j}\frac{\partial x_j}{\partial \bar{x}_l}$$

$$= \frac{\partial f}{\partial x_i}\frac{\partial g}{\partial x_j}\epsilon_{kl}\frac{\partial x_i}{\partial \bar{x}_k}\frac{\partial x_j}{\partial \bar{x}_l} = \frac{\partial f}{\partial x_i}\frac{\partial g}{\partial x_j}\epsilon_{ij}|c_{pq}| = J_{fg}|c_{pq}|.$$

If the modulus $|c_{pq}|$ of the projectivity is denoted by J as before, it is seen that

$$\bar{J}_{\bar{f}\bar{g}} = J_{fg}J,$$

which completes the proof.

Remark: A form such as $f \equiv a_{ij}x_i x_j$ is a covariant itself, because $f = fJ^0 = f$ under $x_i = c_{ij}\bar{x}_j$.

The jacobian J_{fg}, being a binary quadratic form, represents two "jacobian" points (denote them by J_1, J_2) on the line containing the points P_1, P_2, given by $f = 0$, and the points Q_1, Q_2, given by $g = 0$. A geometrical property of J_1, J_2 is seen in the

THEOREM: *A form u separates the forms $f \equiv a_{ij}x_i x_j$ and $g \equiv b_{ij}x_i x_j$ harmonically if and only if u is the jacobian form J_{fg}.*

Proof: The "if" part of the proof will be given first. To effect this, let the form u be J_{fg}, and calculate the harmonic invariant of f and J_{fg} [denote it by $h(f, J_{fg})$] to obtain

$$h(f, J_{fg}) \equiv a_{11}(a_{12}b_{22} - a_{22}b_{12}) - a_{12}(a_{11}b_{22} - a_{22}b_{11}) + a_{22}(a_{11}b_{22} - a_{12}b_{11}) \equiv 0.$$

Similarly, find $h(g, J_{fg}) \equiv 0$. Hence the jacobian form separates f and g harmonically.

The reader may be interested to see that if the notation in Section 3-5 is used for the harmonic invariant—that is, $h_{fg} \equiv \epsilon_{pq}\epsilon_{rs}a_{pr}b_{qs}$—then, on replacing the b_{qs} by the coefficients $\epsilon_{ij}a_{iq}b_{js}$ in the jacobian form, the calculation for $h(f, J_{fg})$ may be carried out as follows. First,

$$h(f, J_{fg}) \equiv \epsilon_{pq}\epsilon_{rs}a_{pr}(\epsilon_{ij}a_{iq}b_{js}) = (\epsilon_{ij}\epsilon_{pq}a_{pr}a_{iq})(\epsilon_{rs}b_{js}) = (\epsilon_{ij}\epsilon_{ri}a)(\epsilon_{rs}b_{js}),$$

where a is the determinant

$$\begin{vmatrix} a_{11} & a_{12} \\ a_{21} & a_{22} \end{vmatrix}.$$

Now verify that $\epsilon_{ij}\epsilon_{ri} = -\delta_{jr}$, where δ_{jr} is the Kronecker delta. Thus, to continue,

$$h(f, J_{fg}) = -\delta_{jr}\epsilon_{rs}b_{js}a = \delta_{jr}\epsilon_{sr}b_{js}a = (\epsilon_{sj}b_{js})a,$$

which is identically zero because $\epsilon_{sj}b_{js} = \epsilon_{1j}b_{j1} + \epsilon_{2j}b_{j2} = b_{21} - b_{12} \equiv 0$.

Next, to prove the "only if" part of the theorem, suppose there is another form $u \equiv lx_1^2 + 2mx_1x_2 + nx_2^2$ such that the points $u = 0$ separate the points $f = 0$ and the points $g = 0$ harmonically. Then the conditions

$$h(u, f) \equiv a_{11}n - 2a_{12}m + a_{22}l = 0,$$

$$h(u, g) \equiv b_{11}n - 2b_{12}m + b_{22}l = 0$$

must obtain. The solution for the ratios $n:m:l$ is given by

$$n:m:l = \begin{vmatrix} -2a_{12} & a_{22} \\ -2b_{12} & b_{22} \end{vmatrix} : \begin{vmatrix} a_{22} & a_{11} \\ b_{22} & b_{11} \end{vmatrix} : \begin{vmatrix} a_{11} & -2a_{12} \\ b_{11} & -2b_{12} \end{vmatrix},$$

so that the form u is

$$u \equiv (a_{11}b_{12} - a_{12}b_{11})x_1^2 + (a_{11}b_{22} - a_{22}b_{11})x_1x_2 + (a_{12}b_{22} - a_{22}b_{12})x_2^2,$$

which is the jacobian J_{fg}. This completes the proof.

In order to study further the jacobian points J_1 and J_2, it will now be shown that the discriminant of the jacobian of f and g is equal to the resultant of f and g. That is, in symbols,

$$D_{J_{fg}} \equiv R_{fg}.$$

It will be remembered that the discriminant D_f of the form $f \equiv a_{ij}x_ix_j$, for instance, is the negative of the determinant

$$\begin{vmatrix} a_{11} & a_{12} \\ a_{21} & a_{22} \end{vmatrix}$$

of the same form.

The discriminant $D_{J_{fg}}$ of the jacobian form (11) is given by

$$D_{J_{fg}} \equiv (a_{11}b_{22} - a_{22}b_{11})^2 - 4(a_{11}b_{12} - a_{12}b_{11})(a_{12}b_{22} - a_{22}b_{12}),$$

which can be cast into the form of R_{fg} in Section 3-6. Hence,

(13) $$D_{J_{fg}} = R_{fg} = h_{fg}^2 - 4d_fd_g.$$

Several facts can be deduced from equation (13). First, if the points P_1, P_2 are real ($d_f > 0$), and Q_1, Q_2 are given by complex numbers ($d_g < 0$), then, since h_{fg} is real, $D_{J_{fg}}$ is positive, so J_1, J_2 are real points. Of course, interchanging the roles of P_1, P_2 and Q_1, Q_2 gives the same conclusion.

In order to deduce another fact from (13), the cross ratio $(P_1P_2Q_1Q_2)$ will be calculated. Denote the roots of $f = 0$ and $g = 0$ by x', x'' and y', y''. Then,

$$(P_1P_2Q_1Q_2) = (x'x''y'y'') = \frac{x'x'' + y'y'' - x'y'' - x''y'}{x'x'' + y'y'' - x''y'' - x'y'}.$$

If the roots are substituted into the last member of the cross-ratio expression, it can be reduced to

$$\frac{a_{11}b_{22} + a_{22}b_{11} - 2a_{12}b_{12} + 2\sqrt{d_f d_g}}{a_{11}b_{22} + a_{22}b_{11} - 2a_{12}b_{12} - 2\sqrt{d_f d_g}} = \frac{h_{fg} + 2\sqrt{d_f d_g}}{h_{fg} - 2\sqrt{d_f d_g}}.$$

Rationalizing the last fraction and using equation (13) lead to

(14) $$(P_1P_2Q_1Q_2) = \frac{R_{fg}}{(h_{fg} - 2\sqrt{d_f d_g})^2}.$$

It can be seen from equations (13) and (14) that if the pairs P_1, P_2; Q_1, Q_2; J_1, J_2 are all real, then

$$(P_1P_2Q_1Q_2) > 0,$$

so that Q_1, Q_2 do not separate P_1, P_2.

A geometrical construction of J_1, J_2, for the case just discussed, will now be shown. Let the points P_1, P_2 and Q_1, Q_2 be given on line l (Fig. 11). Take any circles C_1 and C_2 through P_1, P_2 and Q_1, Q_2, respectively, and such that they intersect in points R, S. Let RS intersect l at O. From analytical geometry it is known that the lengths of the tangents OT_1 and OT_2 from O to C_1 and C_2 are equal. The circle with radius $OT_1 = OT_2$ and center at O intersects l in the jacobian points J_1 and J_2. (It is understood that point O is outside both C_1 and C_2.)

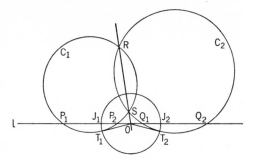

Figure 11

Proof of the Construction: It is required to show that $(J_1J_2Q_1Q_2) = (J_1J_2P_1P_2) = -1$. It will suffice to show that $(J_1J_2Q_1Q_2) = -1$. Observe that if $OJ_2 = OT_2 = r$, $OQ_1 = p$, $OQ_2 = q$, then by a theorem in plane geometry,

$$r^2 = pq,$$

so that

$$(J_1J_2Q_1Q_2) = (-r, r, p, q) = \frac{p+r}{p-r} \div \frac{\dfrac{r^2}{p} + r}{\dfrac{r^2}{p} - r} = -1.$$

Therefore, the jacobian points of f and g separate Q_1, Q_2 harmonically.

A third fact to be deduced from equation (13) is that if the jacobian points coincide, then the resultant of f and g vanishes; thus $f = 0$ and $g = 0$ have a point in common.

Finally, if the pairs P_1, P_2 and Q_1, Q_2 are real and if the jacobian points are not real, then, from (14), $(P_1P_2Q_1Q_2) < 0$, so that P_1, P_2 separate Q_1, Q_2.

The Hessian

The jacobian of two forms was defined as the determinant of their first partial derivatives. Another covariant arises as follows. The *hessian* (after Otto Hesse, 1811–1874) of a single binary form f is defined as the jacobian of the two first partial derivatives f_1 and f_2. Thus, if H_f denotes the hessian of f,

$$H_f \equiv \begin{vmatrix} \dfrac{\partial^2 f}{\partial x_1^2} & \dfrac{\partial^2 f}{\partial x_1 \partial x_2} \\[2mm] \dfrac{\partial^2 f}{\partial x_2 \partial x_1} & \dfrac{\partial^2 f}{\partial x_2^2} \end{vmatrix},$$

then the hessian of f is the determinant of the second partial derivatives of f. Note that if f is a function of degree $p \geq n$ in n variables $x_1, \cdots, x_n$, then the hessian H_f of f is given by the functional determinant

$$H_f \equiv \begin{vmatrix} f_{11} & f_{12} & \cdots & f_{1n} \\ f_{21} & f_{22} & \cdots & f_{2n} \\ \cdots & \cdots & \cdots \\ f_{n1} & f_{n2} & \cdots & f_{nn} \end{vmatrix} \equiv |f_{ij}|, \qquad i, j = 1, \cdots, n.$$

THEOREM: *The hessian of a binary n-ic is a covariant of weight two.*

Proof: Let the form $f(x_1, x_2)$ of degree n be transformed into $\bar{f}(\bar{x}_1, \bar{x}_2)$ by the substitution $x_i = c_{ij}\bar{x}_j$. By the chain rule,

$$\frac{\partial \bar{f}}{\partial \bar{x}_j} = \frac{\partial f}{\partial x_i}\frac{\partial x_i}{\partial \bar{x}_j} = c_{ij}\frac{\partial f}{\partial x_i}, \qquad i, j = 1, \cdots, n,$$

and

(15) $$\frac{\partial^2 \bar{f}}{\partial \bar{x}_k \partial \bar{x}_j} = c_{ij}\frac{\partial}{\partial x_l}\left(\frac{\partial f}{\partial x_i}\right)\frac{\partial x_l}{\partial \bar{x}_k} = c_{ij}\frac{\partial^2 f}{\partial x_l \partial x_i} c_{lk}.$$

On taking the determinant of the first and last members of (15), there results

$$\overline{H}_f \equiv \left|\frac{\partial^2 \bar{f}}{\partial \bar{x}_k \partial \bar{x}_j}\right| = \left|c_{ij}\frac{\partial^2 f}{\partial x_l \partial x_i} c_{lk}\right| = \left|c_{ij}\frac{\partial^2 f}{\partial x_l \partial x_i}\right| |c_{lk}| = |c_{pq}|^2 \left|\frac{\partial^2 f}{\partial x_l \partial x_i}\right|,$$

from which

(16) $$\overline{H}_f = H_f J^2,$$

which proves the theorem.

If, for instance, f is a binary cubic form, then the functional determinant

$$H_f \equiv \begin{vmatrix} f_{11} & f_{12} \\ f_{21} & f_{22} \end{vmatrix}$$

is of degree 2 in the two variables. This is seen as follows. If f is of degree 3, then each second partial derivative is of degree $3 - 2$, and the expansion of the determinant gives a form of degree $2(3 - 2) = 2$. To generalize to a binary n-ic, note that each term in the hessian is of degree $n - 2$; therefore the degree of the second-order determinant is $2(n - 2)$. For a ternary n-ic, the hessian is of degree $3(n - 2)$. A binary quadratic form represents two points. Its hessian is its determinant (see Exercise 6), so the vanishing of the hessian is a condition for the two points represented by f to coincide. If f is a binary cubic, it represents three points, and its hessian represents two points. A geometrical interpretation of the "hessian points" in this more general case appears in Section 3-10. The vanishing of a ternary cubic form represents a set of points which will be seen later to be a cubic curve in the plane. The hessian for such a form is of degree $3(3 - 2) = 3$, and its vanishing also represents a cubic curve.

The geometrical interpretation of the vanishing of the jacobian of two binary quadratic forms f and g is seen in the fact that the jacobian points J_1, J_2 are the double points of the involution determined by the pairs of points given by $f = 0$ and $g = 0$. (See Section 2-5.) The proof is left to the reader.

3-8. A pencil of binary quadratic forms

The definition of a *linear combination* of the elements of a set will be given, and then some examples of this concept will be shown.

DEFINITION: *If the elements of a set are* A_1, A_2, $\cdots$, A_n, *the expression* $c_1 A_1 + c_2 A_2 + \cdots + c_n A_n$, *where* c_1, c_2, $\cdots$, c_n *(not all zero) are arbitrary constants, is called a* linear combination *of the elements of the set.* (It is to be understood that the operations of multiplication and addition are defined here as in elementary algebra.)

As a first instance, consider a set of two elements A_1, A_2 to be the pair of linear functions $x + y - 3$, $2x - y + 9$. The combination $\lambda_1(x + y - 3) + \lambda_2(2x - y + 9)$ with λ_1 and λ_2 arbitrary constants (not both zero), is again a linear function for every choice of λ_1 and λ_2. For $\lambda_1 = 0$, $\lambda_2 = 1$, the element $2x - y + 9$ is represented, and for $\lambda_1 = 1$, $\lambda_2 = 0$, the element $x + y - 3$ is obtained. A geometrical interpretation is that the lines l_1: $x + y - 3 = 0$, l_2: $2x - y + 9 = 0$, give rise to all the lines exhibited by the linear combination $\lambda_1 l_1 + \lambda_2 l_2 = 0$, or $\lambda_1(x + y - 3) + \lambda_2(2x - y + 9) = 0$. Only the ratio $\lambda_1 : \lambda_2$ is significant here, so that $\lambda_1 l_1 + \lambda_2 l_2 = 0$ represents a singly infinite set of lines, all of which contain the point which makes both $x + y - 3$ and $2x - y + 9$ zero. This set of elements (lines in this case), is called a *pencil* of lines, which is determined by the *base* lines l_1 and l_2. Observe that the essence of the problem of solving $x + y - 3 = 0$ with $2x - y + 9 = 0$ for the intersection $(-2, 5)$ is to find the line $x + 2 = 0$ (corresponding to $\lambda_1 : \lambda_2 = 1 : 1$) of the pencil, and the line $y - 5 = 0$ (corresponding to $\lambda_1 : \lambda_2 = 2 : -1$).

As a second example, consider three lines l_1, l_2, l_3 in the plane. If constants α_1, α_2 can be found such that $l_3 \equiv \alpha_1 l_1 + \alpha_2 l_2$, then, by the previous example, $l_3 = 0$ is a member of the pencil of lines determined by l_1 and l_2. In this case, l_3 is said to be *linearly dependent* on l_1 and l_2, or that l_1, l_2, l_3 are three *linearly dependent* lines. Note that in this case $\lambda_1 l_1 + \lambda_2 l_2 + \lambda_3 l_3 = 0$, where $\lambda_1 = \alpha_1$, $\lambda_2 = \alpha_2$, $\lambda_3 = -1$. In general, if constants λ_1, λ_2, λ_3 (not all zero) can be found such that $\lambda_i l_i = 0$, with $i = 1, 2, 3$, then the three lines $l_i = 0$, are said to be *linearly dependent*, which means that they have a point in common.

If the lines $l_i = 0$, with $i = 1, 2, 3$, are *linearly independent* (that is, not linearly dependent), then they form a triangle of nonzero area. It can be shown (see Exercise 9 on p. 61) that any line $l_4 = 0$ in the plane can be expressed as a linear combination of l_1, l_2, l_3. That is, any four lines in the plane are linearly dependent.

If the two elements A_1, A_2 are the points with coordinates (x_1, y_1), (x_2, y_2), then the linear combination $\lambda_1 A_1 + \lambda_2 A_2$ is interpreted as the point with coordinates $(\lambda_1 x_1 + \lambda_2 x_2, \lambda_1 y_1 + \lambda_2 y_2)$, which is on the line determined by A_1 and A_2. Further instances of linear combinations appear later.

To return to the geometry of points on a line l, consider the *pencil of forms* $\lambda_1 f + \lambda_2 g$ determined as a linear combination of the base forms f and g. To each choice of λ_1, λ_2 (not both zero) there corresponds a form which represents the two points given by $\lambda_1 f + \lambda_2 g = 0$. Here only the ratio $\lambda_1 : \lambda_2$ is significant, so if $\lambda_1 \neq 0$, division by λ_1 gives $f + \lambda g = 0$, with $\lambda = \lambda_2 / \lambda_1$ as the nonhomogeneous parameter. The singly infinite set of forms $f + \lambda g$ is called a *one-parameter amily* of forms, or a *pencil* of forms determined by f and g.

It should be noted that no value of λ gives the form g. However, when considering the points represented by $f + \lambda g = 0$, one may divide by λ and then allow λ to become infinite to obtain $g = 0$. This limiting procedure is not necessary if the homogeneous parameters are employed.

A geometrical interpretation of the pencil $f + \lambda g = 0$ is given by the next

THEOREM: *The singly infinite set of pairs of points given by $f + \lambda g = 0$ constitute an involution.*

Proof: If the forms f, g are given by $a_{ij} x_i x_j$, $b_{ij} x_i x_j$, then

$$f + \lambda g \equiv a_{ij} x_i x_j + \lambda b_{ij} x_i x_j = (a_{ij} + \lambda b_{ij}) x_i x_j = 0$$

represents two points for every λ. For convenience, let the two ratios $x_1 : x_2$ for each λ be denoted by x and $\bar{x}$. Then, from the quadratic equation, the sum and product of the roots are expressed by

$$x + \bar{x} = -\frac{2(a_{12} + \lambda b_{12})}{a_{11} + \lambda b_{11}}, \quad x\bar{x} = \frac{a_{22} + \lambda b_{22}}{a_{11} + \lambda b_{11}},$$

and these two equations can be put into the respective forms

$$\lambda[b_{11}(x + \bar{x}) + 2b_{12}] + [a_{11}(x + \bar{x}) + 2a_{12}] = 0,$$
$$\lambda[b_{11} x\bar{x} - b_{22}] + [a_{11} x\bar{x} - a_{22}] = 0.$$

Elimination of λ from these last two equations gives an equation which holds for all values of λ; that is,

$$\begin{vmatrix} b_{11}(x + \bar{x}) + 2b_{12} & a_{11}(x + \bar{x}) + 2a_{12} \\ b_{11}x\bar{x} - b_{22} & a_{11}x\bar{x} - a_{22} \end{vmatrix} = 0,$$

which may be written as

$$2(a_{11}b_{12} - a_{12}b_{11})x\bar{x} + (a_{11}b_{22} - a_{22}b_{11})(x + \bar{x}) + 2(a_{12}b_{22} - a_{22}b_{12}) = 0.$$

This result is recognized as a homography symmetric in x and $\bar{x}$, and therefore (Section 2-5) the pairs of points given by $f + \lambda g = 0$, as λ varies, constitute an involution. This completes the proof.

3-9. Polar forms

The concept of *polarity* for binary forms will be approached by considering first the case of the *polar* of the point y_i, where $i = 1, 2$, with respect to the binary quadratic form $f \equiv a_{ij}x_ix_j$. The *polar form* of y_i with respect to $a_{ij}x_ix_j$ is defined by

$$(17) \qquad y_i \frac{\partial f}{\partial x_i} \equiv y_1 \frac{\partial f}{\partial x_1} + y_2 \frac{\partial f}{\partial x_2} = y_1(a_{11}x_1 + a_{12}x_2) + y_2(a_{21}x_1 + a_{22}x_2).$$

(Notice that a factor 2 is neglected here.) The linear form $y_i(\partial f/\partial x_i)$ in x_i represents one point, with coordinates x_i given by

$$\frac{x_1}{x_2} = -\frac{a_{12}y_1 + a_{22}y_2}{a_{11}y_1 + a_{12}y_2}.$$

Hence, the homogeneous coordinates x_i of the polar point of the point y_i with respect to the form f may be written as $(-a_{12}y_1 - a_{22}y_2, a_{11}y_1 + a_{12}y_2)$ or therefore as $(-\partial f/\partial x_2, \partial f/\partial x_1)$ evaluated at y_i. By virtue of the symmetry of the polar form $y_i(\partial f/\partial x_i)$, it is seen that $y_i(\partial f/\partial x_i) \equiv x_i(\partial f/\partial y_i)$, so that the polar point of the polar point of y_i is the point y_i itself. Another property of any point and its polar point with respect to f is given by the

THEOREM: *Any point y_i and its polar point with respect to $f \equiv a_{ij}x_ix_j$ separate the points represented by $f = 0$ harmonically.*

Proof: Let x' and x'' denote the points given by $f = 0$. It is necessary to show that the equation

$$\left(x', x'', \frac{y_1}{y_2}, -\frac{a_{12}y_1 + a_{22}y_2}{a_{11}y_1 + a_{12}y_2}\right) = -1$$

holds identically in y_1 and y_2. The equation of condition may be cast into the form

$$x'x'' - \frac{y_1}{y_2}\frac{a_{11}y_1 + a_{22}y_2}{a_{11}y_1 + a_{12}y_2} - \frac{1}{2}(x' + x'')\left(\frac{y_1}{y_2} - \frac{a_{12}y_1 + a_{22}y_2}{a_{11}y_1 + a_{12}y_2}\right) = 0.$$

On using the sum $x' + x'' = -2a_{12}/a_{11}$, and the product $x'x'' = a_{22}/a_{11}$, of the roots of $f = 0$, the left side of the last equation reduces identically to zero. This proves the theorem.

To return to the concept of polarity, observe that the polar of y_i with respect to f in equation (17) is obtained by applying the *polar operator* $y_i(\partial/\partial x_i)$ to the function f. The result, $y_i(\partial f/\partial x_i)$, is called the *first polarized form* of f with respect to y_i. If f is a binary quadratic, the first polarized form of f is a linear form (in x_i) and therefore represents a single point. But if f is a binary form of the nth degree, the first polarized form is of degree $n - 1$ (in x_i) and therefore represents $n - 1$ points. The polar of one given point y_i is then the set of $n - 1$ points given by $y_i(\partial f/\partial x_i) = 0$, where the y_i are considered as constants. The polar of another point z_i with respect to $y_i(\partial f/\partial x_i)$, expressed by

$$z_i \frac{\partial}{\partial x_i}\left(y_j \frac{\partial f}{\partial x_j}\right) \equiv z_i y_j \frac{\partial^2 f}{\partial x_i \partial x_j},$$

is styled the *mixed* polar of y_i and z_i with respect to f. It represents a set of $n - 2$ points. This process may be continued. For a third point w_i, the polarized form

$$w_i \frac{\partial}{\partial x_i}\left(z_j y_k \frac{\partial^2 f}{\partial x_j \partial x_k}\right) \equiv w_i z_j y_k \frac{\partial^3 f}{\partial x_i \partial x_j \partial x_k}$$

represents $n - 3$ points. The process terminates after n iterations. The nth derivatives are constants, so a multilinear form in $y_i, z_i, w_i, \cdots$ is obtained. The form is then completely polarized with respect to the n points $y_i, z_i, w_i, \cdots$.

If the $y_i, z_i, w_i, \cdots$, which were just used to obtain the mixed polar forms of various orders, are all taken to be y_i, then

$$y_i \frac{\partial f}{\partial x_i}, \quad y_i y_j \frac{\partial^2 f}{\partial x_i \partial x_j}, \quad y_i y_j y_k \frac{\partial^3 f}{\partial x_i \partial x_j \partial x_k}, \quad \cdots$$

are called the first, second, third, $\cdots$ polars of y_i with respect to f. The $(n - 1)$th polar of y_i is a point, and the nth polar is a constant. It is to be understood that repeated indices indicate summation over the range 1, 2. For instance, $y_i y_j(\partial^2 f/\partial x_i \partial x_j)$ sums to give

$$y_1^2 \frac{\partial^2 f}{\partial x_1^2} + 2y_1 y_2 \frac{\partial^2 f}{\partial x_1 \partial x_2} + y_2^2 \frac{\partial^2 f}{\partial x_2^2},$$

which may be written as

$$\left(y_1 \frac{\partial}{\partial x_1} + y_2 \frac{\partial}{\partial x_2}\right)^2 f.$$

Use of the operator $y_i(\partial/\partial x_i)$ p times on f gives a form which can be written as

$$\left(y_1 \frac{\partial}{\partial x_1} + y_2 \frac{\partial}{\partial x_2}\right)^p f.$$

This latter form is of degree $n - p$ (if f is of degree n) and represents therefore $n - p$ points, which constitute the pth polar of y_i with respect to f.

EXERCISES

1. Carry out the details to arrive at equation (13).

2. Find the double points of the involution determined by the pencil of forms

$$\lambda_1(x^2 - 3x + 2) + \lambda_2(x^2 - 7x + 12).$$

(This should be done in two ways. Use the jacobian points of the base forms. Also find the involution and then obtain its double points.)

Ans. $(5 \pm \sqrt{3})/2$.

3. Prove that if two binary quadratic forms have a common factor, the jacobian of these forms has the same factor.

4. Deduce from Fig. 11 how to construct pairs of points in the hyperbolic involution determined by two given pairs P_1, P_2 and Q_1, Q_2 which do not separate each other. Consider next the case in which line l is taken so the point O is between R and S. The pairs P_1, P_2 and Q_1, Q_2 separate each other, and the involution is elliptic. What is the case if O coincides with S?

5. Extend equation (11′) to apply to three forms f_1, f_2, f_3 in the variables x_1, x_2, x_3.

6. Show that the hessian of a binary quadratic form is its determinant.

7. Find the polar point of (1, 2) with respect to the form $x_1^2 - x_2^2$. Verify that the four points are harmonic.

8. Find the second polar of the point (1, 2) with respect to the cubic form

$$x_1^3 + 2x_1^2 x_2 + x_1 x_2^2 - x_2^3.$$

Ans. (2, 5).

9. Show that the lines

$$l_1: \quad x + y - 1 = 0, \qquad l_2: \quad x - y + 2 = 0, \qquad l_3: \quad 2x + y - 3 = 0$$

are linearly independent, and that l_4: $9x + 2y - 6 = 0$ can be expressed as a linear combination of l_1, l_2, l_3. Show that any line l: $ax + by + c = 0$ can be written as a linear combination of l_1, l_2, l_3, and indicate how the hypothesis of linear independence of l_1, l_2, l_3 is used.

10. If f is a binary form of degree n, show that

$$x_i \frac{\partial f}{\partial x_i} = nf.$$

Hint: Use the fact that $f(tx_1, tx_2) \equiv t^n f(x_1, x_2)$ is an identity in t, and differentiate to find

$$\frac{\partial f}{\partial (tx_1)} \frac{\partial (tx_1)}{\partial t} + \frac{\partial f}{\partial (tx_2)} \frac{\partial (tx_2)}{\partial t} = nt^{n-1} f(x_1, x_2).$$

Then put $t = 1$. Continue the process to find

$$x_i x_j \frac{\partial^2 f}{\partial x_j \partial x_i} = n(n - 1)f,$$

and, in general,

$$\left(x_i \frac{\partial f}{\partial x_i} \right)^p f = n(n - 1) \cdots (n - p + 1)f.$$

(This is Euler's theorem on homogeneous functions.)

3-10. Binary cubic forms

The binary cubic form

$$f \equiv a_0x_1^3 + 3a_1x_1^2x_2 + 3a_2x_1x_2^2 + a_3x_2^3$$

represents three points P_1, P_2, P_3 on line l. The hessian H_f of the form f was shown (Section 3-7) to be a covariant of weight two. It is a quadratic form which represents two points H_1, H_2, the hessian points of f. The geometry of these points relative to P_1, P_2, P_3 is to be investigated. By definition,

$$(18) \qquad H_f \equiv \begin{vmatrix} f_{11} & f_{12} \\ f_{21} & f_{22} \end{vmatrix} = \begin{vmatrix} a_0x_1 + a_1x_2 & a_1x_1 + a_2x_2 \\ a_1x_1 + a_2x_2 & a_2x_1 + a_3x_2 \end{vmatrix}$$

$$= (a_0a_2 - a_1^2)x_1^2 + (a_0a_3 - a_1a_2)x_1x_2 + (a_1a_3 - a_2^2)x_2^2.$$

The points H_1, H_2 represented by $H_f = 0$ are coincident if

$$d_{H_f} \equiv (a_0a_3 - a_1a_2)^2 - 4(a_0a_2 - a_1^2)(a_1a_3 - a_2^2) = 0.$$

It will be shown next that the discriminant d_f (defined below) of the cubic form f may be expressed as d_{H_f}. To do this, demand that $f = 0$ and $\partial f/\partial x = 0$ (where $x = x_1/x_2$) have a root in common; that is, require that the equations

$$a_0x^3 + 3a_1x^2 + 3a_2x + a_3 = 0,$$
$$a_0x^2 + 2a_1x + a_2 \qquad\; = 0$$

hold simultaneously. To find the eliminant of these equations, first multiply the second of them by x and subtract the result from the first equation to find $a_1x^2 + 2a_2x + a_3 = 0$. Form the set of equations

$$a_0x^4 + 3a_1x^3 + 3a_2x^2 + \quad a_3x + 0 \;= 0,$$
$$a_0x^3 + 3a_1x^2 + 3a_2x + a_3 = 0,$$
$$a_1x^2 + 2a_2x + a_3 = 0,$$
$$a_1x^3 + 2a_2x^2 + \quad a_3x + 0 \;= 0,$$
$$a_1x^4 + 2a_2x^3 + \quad a_3x^2 + 0 \quad\; + 0 = 0,$$

which have a common solution if and only if

$$d_f \equiv \begin{vmatrix} a_0 & 3a_1 & 3a_2 & a_3 & 0 \\ 0 & a_0 & 3a_1 & 3a_2 & a_3 \\ 0 & 0 & a_1 & 2a_2 & a_3 \\ 0 & a_1 & 2a_2 & a_3 & 0 \\ a_1 & 2a_2 & a_3 & 0 & 0 \end{vmatrix} = 0.$$

Subtract the third row from the second row to obtain

$$d_f \equiv \begin{vmatrix} a_0 & 3a_1 & 3a_2 & a_3 \\ 0 & a_0 & 2a_1 & a_2 \\ 0 & a_1 & 2a_2 & a_3 \\ a_1 & 2a_2 & a_3 & 0 \end{vmatrix} = 0,$$

the expansion of which can be expressed in the form

(19) $$d_f \equiv (a_0 a_3 - a_1 a_2)^2 - 4(a_0 a_2 - a_1^2)(a_1 a_3 - a_2^2).$$

Hence, the condition $(d_f = 0)$ for two of the points P_1, P_2, P_3 represented by $f = 0$ to coincide is the condition for the hessian points H_1, H_2 of f to coincide. It will be seen next that P_1, P_2, P_3 coincide if and only if the hessian points are indeterminate. First, assume P_1, P_2, P_3 coincide, which implies that the equations $f = 0$, $df/dx = 0$, $d^2f/dx^2 = 0$ have a common solution; that is, the equations

$$a_0 x^3 + 3a_1 x^2 + 3a_2 x + a_3 = 0,$$

$$a_0 x^2 + 2a_1 x + a_2 = 0,$$

$$a_0 x + a_1 = 0$$

hold simultaneously. It is readily shown that the solution of the third equation satisfies the other two equations only if $a_0 a_2 - a_1^2 = 0$ and $a_0 a_3 - a_1 a_2 = 0$. For $x_2 \neq 0$, these last conditions imply that the remaining coefficient in the hessian (18) is zero, which means that the hessian points of f are indeterminate. Now, to show that if the hessian of f is indeterminate, the points P_1, P_2, P_3 coincide, assume

$$a_0 a_2 - a_1^2 = 0, \quad a_0 a_3 - a_1 a_2 = 0, \quad a_1 a_3 - a_2^2 = 0,$$

which can be solved to find

$$a_1 = a_0^{2/3} a_3^{1/3}, \quad a_2 = a_0^{1/3} a_3^{2/3}.$$

When these values are placed in the form f it becomes $(a_0^{1/3} x_1 + a_3^{1/3})^3$, which represents three coincident points.

An important utilization of the covariance of the hessian will now be illustrated in the investigation of the geometric relation between the hessian points H_1, H_2 and the points P_1, P_2, P_3 given by $f = 0$. Suppose d_f in (19) is positive— that is, the points given by (18) are real. Therefore, the hessian is the product of two distinct real linear factors. If these two factors are used for $c_{1j} x_j$ and $c_{2j} x_j$ in the transformation $\bar{x}_i = c_{ij} x_j$, the hessian transforms to the simple form $\bar{x}_1 \bar{x}_2$. The use of this *canonical* form $\bar{x}_1 \bar{x}_2$ renders the analysis much simpler than that by use of the general quadratic form. It is to be realized that a linear substitution of the form $\bar{x}_i = c_{ij} x_j$ (or its inverse) may be regarded in two ways— either a change of coordinates on line l with the points left undisturbed or a projection of l into itself or into another line $\bar{l}$. Let the substitution be considered at present as a change of coordinates. The coordinates of the hessian points depend upon the coordinate system chosen. But the geometric description of the points is invariant under change of coordinates, because the hessian is a covariant.

In view of the foregoing discussion let the hessian be chosen as $h_f = x_1 x_2$, so that H_1 may be assigned the coordinates $(1, 0)$ and H_2 the coordinates $(0, 1)$. This choice of coordinates demands that in equation (18)

$$a_0 a_2 - a_1^2 = 0, \quad a_0 a_3 - a_1 a_2 \neq 0, \quad a_1 a_3 - a_2^2 = 0.$$

Note that the homogeneous equations

$$a_1(a_1) - a_0(a_2) = 0,$$
$$a_3(a_1) - a_2(a_2) = 0$$

have only the trivial solution $a_1 = a_2 = 0$ because the determinant of the coefficients $a_0 a_3 - a_1 a_2 \neq 0$. Hence, the forms f and H_f take the canonical representations

(20) $$f \equiv a_0 x_1^3 + a_3 x_2^3, \quad H \equiv x_1 x_2.$$

A new cubic form will now be introduced—the jacobian of f and H_f; denote it by $J(f, H_f)$. Then, if the representations

$$f \equiv a_0 x_1^3 + 3a_1 x_1^2 x_2 + 3a_2 x_1 x_2^2 + a_3 x_2^3$$

and (18) are used, their jacobian is found to be

$$J(f, H_f) \equiv (a_0^2 a_3 - 3a_0 a_1 a_2 + 2a_1^3)x_1^3 + 3(a_0 a_1 a_3 + a_1^2 a_2 - 2a_0 a_2^2)x_1^2 x_2$$
$$- 3(a_0 a_2 a_3 - 2a_1^2 a_3 + a_1 a_2^2)x_1 x_2^2 - (a_0 a_3^2 - 3a_1 a_2 a_3 + 2a_2^3)x_2^3.$$

The three points represented by this cubic form will be denoted by P_1', P_2', P_3'. In the coordinate system with $(1, 0)$ and $(0, 1)$ as the hessian points of f (that is, with $a_1 = a_2 = 0$), the jacobian of f and H_f reduces to

(21) $$J(f, H_f) \equiv a_0 x_1^3 - a_3 x_2^3,$$

which is the jacobian of the forms in (20). Eight points on line l (Fig. 12) are to be considered—P_1, P_2, P_3 from $f = 0$, P_1', P_2', P_3' from $J(f, H_f) = 0$, and H_1, H_2 from $H_f = 0$, where the forms are given by equations (20) and (21).

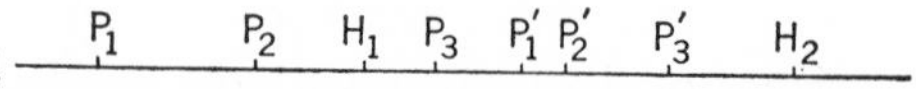

Figure 12

Note first that the hessians of f and $J(f, H_f)$ are the same, so the hessian points of the triple P_1, P_2, P_3 coincide with the hessian points for the triple P_1', P_2', P_3'. Because the hessian points are taken as real, the discriminant of f is $a_0^2 a_3^2$, which is positive. From (20) it is seen that $f = 0$ has one real root and two complex roots. Let r denote the real root of $a_0 x^3 + a_3 = 0$. Then $r = -3\sqrt{a_3/a_0}$ may be assigned to P_1, ωr to P_2, and $\omega^2 r$ to P_3, where $\omega^3 = 1$.

THEOREM: *The sets of points P_1, P_2, P_3, H_1 and P_1, P_2, P_3, H_2 are anharmonic* (Section 1-7).

Proof: Because H_1 has coordinates $(1, 0)$, the cross ratio

$$(P_1 P_2 P_3 H_1) = \lim_{m \to \infty} (r, \omega r, \omega^2 r, m) = \frac{\omega^2 r - r}{\omega^2 r - \omega r} = \frac{\omega + 1}{\omega} = -\frac{\omega^2}{\omega} = -\omega.$$

Similarly, $(P_1 P_2 P_3 H_2) = (r, \omega r, \omega^2 r, 0) = -\omega^2$, which concludes the proof.

Observe that because the roots of $a_0 x^3 + a_3 = 0$ are r, ωr, $\omega^2 r$, the roots of $a_0 x^3 - a_3 = 0$ are $-r$, $-\omega$, $-\omega^2 r$.

THEOREM: *The three sets of points P_2, P_3, P_1, P_1'; P_3, P_1, P_2, P_2'; P_1, P_2, P_3, P_3' are harmonic.*

Proof: The cross ratio

$$(P_2P_3P_1P_1') = (\omega r,\ \omega^2 r,\ r,\ -r) = \frac{1+\omega}{1-\omega^2}\frac{1+\omega^2}{1+\omega} = -1.$$

Similarly, by cyclic permutation of the subscripts, the other two cross ratios are found to be -1.

Three more sets of harmonic points may be selected from the set of eight points on *l*.

THEOREM: *The three sets of points P_1, P_1', H_1, H_2; P_2, P_2', H_1, H_2; P_3, P_3', H_1, H_2 are harmonic.*

Proof: The cross ratio

$$(P_1P_1'H_1H_2) = \lim_{m\to\infty}\ (r,\ -r,\ m,\ 0) = \lim_{m\to\infty}\frac{r-m}{r+m} = -1.$$

Similarly, the other two cross ratios evaluate to -1. This result means that H_1, H_2 are the double points of the involution to which the pairs P_1, P_1'; P_2, P_2'; P_3, P_3' belong.

Observe that the form *f* gives rise not only to the points P_1, P_2, P_3 but also to P_1', P_2', P_3', and H_1, H_2. The last two theorems indicate the relations of P_1', P_2', P_3', and of H_1, H_2 to the points P_1, P_2, P_3. These results were proved by use of canonical forms but—by the fact of invariance under a change of coordinates— the results obtained hold for any binary cubic form.

DEFINITION: *A cubic form f and its hessian are said to be* apolar.

A correspondence has been noted between the algebraic theory of binary forms and the geometry of points on a line. A linear form $a_1x_1 + a_2x_2$ is determined by the ratio $a_1{:}a_2$. The set of all ordered pairs $(ka_1{:}ka_2)$ with $k \neq 0$, corresponds to the set of all points on a projective line. In the case of the binary quadratic forms $a_{ij}x_ix_j$, the set of all ordered triples $(ka_{11}{:}2ka_{12}{:}ka_{22})$ corresponds to the set of *pairs* of points on the line. It will be seen in Section 10-8 that these ordered triples can be interpreted as projective coordinates of points in a projective space of two dimensions. Hence, the geometry of pairs of points on a line is equivalent to projective geometry in the plane. For the case of cubic forms, a correspondence is evident between the totality of triples of points on a line and points with coordinates $(ka_0{:}3ka_1{:}3ka_2{:}ka_3)$ in a projective space of three dimensions. In general, for a binary *n*-ic a correspondence is established between the totality of sets of *n*-points on a line and the $n + 1$ homogeneous coordinates of points in a projective space of *n* dimensions.

EXERCISES

1. Find necessary and sufficient conditions under which the forms

$$\phi \equiv ax_1^2 + 2bx_1x_2 + cx_2^2,$$

$$\psi \equiv \alpha x_1^3 + 3\beta x_1^2 x_2 + 3\gamma x_1 x_2^2 + \delta x_2^3$$

are apolar.

Suggestion: The form ϕ must be the hessian of ψ. That is, the coefficients in ϕ must be proportional to those of

$$\begin{vmatrix} \alpha x_1 + \beta x_2 & \beta x_1 + \gamma x_2 \\ \beta x_1 + \gamma x_2 & \gamma x_1 + \delta x_2 \end{vmatrix},$$

or

$$(\alpha\gamma - \beta^2)x_1^2 + (\alpha\delta - \beta\gamma)x_1x_2 + (\beta\delta - \gamma^2)x_2^2.$$

2. The roots of the cubic $f \equiv x^3 - 2x^2 - 5x + 6 = 0$ are $-2, 1, 3$. Employ homogeneous coordinates, and find the jacobian of the form f and its hessian to be

$$28x_1^3 - 417x_1^2 x_2 + 696x_1 x_2^2 - 91x_2^3 = 0.$$

Use the geometry of Section 3-10 to show that $\frac{7}{4}$ is a root of the latter cubic equation without solving the equation.

3-11. Some projective differential geometry

Algebraic invariants have been introduced and interpreted geometrically in preceding sections. The purpose of this section is to introduce briefly the concept of a *projective differential invariant*.

Consider the motion of a variable point referred to three fixed base points *A, B, C* on a line *l*. As defined in Section 2-6, the projective coordinate *r* is given by

$$r = \frac{x_1}{x_2} = (ABCP).$$

The motion of *P* is described by a function of the time *t*, say, $r = r(t)$. Under a projectivity, *P* projects into $\bar{P}$ with coordinate $\bar{r} = \bar{r}(t)$, and the functions *r*, $\bar{r}$ are related by

(22)
$$\bar{r}(t) = \frac{ar(t) + b}{cr(t) + d}, \qquad\qquad ad - bc \neq 0.$$

Note that corresponding to four successive instants given by t_1, t_2, t_3, t_4, the projective coordinates $r(t_1), r(t_2), r(t_3), r(t_4)$ of *P* at those instants have a cross ratio which is equal to the cross ratio of the four corresponding projected points with coordinates $\bar{r}(t_1), \bar{r}(t_2), \bar{r}(t_3), \bar{r}(t_4)$. The motion of *P* may be styled *projectively equivalent* to the motion of $\bar{P}$. In contrast, the motions of two points (each on a straight line) are equivalent in euclidean geometry if the velocities of the two points are the same functions of the time *t*.

It will be recalled that, because three essential parameters appear in equation (22), this equation exhibits a triply infinite set of projectivities which, moreover, constitute a group. Recall also that a function $y(t) = c_1 f_1(t) + c_2 f_2(t)$, say, where c_1, c_2 are arbitrary constants, is a solution of the differential equation obtained by eliminating c_1, c_2 from $y(t) = c_i f_i$, $y' = c_i f'_i$, $y'' = c_i f''_i$, where the primes indicate derivatives with respect to t. For instance, given the *primitive* $y = c_1 t^2 + c_2 t$, the differential equation for it is found to be $t^2 y'' - 2ty' + 2y = 0$. Analogously, a differential equation corresponding to equation (22) will be found by eliminating the parameters a, b, c, d. Differentiate equation (22) to obtain

$$(23) \qquad \bar{r}' = \frac{(ad - bc)r'}{(cr + d)^2}.$$

It is advisable to differentiate equation (23) logarithmically to arrive at

$$(24) \qquad \frac{\bar{r}''}{\bar{r}'} = \frac{r''}{r'} - 2\frac{r'}{r + d/c}.$$

Differentiate equation (24) and eliminate $r + d/c$ by means of equation (24) to obtain

$$(25) \qquad \frac{\bar{r}'''}{\bar{r}'} - \frac{3}{2}\left(\frac{\bar{r}''}{\bar{r}'}\right)^2 = \frac{r'''}{r'} - \frac{3}{2}\left(\frac{r''}{r'}\right)^2.$$

The result expressed by equation (25) means that the function

$$(26) \qquad \frac{\phi'''(t)}{\phi'(t)} - \frac{3}{2}\left(\frac{\phi''(t)}{\phi'(t)}\right)^2$$

has the same value whether ϕ is $r(t)$ or $\bar{r}(t)$. The function (26) of derivatives of ϕ is therefore unchanged (or invariant) under a projective mapping (22), so it is called a *projective differential invariant*. H. A. Schwarz (1843–1921) came across this function in a study of conformal mapping, so it may be styled the Schwarz derivative of ϕ and denoted by $S\phi$. A differential equation of the third order is obtained by setting $S\phi$ equal to a function of t—say, $g(t)$. Thus, the differential equation

$$(27) \qquad S\phi \equiv \frac{\phi'''(t)}{\phi'(t)} - \frac{3}{2}\left(\frac{\phi''(t)}{\phi'(t)}\right)^2 = g(t)$$

defines a class of projectively equivalent motions in the following sense. If one solution, say, $\phi(t) = x(t)$, is known for equation (27), then all linear fractional functions

$$\frac{ax(t) + b}{cx(t) + d},$$

with a, b, c, d arbitrary constants, are likewise solutions of equation (27). This is to say that if a particular function $x(t)$ can be found to satisfy (27), then a general solution is known.

Solution of (27) is forbidding even for a rather simple function $g(t)$. Some discussion will be adduced, however, for the case of $g(t) = H$, a constant. Three cases arise according as $H < 0$, $H = 0$, $H > 0$.

However, instead of integrating the third-order equation (27), a second-order equation equivalent to it will be introduced. The method to be employed was used by E. J. Wilczynski (1876–1932) in studying projective properties of curves and ruled surfaces. Instead of the nonhomogeneous coordinate $r(t)$ used in (22), use the homogeneous coordinates $x_i(t)$, with $i = 1, 2$, of the moving point P. Note that $r(t) = x_1/x_2 = kx_1/kx_2$, where k may be an arbitrary function of t. Advantage will be taken of the arbitrariness of $k(t)$ later, in choosing this function to satisfy a certain condition.

If A and B, with coordinates a_i and b_i, are two fixed points on line l, the coordinates $x_i(t)$ of P can be expressed as a linear combination $x_i = \lambda a_i + \mu b_i$, where λ and μ are functions of t. Differentiation gives $x_i' = \lambda' a_i + \mu' b_i$, and $x_i'' = \lambda'' a_i + \mu'' b_i$. Elimination of a_i, b_i from the last three equations, with $i = 1$, and elimination of a_2, b_2, with $i = 2$, yields the two differential equations

$$\begin{vmatrix} x_1 & \lambda & \mu \\ x_1' & \lambda' & \mu' \\ x_1'' & \lambda'' & \mu'' \end{vmatrix} = 0, \quad \begin{vmatrix} x_2 & \lambda & \mu \\ x_2' & \lambda' & \mu' \\ x_2'' & \lambda'' & \mu'' \end{vmatrix} = 0.$$

On expanding each of the determinants it is seen that the x_i, with $i = 1, 2$, both satisfy a single linear differential equation of the second order—that is, an equation of the type

$$(28) \qquad \theta'' + p(t)\theta' + q(t)\theta = 0,$$

in which it is unnecessary to specify the forms for p and q as functions of λ, μ and their derivatives. If x_1, x_2 are two independent functions which satisfy (28), then $\bar{x}_1$, $\bar{x}_2$ are general solutions, where

$$\bar{x}_1 = \alpha_1 x_1 + \alpha_2 x_2,$$
$$\bar{x}_2 = \beta_1 x_1 + \beta_2 x_2,$$

$$\alpha_1\beta_2 - \alpha_2\beta_1 \neq 0.$$

Thus, x_i and $\bar{x}_i$ are related by a projectivity. The motion of $P(x_i)$ is projectively equivalent to the motion of $\bar{P}(\bar{x}_i)$. The equation (28) defines a class of projectively equivalent motions. Observe, however, that the motion of P is unchanged if x_i are replaced by $k(t)x_i$. Instead of writing both $k(t)x_1$, and $k(t)x_2$, it is simpler to write θ for x_i, and θ^* for $k(t)\theta$. In order to determine the effect of the multiplying function $\lambda(t)$, differentiate $\theta^* = k\theta$, twice to obtain $\theta^{*\prime} = k'\theta + k\theta'$, $\theta^{*\prime\prime} = k''\theta + 2k'\theta' + k\theta''$. Use the fact that θ^* must satisfy equation (28) to have

$$\theta'' + \left(\frac{2k'}{k} + p\right)\theta' + \left(\frac{k''}{k} + p\frac{k'}{k} + q\right)\theta = 0.$$

The arbitrariness of the function $k(t)$ is now exploited by choosing $k(t)$ so that

$$\frac{2k'}{k} + p = 0,$$

which has for solution

$$k = C_1 \exp\left(-\int \frac{p}{2} dt\right),$$

where C_1 is an arbitrary constant. Hence, with this choice of $k(t)$ the equation in θ takes the form

$$(29) \qquad \theta'' + \sigma(t)\theta = 0,$$

where $\sigma(t)$ is readily calculated to be

$$\sigma(t) = -\frac{p^2}{4} - \frac{p'}{2} + q.$$

Equation (29) is satisfied by $x_i(t)$, with $i = 1, 2$, and therefore by any functions $\bar{x}_i(t)$ projectively related to x_i. The function $\sigma(t)$ is, like the Schwarz derivative $S\phi$ in equation (27), a projective differential invariant. It will be shown next that $\sigma(t)$ is the same as $S\phi$, at least up to a constant factor.

Denote the ratio x_1/x_2 by r, so $x_1 = ur$, $x_2 = u$, where u may be a function of t. Because x_1 and x_2 satisfy (29), one has the two equations $(ur)'' + \sigma(ur) = 0$ and $u'' + \sigma u = 0$, or, on eliminating σ, $(ur)'' - ru'' = 0$; this reduces to

$$\frac{r''}{r'} + \frac{2u'}{u} = 0,$$

a solution of which is

$$u = \frac{C}{\sqrt{r'}},$$

where C is an arbitrary constant.

If the expression just found for u is used in the equation $u'' + \sigma u = 0$, the result can be written as

$$(30) \qquad \sigma(t) = \frac{1}{2}\left[\frac{r'''}{r'} - \frac{3}{2}\left(\frac{r''}{r'}\right)^2\right].$$

Hence, the projective differential invariant $\sigma(t)$ is (aside from the factor $\frac{1}{2}$) the same as the Schwarz derivative Sr in the right member of equation (25). Because equation (29) is invariant under a projectivity, the equation is said to *admit* a projective transformation. The same can be said for equation (30).

The three instances of equation (29) which will now be considered are those for which $\sigma(t)$ is a constant H. The cases are $H < 0$, $H = 0$, $H > 0$.

Case 1. If $H < 0$, say $H = -h^2$, the solutions of $\theta'' - h^2\theta = 0$ may be written as $x_1 = e^{ht}$, $x_2 = e^{-ht}$, and the linear combinations

$$\bar{x}_1 = \alpha_1 x_1 + \alpha_2 x_2 = \alpha_1 e^{ht} + \alpha_2 e^{-ht},$$
$$\bar{x}_2 = \beta_1 x_1 + \beta_2 x_2 = \beta_1 e^{ht} + \beta_2 e^{-ht}$$

exhibit general solutions, where α_1, α_2, β_1, β_2 are arbitrary constants. The solutions may be written as

$$\bar{x}_1 = \alpha_1 e^{2ht} + \alpha_2,$$
$$\bar{x}_2 = \beta_1 e^{2ht} + \beta_2.$$

Let the point where t becomes $-\infty$ correspond to the point $A(k, 0)$. Then $\alpha_2 = k$, $\beta_2 = 0$. Let the point where t becomes ∞ correspond to $B(0, m)$. Then, from

$$\bar{x}_1 = \alpha_1 + \alpha_2 e^{-2ht},$$
$$\bar{x}_2 = \beta_1 + \beta_2 e^{-2ht},$$

it is seen that $\alpha_1 = 0$, $\beta_1 = m$. Hence,

$$\bar{r} = \frac{\bar{x}_1}{\bar{x}_2} = \frac{k}{m} e^{-2ht} = ce^{-2ht}.$$

If r is the point where P is at time $t + \tau$, then

$$r = ce^{-2h(t+\tau)} = ce^{-2h\tau}e^{-2ht} = e^{-2h\tau}\bar{r}$$

or

$$\bar{r} = e^{2h\tau}r,$$

which is a hyperbolic projectivity with the two fixed points at 0 and ∞. If $r = r_1$ when $t = t_1$, then $r = ce^{-2ht}$ gives $r_1 = ce^{-2ht_1}$, and if $r = r_2$ when $t = t_2$, then $r_2 = ce^{-2ht_2}$. Hence,

$$t_2 - t_1 = \frac{1}{2h} \log \left(\frac{r_1}{r_2}\right).$$

A metric may be introduced by taking the "distance" from P_1 at r_1 to P_2 at r_2 as the time $t_2 - t_1$ required for P to move from P_1 to P_2. The cross ratio

$$(r_1, r_2, \infty, 0) = (P_1P_2AB) = \frac{r_2}{r_1}.$$

Hence, the distance $\overline{P_1P_2}$ is expressible as

$$t_2 - t_1 = -\frac{1}{2h} \log (ABP_1P_2).$$

This is the hyperbolic metric of Cayley, which will appear again in Chapter 9. (See Exercise 10 on p. 201.)

Case 2. If $H = 0$, equation (29) becomes $\theta'' = 0$, which has the solutions

$$x_1 = c_1t + c_2,$$
$$x_2 = c_3t + c_4,$$

so that

$$r = \frac{x_1}{x_2} = \frac{c_1t + c_2}{c_3t + c_4}.$$

Choose $c_3 = 0$ to insure that finite values of t always give rise to finite values of r. Hence, take $r = \alpha t + \beta$, where α and β are arbitrary constants. If r and $\bar{r}$ correspond to t and $t + h$ then

$$\bar{r} = \alpha(t + h) + \beta = r + \alpha h,$$

which is a parabolic projectivity with both fixed points coinciding with the ideal point on the line. Suppose again that P is at P_1 when $t = t_1$, and at P_2 when $t = t_2$; then from $r_1 = \alpha t_1 + \beta$ and $r_2 = \alpha t_2 + \beta$ it follows that

$$r_2 - r_1 = \alpha(t_2 - t_1).$$

If the projective (parabolic) measure of the segment P_1P_2 is taken again as $t_2 - t_1$, it is seen that the parabolic measure differs from the euclidean measure by only the scale factor α. Parabolic measure as euclidean measure will appear again in Chapter 9.

Case 3. Finally, if $H > 0$, say $H = h^2$, equation (29) becomes $\theta'' + h^2\theta = 0$, which has particular solutions

$$x_1 = \sin(ht), \quad x_2 = \cos(ht),$$

so that

$$r(t) = \frac{x_1}{x_2} = \tan(ht).$$

At $t = 0$, $r = 0$, and as $t \to \pi/2h$, r becomes infinite, so the point P moves over the entire projective line in the finite time π/h. If $\bar{r}$ corresponds to $t + \tau$,

$$\bar{r} = \tan(ht + h\tau) = \frac{\tan(h\tau) + \tan(ht)}{1 - \tan(h\tau)\tan(ht)} = \frac{r + \gamma}{1 - \gamma r},$$

where $\gamma = \tan(h\tau)$. This is an elliptic projectivity (for every choice of the parameter τ) with fixed points $\pm i$. As in the hyperbolic case, an elliptic metric may be defined as the time $(t_2 - t_1)$ required for P to move from P_1 to P_2. (See Chapter 9 for elliptic measure in the plane.)

CHAPTER 4

Homogeneous Coordinates in Two Dimensions

The projective line has been studied in the three preceding chapters, and, in the treatment of it, it has been seen that geometry and analysis complement each other. Although the real projective line, obtained by adding an ideal point to the real euclidean line, has been the principal object of interest, complex numbers have appeared through the analytical aspect. These complex numbers have been associated with complex points, which are added to the real line in order to maintain the complementation of the analysis and the geometry. For instance, the fixed points of an elliptic involution were found to be represented by complex coordinates. In the *real* projective line there are no fixed points for an elliptic involution, but for the *complex* projective line there are two fixed points. Because a complex number $x + iy$ is determined by a pair of real numbers x and y, the real numbers constitute a subset of the field of complex numbers for which $y = 0$. The projective mappings considered are those which carry the real line into itself, but one may consider the invariants of the complex projective line. A similar situation arises in the plane. Complex numbers will be useful in the complementation of the geometry and analysis. The projective plane will be introduced in Chapter 6 following a treatment in the present chapter of homogeneous point and line coordinates in the euclidean plane, and a study of the homography in two dimensions in Chapter 5.

4-1. The principle of duality

A reciprocal one-to-one correspondence between point and line can be observed in many theorems and constructions of plane geometry. For instance, corresponding to the statement "three points determine a triangle," there is the statement "three lines determine a triangle." These are called *dual* statements. A point and a line are *dual* elements. If a point is on a line, then the line is "on" (that is, "through") the point. In this case the dual elements are said to be *incident*. A triangle is determined by three points or by three lines. If it happens that the three points are *on* a line (collinear points) then the three lines of the dual configuration are *through* a point (concurrent lines). It is evident that some minor changes in the wording may be desirable in making dual statements. A one-to-one correspondence can be established between the points on a line (a point *range*) and the lines through a point (a line *pencil*). Hence, a point range and a line pencil are dual configurations.

Observe that in three-space a plane is determined by a point and a line which is not incident with the point. The dual statement says that a plane is determined by a line and a point not incident with the line. In the plane, a point and a line are dual elements. A point S_0 (a space of dimensionality 0) and a line S_1 (a space of dimensionality 1) determine a plane S_2 (a space of dimensionality 2). Thus, the point and line may be styled *complementary spaces* in the plane. However, in three-space S_3, a point and a line are not complementary. With a point (S_0) a plane (S_2) is required to determine a three-space (S_3). Hence, in three-space, point and plane are complementary spaces; they may be called *dual* elements. Thus, the dual of a given element depends upon the dimensionality of the space considered. The dual of a point in n-space S_n is a space of $n - 1$ dimensions (S_{n-1}) called a *hyperplane*. Note that a line (S_1) is determined by two points, a plane (S_2) by three points, a three-space (S_3) by four points. A space S_n is determined by $n + 1$ points, so to any point (S_0) the complementary (or dual) space is determined by the remaining n points, which determine a space S_{n-1}.

The dual of a line in three-space is a line. Think of two points A and B as determining a line and two points C and D as determining another line. (It is assumed that lines AB and CD are not coplanar.) The point A and the plane determined by B, C, D together determine the three-space. It can also be said that the four points A, B, C, D determine the

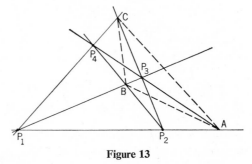

Figure 13

three-space, or that the lines AB and CD are complementary spaces—that is, dual elements.

To return to plane geometry, consider the configuration (Fig. 13) determined by four points P_1, P_2, P_3, P_4 in general position, that is, with no three of them collinear. (Points are usually denoted by capital letters and corresponding lines by the corresponding lower case letters.) In the case of the triangle P_1, P_2, P_3, the three points can be selected two at a time in three ways to determine the three lines P_2P_3, P_3P_1, P_1P_2. But the number of ways in which four points can be selected two at a time is $_4C_2 = 6$. The six lines determined by the four points are shown in Fig. 13. The six lines intersect by pairs in three points A, B, C. Note that lines (P_1P_2) and (P_3P_4) meet in A, (P_1P_3) and (P_4P_2) meet in B, and (P_1P_4) and (P_2P_3) meet in C. The entire configuration determined by the four given points is called a *complete quadrangle*. This includes the triangle *ABC* which is called the *diagonal triangle* of the complete quadrangle. Some projective geometry of the quadrangle will be studied after projective coordinates are introduced in Chapter 6.

What is the dual configuration of the complete quadrangle? It is the complete configuration determined by four lines p_1, p_2, p_3, p_4 in general position in the plane, that is, with no three of the lines concurrent. This configuration (Fig. 14)

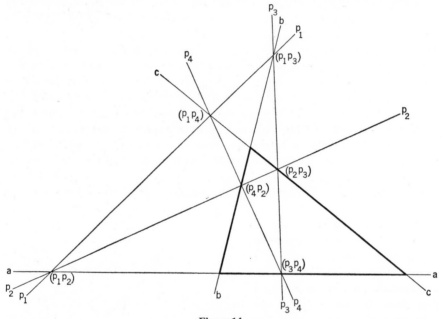

Figure 14

is called a *complete quadrilateral*. Whereas (P_1P_2) denotes the line determined by points P_1 and P_2 (or the join of P_1, P_2), the notation (p_1p_2) indicates the point determined by the lines p_1 and p_2 (or the *intersection* of p_1, p_2). Thus, join and intersection are dual expressions.

In the complete quadrilateral of Fig. 14, note first that the four lines may be selected by pairs in six ways to determine six points. (Observe how the paragraph on the complete quadrangle is being dualized here.) The six points are joined by pairs to form the three lines *a*, *b*, *c*. Note that points (p_1p_2) and (p_3p_4) are joined by *a*, (p_1p_3) and (p_4p_2) by *b*, and (p_1p_4) and (p_2p_3) by *c*. The complete quadrilateral includes the diagonal triangle *abc*.

Any theorems which may be stated relative to the quadrangle hold also for the quadrilateral provided the words "point" and "line" are interchanged. It may be desirable also to effect certain changes in the wording, such as interchanging the terms "join" and "intersection," and "collinear" and "concurrent." This principle by which one theorem has two interpretations is called the *principle of duality.* Its use effects not only economy of language but also a better appreciation for the structure of geometry. J. V. Poncelet (1788–1867) observed the principle of duality in geometry in 1818. J. D. Gergonne (1771–1859) formulated the principle first in 1826.

Besides the already mentioned three-point (triangle) and four-point (quadrangle) configurations in the plane, there are the five-point, six-point, $\cdots$, n-point plane configurations. The duals consist of the three-line (triangle), four-line (quadrilateral), five-line, six-line, $\cdots$, n-line configurations. The total number of incidences of lines with points or lines, and of points with points or lines, for a general complete configuration in the plane will be shown.

In the case of a three-point configuration it can be said that a point may be incident with any one of three points, a line with two points, a point with two lines, and a line with any one of three lines. This fact may be shown by the "incidence" matrix,

$$\begin{array}{c} \\ \text{Points} \\ \text{Lines} \end{array} \begin{array}{cc} \text{Points} & \text{Lines} \\ \left(\begin{array}{cc} 3 & 2 \\ 2 & 3 \end{array} \right), \end{array}$$

which is called the *symbol* of the configuration. Observe that the symbol for a three-point is precisely the same as that for a three-line (interchange the words "points" and "lines"). This means that the figure is self-dual.

The complete four-point has the symbol

$$\begin{array}{c} \\ \text{Points} \\ \text{Lines} \end{array} \begin{array}{cc} \text{Points} & \text{Lines} \\ \left(\begin{array}{cc} 4 & 3 \\ 2 & 6 \end{array} \right), \end{array}$$

because a point may be incident with four points, a line with six ($_4C_2$) lines, a line with two points, and a point with three lines (see Fig. 13).

The complete four-line has the symbol

$$\begin{array}{c} \\ \text{Points} \\ \text{Lines} \end{array} \begin{array}{cc} \text{Points} & \text{Lines} \\ \left(\begin{array}{cc} 6 & 2 \\ 3 & 4 \end{array} \right), \end{array}$$

because a point may be incident with six points, a point with two lines, a line with three points, and a line with four lines. Note that the complete four-line and complete four-point do not have the same symbol, so the complete quadrangle is not a self-dual configuration.

The symbol for a complete n-point is

$$\begin{array}{c} \\ \text{Points} \\ \text{Lines} \end{array} \begin{array}{cc} \text{Points} & \text{Lines} \\ \left(\begin{array}{cc} n & n-1 \\ 2 & _nC_2 \end{array} \right), \end{array}$$

and the symbol for a complete n-line is

$$\begin{array}{c} \\ \text{Points} \\ \text{Lines} \end{array} \begin{array}{cc} \text{Points} & \text{Lines} \\ \left(\begin{array}{cc} _nC_2 & 2 \\ n-1 & n \end{array} \right). \end{array}$$

Clearly, when incidences of points, lines, *and planes* are considered for complete configurations in three-space, the symbols must be square matrices of the *third* order. (See Section 6-3.)

4-2. Orthogonal cartesian point coordinates

The coordinates most employed in elementary plane analytical geometry are the orthogonal cartesian coordinates. Two perpendicular lines are taken as a frame of reference, with a positive direction and a unit of length assigned to each line. The coordinates x, y of a point P are the distances from P to the axes with the proper sign attached. This is a very convenient coordinate system for many purposes, because it establishes a one-to-one correspondence between the totality of points in the euclidean plane and the totality of ordered pairs of real numbers (x, y). To every point there is a unique ordered pair of numbers, and to every ordered pair of numbers there is a unique point. This is not true for every coordinate system. For instance, in polar coordinates (ρ, θ) for the plane, the origin is a point where ρ is zero, but θ is arbitrary, so there is not a one-to-one correspondence between number pairs and points in the polar coordinate system. Orthogonal cartesian coordinates originated with R. Descartes (1596–1650), when he wedded algebra and geometry in the publication of *La Géométrie* in 1637.

It is well known to the reader that the set of points (x_i, y_i), which satisfy the equation $Ax + By + C = 0$, constitute a straight line in the plane. The origin is a point of the set if and only if $C = 0$. The line is parallel to the x-axis if and only if $A = 0$, and it is parallel to the y-axis if and only if $B = 0$. In euclidean geometry, one restriction must be imposed on the coefficients A, B, C in addition to the obvious restriction that A, B, C are not all zero. It is that A and B cannot both be zero, for this would lead to the apparent contradiction that $C = 0$ in cases where C is nonzero. This restriction will be removed for the case of a line in the affine or projective plane. The linear equation $Ax + By + C = 0$ is a special case of the equation $f(x, y) = 0$. If the function $f(x, y)$ is not linear in x and y, the set of points with coordinates (x_i, y_i) which satisfy $f(x, y) = 0$ constitute a curve. The equation $f(x, y) = 0$, or in solved form $y = \phi(x)$, defines a set of points which may be styled a *point locus*.

Three constants A, B, C (called parameters) appear in the general linear equation $Ax + By + C = 0$. Observe, however, that only the ratios $A:B:C$ have significance, so that A, B, and C may each be divided by any one of the three which is not zero. Hence, two *essential* parameters remain in the linear equation. Note that for any specified line l_1 the ratios $A:B:C$ are fixed—say, $A_1:B_1:C_1$—and the variable point coordinates (x, y) represent a variable point P on the fixed line given by $A_1x + B_1y + C_1 = 0$. The line is determined by the ratios $A_1:B_1:C_1$. Hence, A_1, B_1, C_1 can be called *coordinates* of the line l_1. Suppose $A \neq 0$ in the general equation $Ax + By + C = 0$. Divide by A to obtain the line equation in the form $x + B'y + C' = 0$. Because a singly infinite set of values can be assigned independently to each of the parameters B' and C', the equation $x + B'y + C' = 0$ may be said to represent a doubly infinite set of lines. A doubly infinite set of values can be assigned to the ratios $A:B:C$. Hence, the plane contains a doubly infinite set of straight lines or a *two-parameter* set of lines. The coordinates (x, y) of any point in the plane may each be assigned a singly infinite set of values. Hence, the plane contains a doubly infinite set of points. Consider the doubly infinite set of lines in a plane π, and the doubly infinite set of points in a plane π'. A one-to-one correspondence can be established between the sets π and π' such that to each point in π' there corresponds a unique line in π, and to each line in π there corresponds a unique point in π'. If $C \neq 0$, a correspondence could be effected by allowing the point (x, y) in π' to correspond to the line determined by $(A/C, B/C)$ in π. This does not account for the lines through the origin in π. By the duality principle, one would expect the lines through a point (here the origin) to correspond to the points on a line. (The case $C = 0$ will be postponed until help arrives in the form of homogeneous coordinates.)

Suppose it is desired to select all of the lines of the doubly infinite set $Ax + By + C = 0$, which contain, say, the point (x_0, y_0). The condition $Ax_0 + By_0 + C = 0$ must obtain. Subtract the second equation from the first to have

$$(1) \qquad A(x - x_0) + B(y - y_0) = 0.$$

A singly infinite set of values may be assigned for the ratio $A:B$. Hence, a singly infinite set of lines, or a one-parameter set of lines has been selected to pass through the point (x_0, y_0). A single line of this pencil of lines through (x_0, y_0) can be found which will contain another point (x_1, y_1). The condition for this is that

$$(2) \qquad A(x_1 - x_0) + B(y_1 - y_0) = 0.$$

The eliminant of equations (1) and (2) is

$$\begin{vmatrix} x - x_0 & y - y_0 \\ x_1 - x_0 & y_1 - y_0 \end{vmatrix} = 0,$$

which is the equation of the required line.

The preceding discussion on parameters in the linear equation may be extended to circles and other plane curves. Because the equation of a circle— $(x - h)^2 + (y - k)^2 = r^2$—has three essential parameters, there is a triply infinite set of circles in the plane. The fixed quantities h, k, r for a given circle may be called the coordinates of the circle. A one-to-one correspondence exists between the circles in the plane and the points of three-space. Similarly, the general equation of a conic section,

$$ax^2 + 2hxy + by^2 + 2gx + 2fy + c = 0,$$

has five essential parameters, so one may establish a one-to-one correspondence between the conics in the plane and the points of a five-dimensional space.

4-3. Plückerian line coordinates

Consider any line $Ax + By + C = 0$ in the plane, but with the assumption that the line does not contain the origin, that is, $C \neq 0$. Write the equation in the form $(A/C)x + (B/C)y + 1 = 0$, or as $ux + vy + 1 = 0$. For fixed values of u and v this is a fixed line, with (x, y) the variable coordinates of a point which ranges on the line. If x and y are held fixed and u and v are allowed to vary, the equation represents a singly infinite set of lines, each of which contains the fixed point (x, y). That is, $ux + vy + 1 = 0$ represents a pencil of lines through every given point (x, y). Because a one-to-one correspondence exists between the totality of ordered number pairs (u, v) and the totality of lines in the plane (not through the origin), a pair of values for u and v may be called coordinates of a line. The equation $ux + vy + 1 = 0$, with u, v fixed and x, y variable, is the point equation of the line (u, v). The same equation with x, y fixed and u, v variable is the *line equation* of the point (x, y). The equation $ux + vy + 1 = 0$ is an incidence condition. It states that the point (x, y) is on the line (u, v), and conversely, that the line (u, v) is "on," or incident with, the point (x, y). J. Plücker (1801–1868) introduced line coordinates. They are therefore called plückerian coordinates. Observe that because the x and y intercepts of the line $ux + vy + 1 = 0$ are respectively $-1/u$ and $-1/v$, the plückerian coordinates u and v may be defined as the negative reciprocals of the intercepts of the line on the x- and y-axes. It is clear then why lines through the origin $(C = 0)$ have no plückerian coordinates. A more satisfactory situation will obtain after homogeneous coordinates are introduced.

EXAMPLE 1

Find the line coordinates of the line $3x + 4y = 5$ and the point coordinates of the point $3u + 4v = 5$.

Solution: Each equation should be changed to the form $ux + vy + 1 = 0$. The first is $-(3/5)x - (4/5)y + 1 = 0$, so the line coordinates are $(-3/5, -4/5)$. The second is $u(-\frac{3}{5}) + v(-\frac{4}{5}) + 1 = 0$, so the point coordinates of the center of the line pencil are $(-3/5, -4/5)$.

Note the following dual statements relative to the linear equation $ux + vy + 1 = 0$. Subscripts indicate fixed quantities.

1. The point of intersection of the lines

$$l_1: \quad u_1 x + v_1 y + 1 = 0,$$

$$l_2: \quad u_2 x + v_2 y + 1 = 0,$$

where $u_1 v_2 - u_2 v_1 \neq 0$, is obtained by solving the equations for x and y. The condition $u_1 v_2 - u_2 v_1 \neq 0$ means that the lines are not parallel.

1. The line joining the points

$$P_1: \quad x_1 u + y_1 v + 1 = 0,$$

$$P_2: \quad x_2 u + y_2 v + 1 = 0,$$

where $x_1 y_2 - x_2 y_1 \neq 0$, is obtained by solving the equations for u and v. The condition $x_1 y_2 - x_2 y_1 \neq 0$ means that the points are not on a line through the origin.

2. The equation of the join of the points $P_1(x_1, y_1)$, $P_2(x_2, y_2)$ is

$$\begin{vmatrix} x & y & 1 \\ x_1 & y_1 & 1 \\ x_2 & y_2 & 1 \end{vmatrix} = 0.$$

2. The equation of the intersection of the lines $l_1(u_1, v_1)$, $l_2(u_2, v_2)$ is

$$\begin{vmatrix} u & v & 1 \\ u_1 & v_1 & 1 \\ u_2 & v_2 & 1 \end{vmatrix} = 0.$$

The equation $bx = ay$ is clearly a line through the origin. What is the interpretation of $bu = av$? Write $v = (b/a)u$ in the equation $ux + vy + 1 = 0$ to obtain $ax + by + a/u = 0$, which, as u varies, is a family of parallel lines with common slope $-a/b$. As u becomes infinite the limiting line of the family is the line through the origin. But as u becomes infinite v also becomes infinite. Hence, $bu = av$ determines not a point but a direction—that is, the direction of the line $ax + by = 0$. Duality breaks down for this situation, but the following statements can be made.

3. The equation $cx = dy$ gives a line through the origin with slope c/d.

3. The equation $bu = av$ determines the direction of a family of parallel lines with slope $-a/b$.

Now that linear equations in x and y and linear equations in u and v have been discussed, a study of curves is next in order.

The reader is familiar with the fact that the graph of the equation $y = f(x)$ is a point locus. Suppose the function $f(x)$ is continuous in the domain of x under consideration. A tangent to the point locus (curve) at a point (x_1, y_1) is conceived as follows. Consider the secant line determined by the points $P_1(x_1, y_1)$ and $P'(x_1 + \Delta x, y_1 + \Delta y)$ on the locus. Any point $P(x, y)$ on this line satisfies the equation

$$\begin{vmatrix} x & y & 1 \\ x_1 + \Delta x & y_1 + \Delta y & 1 \\ x_1 & y_1 & 1 \end{vmatrix} = 0,$$

which reduces to

$$\frac{y - y_1}{x - x_1} = \frac{\Delta y}{\Delta x}.$$

In the limit as $P' \to P_1$, the secant line becomes the tangent line at $P_1(x_1, y_1)$, with equation

$$y - y_1 = \left(\frac{dy}{dx}\right)_1 (x - x_1).$$

Dually, instead of two points determining a secant line, one has two tangents intersecting in a point. Instead of the condition $y = f(x)$ on points of the plane, one has the condition $v = f(u)$ on lines in the plane. From here on the analysis follows precisely the steps as outlined for $y = f(x)$. However, instead of the variable point (x, y) generating a curve, the variable line (u, v) *envelops* a curve; that is, as the variable line moves it is always tangent to a curve, which is called the *envelope* of the line. Relative to $y = f(x)$ one seeks the *tangent line* to the curve at a point. Relative to $v = f(u)$ one seeks the *contact point* of the curve "at" (or on) a given tangent line.

Suppose again that $f(u)$ is continuous in the domain of u under consideration. A point on the line locus (curve, or envelope) at the line $p_1(u_1, v_1)$ is conceived as follows. Consider the intersection of line $p_1(u_1, v_1)$ and a neighboring line $p'(u_1 + \Delta u, v_1 + \Delta v)$ of the envelope. Any line $l(u, v)$ through this point satisfies the equation

$$\begin{vmatrix} u & v & 1 \\ u_1 + \Delta u & v_1 + \Delta v & 1 \\ u_1 & v_1 & 1 \end{vmatrix} = 0,$$

which reduces to

$$\frac{v - v_1}{u - u_1} = \frac{\Delta v}{\Delta u}.$$

In the limit as $p' \to p_1$ the intersection point becomes the desired contact point [of the line $p_1(u_1, v_1)$], with equation

$$v - v_1 = \left(\frac{dv}{du}\right)_1 (u - u_1).$$

For curves, the following dual statements may be compared.

4. The graph of $y = f(x)$ is a point locus.

4. The graph of $v = f(u)$ is a line envelope.

5. The equation of the tangent line at a point (x_1, y_1) is

$$y - y_1 = \left(\frac{dy}{dx}\right)_1 (x - x_1).$$

5. The equation of the contact point of a line (u_1, v_1) is

$$v - v_1 = \left(\frac{dv}{du}\right)_1 (u - u_1).$$

6. The *order* of a point locus is the number of points (real or complex) in which a line meets it.

6. The *class* of a line envelope is the number of tangents (real or complex) to it through a point.

EXAMPLE 2

Find the line equation of the hypocycloid of four cusps given by the point equation $x^{2/3} + y^{2/3} = a^{2/3}$.

Solution: A parametric representation of the point locus is

$$x = a \cos^3 \theta, \quad y = a \sin^3 \theta.$$

The slope of the tangent line to the curve at any point θ is $dy/dx = -\tan \theta$, so the equation of the tangent line is

$$y - a \sin^3 \theta = -\tan \theta (x - a \cos^3 \theta)$$

or, in another form,

$$-\frac{x}{a \cos \theta} - \frac{y}{a \sin \theta} + 1 = 0.$$

On comparing the last equation with $ux + vy + 1 = 0$, it is seen that the line coordinates u, v in terms of θ are

$$u = -\frac{1}{a}\sec\theta, \quad v = -\frac{1}{a}\csc\theta.$$

For the line envelope, elimination of θ gives the equation

$$\frac{1}{u^2} + \frac{1}{v^2} = a^2.$$

Observe that if the equation $x^{2/3} + y^{2/3} = a^{2/3}$ is rationalized, there results the sixth degree equation $(x^2 + y^2 - a^2)^3 + 27a^2x^2y^2 = 0$. Hence, the hypocycloid is a curve of the sixth *order*. Also, note that the equation of the line locus can be written as $a^2u^2v^2 - u^2 - v^2 = 0$, an equation of the fourth degree. Hence, the hypocycloid is a curve of the fourth *class*. Therefore, the order and class of a curve are not necessarily the same.

The curve of the preceding example will be treated again in the following section on homogeneous line coordinates.

EXERCISES

1. In the geometry of a line, what would be the complementary space of a given point? On the line, what is therefore the dual element of a point?

2. Sketch figures to show the plane dual configurations of the following:

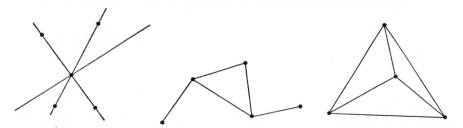

3. In space S_4, what are the duals of (a) a point, (b) a line, (c) a plane?

4. Show that self-dual elements occur only in spaces of an odd number of dimensions.

5. By use of the principle of duality in the plane, formulate the dual of the theorem: If the lines joining corresponding vertices of two triangles are concurrent, then the pairs of corresponding sides intersect in collinear points.

6. Write the symbol for the configuration in Exercise 5 and thus show that it is self-dual.

7. Write the symbol for a complete four-point in three-dimensional space.

8. Draw several lines of the graph of $u + 2v + 1 = 0$.

9. Write the equation of the line with line coordinates (u, v) given as $(\frac{1}{3}, \frac{2}{7})$.

10. Write the equation of the point with point coordinates $(\frac{3}{4}, -8)$.

11. What are the plückerian coordinates of the line $3x - 4y - 7 = 0$?

12. Draw the graph of $3v = 4u$.

13. Show that the distance from the point $(\bar{x}, \bar{y})$ to the line $ax + by + c = 0$ is

$$\frac{a\bar{x} + b\bar{y} + c}{\pm\sqrt{a^2 + b^2}}.$$

14. Show that the distance from the point $au + bv + c = 0$ to the line $(\bar{u}, \bar{v})$ is

$$\frac{a\bar{u} + b\bar{v} + c}{\pm c\sqrt{\bar{u}^2 + \bar{v}^2}}.$$

Observe that if the line in Exercise 13 and the point in this exercise are both given by $ux + vy + 1 = 0$, the two distances are given by the single expression

$$\pm\frac{ux + vy + 1}{\sqrt{u^2 + v^2}}.$$

15. Describe the line pencil represented by $u = c$, where c is a nonzero constant.

16. Show that the intersection (x, y) of $u_i x + v_i y + 1 = 0$, where $i = 1, 2$, is given by

$$x:y:1 = \begin{vmatrix} v_1 & 1 \\ v_2 & 1 \end{vmatrix} : \begin{vmatrix} 1 & u_1 \\ 1 & u_2 \end{vmatrix} : \begin{vmatrix} u_1 & v_1 \\ u_2 & v_2 \end{vmatrix},$$

and that the join (u, v) of $x_i u + y_i v + 1 = 0$, where $i = 1, 2$, is given by

$$u:v:1 = \begin{vmatrix} y_1 & 1 \\ y_2 & 1 \end{vmatrix} : \begin{vmatrix} 1 & x_1 \\ 1 & x_2 \end{vmatrix} : \begin{vmatrix} x_1 & y_1 \\ x_2 & y_2 \end{vmatrix}.$$

17. Find a necessary and sufficient condition for (a) the three points (x_i, y_i), where $i = 1, 2, 3$, to be collinear, (b) the three lines (u_i, v_i), where $i = 1, 2, 3$, to be concurrent.

18. Given the equation $x^2 + xy + y^2 = 3$ of a point locus, find the equation of the tangent line at the point $(1, 1)$.

19. Given the equation $4(u^2 - uv + v^2) = 1$ of a line locus, find the equation of the contact point for the line $(-\frac{1}{2}, -\frac{1}{2})$.

> Ans. $u + v + 1 = 0$.

20. Find the equation in line coordinates of the point locus $x^2 + xy + y^2 = 3$. *Hint:* Write the equation of the tangent line to the curve at any point $(\bar{x}, \bar{y})$, compare with $ux + vy + 1 = 0$ to obtain u and v as functions of $(\bar{x}, \bar{y})$, and use the condition that $(\bar{x}, \bar{y})$ is on the given curve.

> Ans. $4(u^2 - uv + v^2) = 1$.

4-4. Homogeneous point and line coordinates

For much of the work which follows it is convenient to have equations of loci written in homogeneous form. Consider the straight line first. Its equation has been used in the form $Ax + By + C = 0$ in Section 4-2. In Section 1-4 the abscissa x of a point on a line was replaced by a number pair $(kx_1:kx_2)$, with k any nonzero constant. The coordinates x and y of a point in the plane will now be replaced by the respective ratios $(hx_1:hx_3)$ and $(kx_2:kx_3)$, where neither h

nor k is zero. That is, x is replaced by x_1/x_3 and y by x_2/x_3. The general equation of a line is then

(3) $$Ax_1 + Bx_2 + Cx_3 = 0,$$

where the x_i, with $i = 1, 2, 3$, are the homogeneous point coordinates of a variable point on the line. Any numbers proportional to x_1, x_2, x_3 suffice as coordinates of the same point. (The triple $0, 0, 0$ is excluded from consideration.) If u_1, u_2, u_3 are numbers proportional to A, B, C, then equation (3) takes the symmetric form

(4) $$u_1x_1 + u_2x_2 + u_3x_3 = 0.$$

If equation (4) is divided by u_3x_3, the equation is in the previously used form $ux + vy + 1 = 0$, where now $u = u_1/u_3$, $v = u_2/u_3$. Any numbers proportional to u_1, u_2, u_3 are *homogeneous* plückerian coordinates of the line (4). Equation (4) is referred to as an equation of *united position*. It is the condition that a point with homogeneous coordinates x_i lie on a line with homogeneous coordinates u_i. If the x_i are held fixed and the u_i vary, equation (4) represents a point. If the u_i are held fixed and the x_i vary, equation (4) represents a line.

A technique for determining readily the point of intersection of two lines is shown next. Let the two lines be given by

(5) $$a_1x_1 + a_2x_2 + a_3x_3 = 0,$$
$$b_1x_1 + b_2x_2 + b_3x_3 = 0.$$

The ratios $x_1:x_2:x_3$ are desired. Solve the equations (5) for x_1 and x_2 in terms of x_3 to obtain

$$x_1 = \frac{\begin{vmatrix} -a_3x_3 & a_2 \\ -b_3x_3 & b_2 \end{vmatrix}}{\begin{vmatrix} a_1 & a_2 \\ b_1 & b_2 \end{vmatrix}}, \quad x_2 = \frac{\begin{vmatrix} a_1 & -a_3x_3 \\ a_2 & -b_3x_3 \end{vmatrix}}{\begin{vmatrix} a_1 & a_2 \\ b_1 & b_2 \end{vmatrix}},$$

or

$$x_1:x_2:x_3 = x_3 \begin{vmatrix} -a_3 & a_2 \\ -b_3 & b_2 \end{vmatrix} : x_3 \begin{vmatrix} a_1 & -a_3 \\ b_1 & -b_3 \end{vmatrix} : x_3 \begin{vmatrix} a_1 & a_2 \\ b_1 & b_2 \end{vmatrix}$$

(6)

$$= \begin{vmatrix} a_2 & a_3 \\ b_2 & b_3 \end{vmatrix} : \begin{vmatrix} a_3 & a_1 \\ b_3 & b_1 \end{vmatrix} : \begin{vmatrix} a_1 & a_2 \\ b_1 & b_2 \end{vmatrix}.$$

Note that the three second-order determinants arrived at are the three determinants formed from the matrix of the coefficients in equations (5)—that is, from

$$\begin{pmatrix} a_1 & a_2 & a_3 \\ b_1 & b_2 & b_3 \end{pmatrix}.$$

The three determinants are obtained in order by leaving out the first, second, and third columns of the matrix. *Caution:* Be sure to note that when the second column is omitted the second determinant is taken as

$$\begin{vmatrix} a_3 & a_1 \\ b_3 & b_1 \end{vmatrix}.$$

With a little practice, one writes the intersection point of equations (5) without writing the determinants.

EXAMPLE 1

Write the coordinates of the intersection of the lines

$$x_1 - 2x_2 + 5x_3 = 0,$$

$$2x_1 + x_2 - x_3 = 0.$$

Solution: $x_1:x_2:x_3 = (-2)(-1) - (5)(1):(5)(2) - (1)(-1):(1)(1) - (-2)(2)$
$$= -3:11:5.$$

By the same technique, the coordinates of the join of two points are readily determined. Let the points have line equations

(7)
$$u_1\alpha_1 + u_2\alpha_2 + u_3\alpha_3 = 0,$$

$$u_1\beta_1 + u_2\beta_2 + u_3\beta_3 = 0.$$

From (6), the ratios $u_1:u_2:u_3$ are given by

$$u_1:u_2:u_3 = \begin{vmatrix} \alpha_2 & \alpha_3 \\ \beta_2 & \beta_3 \end{vmatrix} : \begin{vmatrix} \alpha_3 & \alpha_1 \\ \beta_3 & \beta_1 \end{vmatrix} : \begin{vmatrix} \alpha_1 & \alpha_2 \\ \beta_1 & \beta_2 \end{vmatrix}.$$

EXAMPLE 2

Write the coordinates of the join of the points

$$2u_1 - u_2 + u_3 = 0,$$

$$u_1 + 3u_2 - 4u_3 = 0.$$

Solution: $u_1:u_2:u_3 = (4 - 3):(1 + 8):(6 + 1) = 1:9:7.$

Henceforth, point coordinates will be enclosed by parentheses ( ) and line coordinates by brackets [ ]. Thus, for instance, $(1, 2, -3)$ or $(1:2:-3)$ will denote a point, but $[2, -1, 4]$ or $[2:-1:4]$ will denote a line. In order to exhibit the coordinates of the line determined by the points y_i and z_i, the following notation will be employed:

$$\begin{pmatrix} y_1 & y_2 & y_3 \\ z_1 & z_2 & z_3 \end{pmatrix} \rightarrow [y_2z_3 - y_3z_2, \ y_3z_1 - y_1z_3, \ y_1z_2 - y_2z_1].$$

On the other hand, the dual notation, for the point of intersection of the lines v_i and w_i, is

$$\begin{bmatrix} v_1 & v_2 & v_3 \\ w_1 & w_2 & w_3 \end{bmatrix} \rightarrow (v_2w_3 - v_3w_2, \ v_3w_1 - v_1w_3, \ v_1w_2 - v_2w_1).$$

A useful alternative notation may be introduced here by employing the symbol e^{ijk}, defined as follows:

$e^{ijk} = 1$ if i, j, k take on an even permutation of the numbers 1, 2, 3, i.e. 1, 2, 3; 2, 3, 1; 3, 1, 2.

$e^{ijk} = -1$ if i, j, k take on an odd permutation of 1, 2, 3, i.e. 1, 3, 2; 3, 2, 1; 2, 1, 3.

$e^{ijk} = 0$ if any two of i, j, k take the same value; as instances, $e^{312} = +1$, $e^{321} = -1$, $e^{113} = 0$, $e^{122} = 0$.

A repeated index always denotes a summation, if mention is not made to the contrary; as instances, $e^{1jk}y_jz_k = e^{123}y_2z_3 + e^{132}y_3z_2 = y_2z_3 - y_3z_2$, and $e^{2jk}v_jw_k = e^{231}v_3w_1 + e^{213}v_1w_3 = v_3w_1 - v_1w_3$.

If the reader is familiar with vector analysis he will note that one of the several advantages of homogeneous coordinates is that it allows use of the concise notation of vector analysis. The sum in equation (4)—that is, u_ix_i—is the *inner product* of two vectors **u** and **x** with components u_i and x_i. It is denoted by **u**·**x** in vector analysis, and is also called the *scalar* product of the vectors **u** and **x**. The scalar product of **u** and **x** is a number. In contrast, the *vector product* (or *cross product*) of **u** and **x** is another vector denoted by **u** × **x** (*u* cross *x*). Its components are $e^{ijk}u_jx_k$, for $i = 1, 2$, and 3. Note that $e^{ijk}u_jx_k = -e^{ijk}x_ju_k$.

Observe that if **a**, **b**, **c** have components a_i, b_i, c_i,

$$\mathbf{a} \cdot (\mathbf{b} \times \mathbf{c}) = a_ie^{ijk}b_jc_k.$$

Now perform the sum indicated by i, j, and k to see that

$$\mathbf{a} \cdot (\mathbf{b} \times \mathbf{c}) = \begin{vmatrix} a_1 & a_2 & a_3 \\ b_1 & b_2 & b_3 \\ c_1 & c_2 & c_3 \end{vmatrix}.$$

In the notation just explained, the coordinates of the intersection of lines v_i and w_i are $(e^{ijk}v_jw_k)$, and the coordinates of the join of points y_i and z_i are $[e^{ijk}y_jz_k]$.

Another advantage of homogeneous coordinates is that by their use every equation is rendered homogeneous. If, for instance, $\bar{x}_i$ satisfies the homogeneous equation $x_1^2 + 2x_1x_2 + x_3^2 = 0$, then $k\bar{x}_i$ also satisfies it, whereas this would not be true for a nonhomogeneous equation such as $x_1^2 + 2x_1x_2 + x_3 = 0$.

A further advantage of homogeneous coordinates is that they effect the transition from euclidean geometry to the more general affine and projective geometries. Just as a single ideal point with number pair $(1, 0)$ was added to the euclidean line to obtain a projective space of one dimension, an ideal line is added to the euclidean plane to obtain a projective space of two dimensions. Every line in the plane has one ideal point in common with the ideal line. A line in the projective plane is defined as a point set, whose coordinates x_i satisfy a linear equation

$$a_ix_i \equiv a_1x_1 + a_2x_2 + a_3x_3 = 0.$$

Remark: In an abstract axiomatic development of projective geometry, a set of numbers $(kx_1 : kx_2 : kx_3)$, with k any number except zero, is called a "point," and a set $(lu_1 : lu_2 : lu_3)$, with $l \neq 0$, is called a "line," but no physical interpretation is necessarily attached to "point" and "line." They are merely convenient names for sets of quantities, which may be real or complex numbers. With the additional definition of incidence given by $u_ix_i = 0$, it can be shown that any two distinct points are incident with a unique line and any two distinct lines are incident with a unique point. If the numbers involved are all real, the foregoing is a definition of the *real projective plane*.

If $a_1 = a_2 = 0$ and $a_3 \neq 0$, in $a_i x_i = 0$, one line has the equation $x_3 = 0$, and this line is treated as any other, such as, say, the line $x_1 = 0$. However, in euclidean geometry $x_3 \neq 0$. The ideal line does not exist. The points on $x_3 = 0$ are deleted from the projective plane to obtain the euclidean plane. In spite of this, the extended plane will be found useful in interpretations of results in euclidean geometry.

Observe that, in the solution (6) of equations (5), $x_3 = 0$ implies that $a_1 b_2 - a_2 b_1 = 0$, which means that the lines in (5) are parallel. In euclidean geometry, parallel lines have no intersection, so equations (5) have no solution if $a_1 b_2 - a_2 b_1 = 0$. In projective geometry, this deficiency is removed. Every two lines in the projective plane have an intersection. However, it must be kept in mind that the concept of parallelism as it is realized in euclidean geometry is lost in projective geometry. It was seen in the geometry of the line that euclidean measure of distance is not invariant under a projectivity and is, therefore, not a projective concept. A similar statement holds for the euclidean concept of parallelism. In spite of this loss of certain invariants on generalizing from euclidean to projective transformations in the plane, it will be seen that numerous interesting invariants remain for consideration in projective geometry.

The dual of equations (5) is now considered. Let it be required to find the *line* determined by the points

$$(8) \qquad \begin{aligned} u_1 a_1 + u_2 a_2 + u_3 a_3 &= 0, \\ u_1 b_1 + u_2 b_2 + u_3 b_3 &= 0. \end{aligned}$$

The solution in euclidean geometry is

$$u_i = e^{ijk} a_j b_k,$$

where $u_3 = a_1 b_2 - a_2 b_1 \neq 0$. In Section 4-2, it was realized that lines through the origin of cartesian coordinates have no nonhomogeneous line coordinates. Since u and v were defined as the negatives of the reciprocals of the intercepts of the line on the coordinate axes, a line with intercepts zero has nonexisting u and v coordinates. In euclidean geometry, the ratios $u = u_1/u_3$ and $v = u_2/u_3$ are used with $u_3 \neq 0$, but in projective geometry the line equation $u_3 = 0$, being a particular form of the general equation, $u_i a_i = 0$, with $a_1 = a_2 = 0$ and $a_3 \neq 0$, represents a point, just as does any other equation, say, $u_1 = 0$. Note that as $u_3 \to 0$, both u and v become infinite. This is sometimes described by saying that the u, v coordinates of a line through the origin are infinite. Note that as $u_3 \to 0$ in the equation $a_1 x_1 + a_2 x_2 + u_3 x_3 = 0$, the limiting line $a_1 x_1 + a_2 x_2 = 0$ has a definite direction which is that of the line $a_1 x + a_2 y = 0$. This line has homogeneous coordinates $[a_1, a_2, 0]$. If a_1 and a_2 are parameters, the singly infinite set of coordinates $[a_1, a_2, 0]$ are in one-to-one correspondence with the lines through the origin. Thus, $u_3 = 0$, with u_1 and u_2 arbitrary, characterizes the origin as the center of a pencil of lines. The dual is the ideal line, characterized by $x_3 = 0$, with x_1 and x_2 arbitrary.

Curves

Consider next the use of homogeneous point and line coordinates in the equations of curves. For some purposes the equation of a parabola, for instance, is conveniently taken as $y^2 = ax$, but for other purposes the homogeneous form $x_2^2 = ax_1x_3$ is to be preferred. It is always possible in euclidean geometry to assign the value 1 to x_3. For any curve given by $\psi(x, y) = 0$ or, in solved form, $y = F(x)$, the corresponding equation in homogeneous coordinates $f(x_1, x_2, x_3) = 0$ is obtained by replacing x by x_1/x_3 and y by x_2/x_3. The homogeneous function $f(x_1, x_2, x_3)$ has the property that

$$(9) \qquad f(tx_1, tx_2, tx_3) = t^n f(x_1, x_2, x_3),$$

where n is called the *degree* of homogeneity, and t is a nonzero parameter. In Exercise 10 on p. 61, it was seen that

$$x_i \frac{\partial f}{\partial x_i} \equiv nf.$$

Hence, the equation $f(x_1, x_2, x_3) = 0$ of a curve may be written in the form $x_i(\partial f/\partial x_i) = 0$. Observe that if $t = 1/x_3$ in equation (9), then

$$f\left(\frac{x_1}{x_3}, \frac{x_2}{x_3}, 1\right) = \frac{1}{x_3^n} f(x_1, x_2, x_3),$$

so that $f(x_1, x_2, x_3) = 0$ is equivalent to $f(x, y, 1) = 0$. Similar remarks hold for equations of curves in line coordinates. By letting $u = u_1/u_3$ and $v = u_2/u_3$, the line equation $v = F(u)$ can be cast into the homogeneous form $\phi(u_1, u_2, u_3) = 0$.

For a curve given in parametric form by $x = H(t)$, $y = K(t)$, an equivalent representation $x_1:x_2:x_3 = \phi_1(t):\phi_2(t):\phi_3(t)$ may be used. One has

$$x = \frac{x_1}{x_3} = \frac{\phi_1(t)}{\phi_3(t)} = H(t), \quad y = \frac{x_2}{x_3} = \frac{\phi_2(t)}{\phi_3(t)} = K(t)$$

for the equivalent nonhomogeneous form. Similarly, the curve may be represented in line coordinates by

$$u_1:u_2:u_3 = \psi_1(t):\psi_2(t):\psi_3(t).$$

Tangent Line to a Point Curve

Let it be required to find the equation of the tangent line to the curve $x_i = x_i(t)$, for $i = 1, 2, 3$, at any point t on the curve. It is assumed that the functions $x_i(t)$ have derivatives, denoted by $x_i'(t)$, which are continuous and not all zero at the point $P(y_i)$ where $t = t$. Let $\overline{P}(y_i + \Delta y_i)$ be the point corresponding to $t + \Delta t$. The line $P\overline{P}$ has an equation of the form $a_ix_i = 0$, where the coefficients a_i are to be determined. Because P and $\overline{P}$ lie on this line, it follows that

$$a_iy_i = 0, \quad a_i(y_i + \Delta y_i) = 0,$$

or, by virtue of the first of these equations,

(10) $$a_i y_i = 0, \quad a_i \Delta y_i = 0.$$

The a_i are therefore proportional to $e^{ijk} y_j \Delta y_k$. Divide each of these three quantities by Δt and allow Δt to approach zero to see that the coefficients a_i in the equation $a_i x_i = 0$ of the tangent line to the curve at $P(y_i)$ are given by $e^{ijk} y_j y_k'$. Hence, the tangent line is represented by

(11) $$e^{ijk} x_i y_j y_k' = 0.$$

Another form for the equation of the tangent line is obtained from $f(x_1, x_2, x_3) = 0$ as follows. From $x_i(\partial f/\partial x_i) = nf$, it follows that $y_i(\partial f/\partial y_i) = nf(y_1, y_2, y_3) = 0$. Also, the total differential of $f(x_1, x_2, x_3) = 0$ at $P(y_i)$ gives $df \equiv (\partial f/\partial y_i)dy_i = 0$. From

$$\frac{\partial f}{\partial y_i} y_i = 0, \quad \frac{\partial f}{\partial y_i} dy_i = 0,$$

the coefficients $\partial f/\partial y_i$ have the ratios $e^{ijk} y_j dy_k$, or equivalently $e^{ijk} y_j y_k'$, which are proportional to the a_i. It follows that the tangent line (11) may be written in the form

(12) $$x_i \frac{\partial f}{\partial y_i} = 0,$$

where it is understood that $\partial f/\partial y_i$ means $\partial f/\partial x_i$ evaluated at the point y_i.

Dually, one may proceed in like manner (see Exercise 8) to find the contact point x_i of a tangent line $v_i x_i = 0$ to $f(u_1, u_2, u_3) = 0$, to be given by

(13) $$x_1 : x_2 : x_3 = \frac{\partial f}{\partial v_1} : \frac{\partial f}{\partial v_2} : \frac{\partial f}{\partial v_3}.$$

From Point Equation to Line Equation

A general method will now be outlined for obtaining the line equation of a curve from its point equation. (See Example 2 on p. 80.) First, make the point equation homogeneous; that is, write $x = x_1/x_3$ and $y = x_2/x_3$, to have $f(x_1, x_2, x_3) = 0$ as the equation of the point locus. By equation (12), the tangent line $u_i x_i = 0$ at $P(y_i)$ has the form $(\partial f/\partial y_i)x_i = 0$, so the u_i are proportional to $\partial f/\partial y_i$. One may write the four equations

(14) $$\rho u_i = \frac{\partial f}{\partial y_i}, \quad f(y_1, y_2, y_3) = 0$$

(where ρ is a proportionality factor), from which it is necessary to eliminate the y_i to obtain a homogeneous equation in the u_i which holds for all points y_i on the curve. The result is $\phi(u_1, u_2, u_3) = 0$, which is called the *tangential equation* of the curve (or the *line equation* of the curve) because it is a condition on the line coordinates u_i of the tangent lines to the curve. In practice, it is not necessary to use y_i in (14), as is seen in the following instance.

EXAMPLE 3

Write the line equation of the curve $x^{2/3} + y^{2/3} = a^{2/3}$.

Solution: The homogeneous point equation is $x_1^{2/3} + x_2^{2/3} - a^{2/3}x_3^{2/3} = 0$. Eliminate x_1, x_2, x_3 from this and the equations

$$\rho u_1 = \tfrac{2}{3}x_1^{-1/3}, \quad \rho u_2 = \tfrac{2}{3}x_2^{-1/3}, \quad \rho u_3 = -\tfrac{2}{3}a^{2/3}x_3^{-1/3}$$

to obtain the desired equation

$$\frac{1}{u_1^2} + \frac{1}{u_2^2} - \frac{a^2}{u_3^2} = 0.$$

Compare with the solution of Example 2 on p. 80.

EXERCISES

1. Find the line equation of the point locus $x^2 - 2y^2 + 3 = 0$. For what value(s) of k is the line $kx_1 + x_2 + x_3 = 0$ tangent to the curve? (*Hint:* The line coordinates of the line must satisfy the line equation.)

   Ans. $k = \pm 1/\sqrt{6}$.

2. Find the line equation of the point locus $\sqrt{x} + \sqrt{y} = \sqrt{a}$.

3. Write the coordinates of the intersection of the lines which have coordinates $[6, 2, 1]$ and $[-1, 2, 0]$.

   Ans. $(2, 1, -14)$.

4. Write the coordinates of the line determined by the points $(2, 1, -4)$ and $(1, -2, 5)$.

   Ans. $[3, 14, 5]$.

5. From the definition of the symbol e^{ijk} show that

$$e^{ijk}a_{1i}a_{2j}a_{3k} = \begin{vmatrix} a_{11} & a_{12} & a_{13} \\ a_{21} & a_{22} & a_{23} \\ a_{31} & a_{32} & a_{33} \end{vmatrix}.$$

6. Prove that the three points (lines) with coordinates a_i, b_i, c_i are collinear (concurrent) if and only if $e^{ijk}a_ib_jc_k = 0$.

7. Verify equation (9) for the function

$$f \equiv \frac{x_1^2x_3 + x_1x_2^2}{\sqrt{x_1^2 + x_2^2}},$$

and also verify that $x_i(\partial f/\partial x_i) = nf$.

8. Carry out the details to show that the contact point x_i of a tangent line $v_ix_i = 0$ to $f(u_1, u_2, u_3) = 0$ is given by equation (13).

9. Show that the lines with coordinates $[1, 1, 1]$, $[2, -1, 4]$, $[5, -1, 9]$, $[1, -5, 5]$ are concurrent.

10. Find the points which are on the line joining the points $A(9, -4, 6)$ and $B(13, -8, 7)$ and also on the curve $x_2^2 = 4x_1x_3$. See Section 3-8 on linear dependence. Express a variable point on line AB by the coordinates

$$(9 + 13\lambda, -4 - 8\lambda, 6 + 7\lambda).$$

11. Take four points $A_1(1, 0, 0)$, $A_2(0, 1, 0)$, $A_3(0, 0, 1)$, and $H(1, 1, 1)$ with coordinates as indicated. Line A_1H intersects line A_2A_3 in B_1, A_2H intersects A_3A_1 in B_2, and A_3H intersects A_1A_2 in B_3. Find the coordinates of B_1, B_2, B_3. Then show that the intersections of A_2A_3, B_2B_3; A_3A_1, B_3B_1; and A_1A_2, B_1B_2 are collinear.

12. Find the equation of the tangent line to the curve

$$ax_1^2 + bx_2^2 + cx_3^2 + 2fx_2x_3 + 2gx_3x_1 + 2hx_1x_2 = 0$$

at the point $(\bar{x}_1, \bar{x}_2, \bar{x}_3)$, and show that the result can be written in the form

$$a\bar{x}_1x_1 + b\bar{x}_2x_2 + c\bar{x}_3x_3 + f(\bar{x}_2x_3 + x_2\bar{x}_3) + g(\bar{x}_3x_1 + x_3\bar{x}_1) + h(\bar{x}_1x_2 + x_1\bar{x}_2) = 0.$$

Note: If the x_i are regarded as orthogonal cartesian coordinates in three-space, the first equation here represents a cone, and the second equation represents the tangent plane to the cone along the generator through the origin and the point $\bar{x}_i$.

13. Use equation (11) in the preceding section to find the equation of the tangent line to the curve

$$x_1 = t^3, \quad x_2 = t^2, \quad x_3 = t + 1$$

at the point where $t = 1$.

Ans. $3x_1 - 5x_2 + x_3 = 0$.

CHAPTER 5

Homography in Two Dimensions

5-1. Homography between two planes

A homography between two lines was defined and studied in Chapter 1, and projective significance was attached to the homography in Chapter 2. Thus, the identification of the geometric projectivity with the algebraic homography allowed the use of the terms homography and projectivity to become synonymous. Here, in a similar way, a homography between two planes will be introduced. (The projective aspect of the correspondence between the planes will appear in Chapter 6.)

Consider a plane π and a coordinate system in it by which a point of π is identified uniquely by a number pair (x, y). Take a second plane $\bar{\pi}$ endowed similarly with a coordinate system so that each point of $\bar{\pi}$ is identified uniquely by a number pair $(\bar{x}, \bar{y})$.

DEFINITION: *A homography between the planes π and $\bar{\pi}$ is a one-to-one correspondence between the points of π and $\bar{\pi}$ of the form*

$$(1) \qquad H: \qquad \bar{x} = \frac{a_1 x + b_1 y + c_1}{a_3 x + b_3 y + c_3}, \quad \bar{y} = \frac{a_2 x + b_2 y + c_2}{a_3 x + b_3 y + c_3}.$$

Note that $\bar{x}$ and $\bar{y}$ are linear fractional functions of x and y with the same denominator. If the determinant M of the coefficients in (1), that is,

$$(2) \qquad M \equiv \begin{vmatrix} a_1 & b_1 & c_1 \\ a_2 & b_2 & c_2 \\ a_3 & b_3 & c_3 \end{vmatrix}$$

is zero, the mapping (1) is said to be *singular*. It will be supposed that M (sometimes called the modulus of the homography) is not zero. Let the cofactor of any element in M be denoted by the corresponding capital letter. For instance, the cofactor of a_1 is A_1, and the cofactor of b_3 is B_3. If M is used to denote the *value* of the determinant as well as the determinant (2), it follows that, for instance,

$$M = a_1 A_1 + a_2 A_2 + a_3 A_3 \equiv a_i A_i,$$

and, similarly, $M = b_i B_i = c_i C_i$. Further, $a_i B_i = a_i C_i = 0$, $b_i C_i = b_i A_i = 0$, and $c_i A_i = c_i B_i = 0$, from the property that the sum of the products of the elements of any column (or row) of a determinant by the respective cofactors of the corresponding elements of any other column (or row) is zero.

The inverse H^{-1} of the homography H can be found as follows. Let D denote the denominator $a_3 x + b_3 y + c_3$. One has then, from (1),

$$\begin{aligned} D\bar{x} &= a_1 x + b_1 y + c_1, \\ (3) \qquad D\bar{y} &= a_2 x + b_2 y + c_2, \\ D &\equiv a_3 x + b_3 y + c_3. \end{aligned}$$

Multiply the three equations in (3) respectively by A_1, A_2, A_3 and add to find the first of the equations

$$\begin{aligned} D(A_1\bar{x} + A_2\bar{y} + A_3) &= a_i A_i x = Mx, \\ (4) \qquad D(B_1\bar{x} + B_2\bar{y} + B_3) &= b_i B_i y = My, \\ D(C_1\bar{x} + C_2\bar{y} + C_3) &= c_i C_i \;\; = M. \end{aligned}$$

The last two equations of (4) are obtained by using the multipliers B_i and C_i, in turn, in the place of A_i. Now divide the first and second equations in (4) by the third to obtain the inverse H^{-1} of (1) in the form

$$(5) \qquad H^{-1}: \qquad x = \frac{A_1\bar{x} + A_2\bar{y} + A_3}{C_1\bar{x} + C_2\bar{y} + C_3}, \quad y = \frac{B_1\bar{x} + B_2\bar{y} + B_3}{C_1\bar{x} + C_2\bar{y} + C_3}.$$

It will be seen below that the modulus M_I of the inverse H^{-1} is M^2, so that if $M \neq 0$, then $M_I \neq 0$.

A Change of Notation

For some purposes it is convenient to employ the expressions in (1) and (5) for the homography H and its inverse H^{-1}, but for other purposes it is advantageous to employ homogeneous coordinates. Also, in order to anticipate a useful convention of tensor algebra, the homogeneous point coordinates x_1, x_2, x_3 (with subscripts) introduced in Chapter 4 will be written henceforth with superscripts—as x^1, x^2, x^3. The x^2 (read "x upper 2"), for instance, is not to be confused with the square of x, which would be written as $(x)^2$ if the occasion should arise. The square of x^i (x upper i) would be written as $(x^i)^2$. The subscripts will continue to be used for homogeneous line coordinates u_i (read "u lower i").

Let x, y in (1) be replaced by x^1/x^3, x^2/x^3 respectively, and $\bar{x}$, $\bar{y}$, by $\bar{x}^1/\bar{x}^3$, $\bar{x}^2/\bar{x}^3$. (One may write $\bar{x}^3 \equiv 1$, and interpret $\bar{x}^1$ and $\bar{x}^2$ as the cartesian coordinates $\bar{x}$, $\bar{y}$.) Further, write the matrix of the coefficients in (2) as (a_j^i), so that (1) becomes

$$\frac{\bar{x}^1}{\bar{x}^3} = \frac{a_1^1 x^1 + a_2^1 x^2 + a_3^1 x^3}{a_1^3 x^1 + a_2^3 x^2 + a_3^3 x^3} = \frac{a_i^1 x^i}{a_i^3 x^i}, \quad \frac{\bar{x}^2}{\bar{x}^3} = \frac{a_i^2 x^i}{a_i^3 x^i},$$

which are equivalent to

$$(6) \qquad h\bar{x}^i = a^i_j x^j, \qquad\qquad i, j = 1, 2, 3,$$

where h is a proportionality factor. Denote the cofactor of a^i_j by A^j_i, and the determinant $|a^i_j|$ of the matrix (a^i_j) by a. It follows that, for instance, $a = a^1_j A^j_1 = a^2_j A^j_2 = a^3_j A^j_3$, so that, for any k, $a^{(k)}_j A^j_{(k)} = a$, where the parentheses on k indicate that k is not summed. On the other hand, $a^1_j A^j_2 = 0$, for instance, and $a^k_j A^j_l = 0$ for $k \neq l$. Simplification is achieved by writing

$$(7) \qquad a^i_j A^j_k = a\delta^i_k,$$

where the Kronecker delta δ^i_k is 1 if $i = k$ and zero if $i \neq k$. By means of (7) the inverse of equations (6) can be obtained readily by multiplying by A^k_i and summing on the index i. This gives

$$hA^k_i \bar{x}^i = A^k_i a^i_j x^j = a\delta^k_j x^j = ax^k,$$

or, on writing $\rho = a/h$ and changing the indices,

$$(8) \qquad \rho x^i = A^i_j \bar{x}^j.$$

Observe that the matrix (A^i_j) is the transpose of the cofactors of the matrix (a^i_j) in (6). If equations (8) are divided by the determinant $a \equiv |a^i_j|$, the matrix (A^i_j/a) in the resulting equations

$$(8') \qquad \sigma x^i = \frac{A^i_j}{a} \bar{x}^j$$

is the *inverse* of the matrix (a^i_j). The matrix (A^i_j) is the *adjoint* matrix of (a^i_j). Because of the presence of the nonzero proportionality factor in equations (8), it is immaterial whether one uses the adjoint matrix as in (8) or the inverse matrix as in (8').

THEOREM: *The determinant of the matrix (A^i_j) in (8) is equal to the square of the determinant of the matrix (a^i_j) in (6).*

Proof: Take the determinant of both sides of equation (7) to have

$$|a^i_j A^j_k| = |a^i_j|\,|A^j_k| = |a\delta^i_k| = a^3|\delta^i_k| = a^3,$$

from which

$$a|A^j_k| = a^3,$$

or

$$|A^p_q| = a^2 = |a^i_j|^2.$$

It follows that, in the former notation, $M_I = M^2$, a result promised earlier. The efficacy of the change in notation is apparent from the proof of this theorem. The alternative notation in (6) will be employed in succeeding chapters.

5-2. Properties of a homography

A homography between two lines was seen in Section 1-6 to be determined by three pairs of corresponding points. The extension of this to a homography between two planes is stated in

THEOREM 1: *A nonsingular homography between two planes is determined by four pairs of corresponding points, with no three of the points in either plane being collinear.*

Proof: In equations (1) there are nine coefficients a_i, b_i, c_i. However, the numerators and denominators of both fractional functions in (1) may be divided by any one of the coefficients which is not zero. This operation leaves eight essential parameters to be determined. A pair of corresponding points (x, y) and $(\bar{x}, \bar{y})$ gives rise to two equations in the eight parameters. Hence, four pairs of corresponding points are required to determine the eight parameters. Similarly, if the homography is in the form of equations (6), each of these equations can be divided by any one of the nonzero coefficients a_j^i to leave again eight essential parameters to be determined.

It is left to the reader to show that the eight parameters are not determined uniquely if the homography is singular or if three of the points in one plane are collinear.

EXAMPLE

Determine the homography under which the four points $Q_1(1:1:-1)$, $Q_2(1:-1:1)$, $Q_3(-1:1:1)$, $Q_4(1:2:3)$ map into the four points $P_1(1:0:0)$, $P_2(0:1:0)$, $P_3(0:0:1)$, $P_4(1:1:1)$, respectively.

Solution: The algebra is simpler if, in equations (6), the x^i are taken as coordinates of P_i and the $\bar{x}^i$ as coordinates of Q_i. The requirement that $P_1(1:0:0)$ maps into $Q_1(1:1:-1)$ by equations (6) produces

$$k_1 = a_1^1,$$
$$k_1 = a_1^2,$$
$$-k_1 = a_1^3,$$

from which

$$a_1^2 = a_1^1 = -a_1^3.$$

Similarly, if P_2, P_3, P_4 go into Q_2, Q_3, Q_4, respectively, the equations

$$k_2 = a_2^1, \quad -k_3 = a_3^1, \quad k_4 = a_1^1 + a_2^1 + a_3^1,$$
$$-k_2 = a_2^2, \quad k_3 = a_3^2, \quad 2k_4 = a_1^2 + a_2^2 + a_3^2,$$
$$k_2 = a_2^3, \quad k_3 = a_3^3, \quad 3k_4 = a_1^3 + a_2^3 + a_3^3,$$

must obtain. On using $a_2^3 = a_2^1 = -a_2^2$, and $a_3^1 = -a_3^3$, $a_3^2 = a_3^3$, with $k_4 = 2$ for convenience, in the last set of three equations, the coefficients are determined for the homography. It is

$$\rho \bar{x}^1 = 3x^1 + 4x^2 - 5x^3,$$
$$\rho \bar{x}^2 = 3x^1 - 4x^2 + 5x^3,$$
$$\rho \bar{x}^3 = -3x^1 + 4x^2 + 5x^3.$$

The inverse is readily found to be given by

$$3\sigma x^1 = \bar{x}^1 + \bar{x}^2 \qquad ,$$
$$4\sigma x^2 = \bar{x}^1 \qquad + \bar{x}^3,$$
$$5\sigma x^3 = \qquad \bar{x}^2 + \bar{x}^3.$$

The reader should verify that the latter form of the homography does map the four points Q_i into P_i.

As in the case of homographies between one-dimensional spaces, the totality of homographies in (1) can be shown to constitute a group. Because equations (6) (or equations (1)) involve eight essential parameters, it is seen that these equations constitute ∞^8 homographies between two planes. Another way to express this is to say that the totality of homographies between two spaces (each of dimensionality two) is a group of eight parameters.

It will be shown next that any line $\bar{l}$ in plane $\bar{\pi}$ maps into a line l in π. Let $\bar{l}$ have the equation $A\bar{x} + B\bar{y} + C = 0$. Substitute for $\bar{x}$ and $\bar{y}$ from equations (1) to have

$$A(a_1x + b_1y + c_1) + B(a_2x + b_2y + c_2) + C(a_3x + b_3y + c_3) = 0,$$

a linear equation in x and y which represents the corresponding line l in π to $\bar{l}$ in $\bar{\pi}$. By (5) a line l in π can be mapped into its correspondent $\bar{l}$ in $\bar{\pi}$. Because collinear points map into collinear points under (1), a homography may be called a *collineation*. A study of collineations in the projective plane is set forth in Chapter 7. Note that if planes π and $\bar{\pi}$ coincide, equations (1) determine a mapping of a plane into itself.

Vanishing Lines

Observe from equations (1) and (6) that the line in π with equation $a_3x + b_3y + c_3 = 0$ and the line in $\bar{\pi}$ with equation $C_1\bar{x} + C_2\bar{y} + C_3 = 0$ play exceptional roles. There are no correspondents for these lines in plane euclidean geometry. However, if the euclidean plane is enlarged to the projective plane by the addition of an ideal line, the correspondence (1) and (6) between lines in π and $\bar{\pi}$ becomes complete. The line $a_3x + b_3y + c_3 = 0$ in π takes the ideal line in $\bar{\pi}$ for its correspondent, and the line $C_1\bar{x} + C_2\bar{y} + C_3 = 0$ in $\bar{\pi}$ is matched with the ideal line in π.

DEFINITION: *The line in plane π which corresponds to the ideal line in plane $\bar{\pi}$ is called the* vanishing line *in π.*

A set of parallel lines in plane π maps into a pencil of lines in plane $\bar{\pi}$ with the center of the pencil on the vanishing line in $\bar{\pi}$. In order to see this, consider the family of parallel lines in π given by $ax + by + \lambda = 0$, where λ is a parameter. These lines map by (5) into the family of lines in $\bar{\pi}$ with the equation

(9) $a(A_1\bar{x} + A_2\bar{y} + A_3) + b(B_1\bar{x} + B_2\bar{y} + B_3) + \lambda(C_1\bar{x} + C_2\bar{y} + C_3) = 0.$

As λ varies, all lines in (9) contain the point of intersection of the two lines

$$(aA_1 + bB_1)\bar{x} + (aA_2 + bB_2)\bar{y} + aA_3 + bB_3 = 0,$$
$$C_1\bar{x} + C_2\bar{y} + C_3 = 0,$$

the second of which is the vanishing line in $\bar{\pi}$.

Affine Mapping

In equations (1) it is to be observed that if $a_3 = b_3 = 0$ and $c_3 \neq 0$, then a point (x, y) in the plane π always has a correspondent in plane $\bar{\pi}$. There is therefore no vanishing line in π or $\bar{\pi}$, because $C_1 = C_2 = 0$. From the point of view of projective geometry, the ideal line is required to be a fixed line in each plane, which means that under the mapping of the form

(10)
$$\bar{x} = \alpha_1 x + \beta_1 y + \gamma_1,$$
$$\bar{y} = \alpha_2 x + \beta_2 y + \gamma_2$$

now under consideration, any point (x, y) on the ideal line in π maps into some point $(\bar{x}, \bar{y})$ on the ideal line in $\bar{\pi}$. In other words, the vanishing lines in π and $\bar{\pi}$ are the ideal lines in these respective planes. A special homography of this kind is called an *affine* mapping. Observe that the affine mapping (10) is more general than the rotation and translation of euclidean geometry because the only restriction on (10) is that the inverse must exist, which means that $\alpha_1\beta_2 - \alpha_2\beta_1 \neq 0$. Thus, the group of the affine mappings occupies a position between the euclidean group and the projective group. One generalizes from euclidean geometry to affine geometry, but specializes from projective geometry to affine geometry. Affine geometry may be defined as the study of invariants of configurations under the group of affine mappings given by (10). (See Exercises 3 and 4.) The projective interpretation of affine geometry will appear in Chapter 6.

Singular Homography

The matrix of the mapping (1) has the determinant M shown in (2). If $M \neq 0$ the matrix has rank three. This is the general case which has been considered. Now suppose the rank of the matrix is two. That is, $M = 0$, but not all of the cofactors $A_1, A_2, \cdots$ are zero. Equations (4) reduce to

(10′)
$$A_1\bar{x} + A_2\bar{y} + A_3 = 0,$$
$$B_1\bar{x} + B_2\bar{y} + B_3 = 0,$$
$$C_1\bar{x} + C_2\bar{y} + C_3 = 0.$$

From the equations

$$a_1A_1 + a_2A_2 + a_3A_3 = M = 0,$$
$$b_1A_1 + b_2A_2 + b_3A_3 = 0,$$

it follows that $A_1:A_2:A_3 = C_1:C_2:C_3$. In a similar way show that $A_1:A_2:A_3 = B_1:B_2:B_3$. Hence, the three equations in (10′) represent the same line. This means that all points in plane π map into a single line in plane $\bar{\pi}$.

Next, let the rank of the matrix of the homography be 1. In this case all cofactors A_1, A_2, $\cdots$ are zero, which requires that the elements of any row of the determinant M be proportional to the corresponding elements of any other row. Hence, all points in plane π map into a single point in plane $\bar{\pi}$. (See Exercise 11.) The results on singular homographies can be stated as follows.

In a singular homographic correspondence between two spaces of two dimensions the image of all points in one space is (a) a line in the other if the rank of the matrix of the homography is two, or (b) a point in the other if the rank is one.

For the matrix of a singular homographic correspondence between two spaces π and $\bar{\pi}$ of n dimensions, it can be shown that rank one means again a point in $\bar{\pi}$, rank two a line, rank three a plane, rank four a three-space, etc., to rank $k + 1$ for a k-space.

EXERCISES

1. Use equations of the form (6) to show that the totality of homographies constitute a group.

2. Find the equations of the vanishing lines in π and $\bar{\pi}$ for the homography of the Example in Section 5-2 (p. 94).

3. Show that under the affine mapping

$$\bar{x} = x + y + 2,$$
$$\bar{y} = 2x - y + 4,$$

the distance between the points $P_1(x_1, y_1)$ and $P_2(x_2, y_2)$ is not invariant.

4. Perform the affine mapping in Exercise 3 on the family of parallel lines $\bar{y} = 5\bar{x} + \lambda$. What conclusions can you draw? Is the new family of lines a set of parallel lines? Is the slope of a line changed under an affine mapping?

> *Ans.* Parallelism is an affine invariant. The euclidean measure of an angle is not an affine invariant.

5. Find the line in $\bar{\pi}$ into which the line $x + y + 1 = 0$ maps under the homography of the Example in Section 5-2.

6. Given

$$\bar{x} = \frac{x + y - 1}{x + y + 1}, \quad \bar{y} = \frac{x - y - 1}{x + y + 1},$$

compute the modulus, and find the inverse by means of the method indicated in equations (4).

7. Find both the homogeneous and nonhomogeneous forms of the homography which maps the points $P_1(1, 0)$, $P_2(0, 1)$, $P_3(-1, 0)$, and $P_4(0, -1)$ in π into the respective points $\overline{P}_1(2, 0)$, $\overline{P}_2(0, \frac{1}{2})$, $\overline{P}_3(-2, 0)$, and $\overline{P}_4(0, -\frac{1}{2})$ in $\overline{\pi}$.

> *Ans.* Homogeneous: $k\overline{x}^1 = 4x^1$, $k\overline{x}^2 = x^2$, $k\overline{x}^3 = 2x^3$.
> Nonhomogeneous: $\overline{x} = 2x$, $2\overline{y} = y$.

8. Show that a circle $x^2 + y^2 = r^2$ in π maps into an ellipse $\overline{x}^2 + 16\overline{y}^2 = 4r^2$ in $\overline{\pi}$ by the mapping of Exercise 7.

9. Make a detailed study of the homography

$$\overline{x} = \frac{x + 4y - 2}{x + y - 1}, \quad \overline{y} = \frac{-x + 2y - 2}{x + y - 1}.$$

Suggestions: Use one sheet of paper for π and another for $\overline{\pi}$, and orthogonal cartesian coordinates in both planes, with $\frac{1}{2}$ inch as the unit of length. Find the inverse mapping, and draw the vanishing line in each plane. The homography maps $A(1, -1)$, $B(1, 1)$, $C(-1, 1)$, $D(-1, -1)$ in π into a prescribed set of four points in $\overline{\pi}$. Draw all lines determined by A, B, C, D in π, and by $\overline{A}$, $\overline{B}$, $\overline{C}$, $\overline{D}$ in $\overline{\pi}$. Use colors to indicate corresponding regions in the two planes. Note that if a bounded region in π has no point in common with the vanishing line, then the corresponding region in $\overline{\pi}$ is bounded and has no point in common with the vanishing line in $\overline{\pi}$.

10. Show that the circles $x^2 + y^2 = r^2$ map into the curves given by $9(r^2 - 1)\overline{x}^2 + 6(1 - 3r^2)\overline{x}\overline{y} + (9r^2 - 5)\overline{y}^2 + 12(2 - 3r^2)\overline{x} + 4(2 + 9r^2)\overline{y} + 36r^2 - 32 = 0$ under the mapping of Exercise 9, and that the curves in $\overline{\pi}$ are ellipses, a parabola, or hyperbolas according as $r^2 \lesseqgtr \frac{1}{2}$. If $r^2 = \frac{1}{2}$, the circle $x^2 + y^2 = \frac{1}{2}$ tangent to the vanishing line $x + y - 1 = 0$ in π maps into the parabola in $\overline{\pi}$ with equation $(3\overline{x} + \overline{y})^2 = 4(3\overline{x} + 13\overline{y} - 7)$.

11. (a) Show that the rank of the homography

$$\overline{x} = \frac{x}{y}, \quad \overline{y} = \frac{2x + y}{y}$$

is two, and that it takes all points of π into the line $2\overline{x} - \overline{y} + 1 = 0$ in $\overline{\pi}$.
(b) Show that the rank of the homography

$$\overline{x} = \frac{2x + 2y + 2}{x + y + 1}, \quad \overline{y} = \frac{3x + 3y + 3}{x + y + 1}$$

is one, and that it takes all points of π into the single point $(2, 3)$ in $\overline{\pi}$.

12. Consider the pencil of lines $x + y - 1 + \rho(x - 2y + 3) = 0$ which has its center on the vanishing line $x + y - 1 = 0$ of the homography in Exercise 9. Show that the pencil, under this homography, maps into the set of parallel lines

$$x - 3y - 2 + \frac{2}{\rho} = 0.$$

Note that the distance from the origin in $\overline{\pi}$ to the latter line becomes infinite as $\rho \to 0$. For this reason the vanishing line $x + y - 1 = 0$ may be said to correspond to the "line at infinity" in $\overline{\pi}$.

5-3. Homogeneous point coordinates

In Section 4-4 homogeneous point coordinates were introduced by merely replacing the cartesian coordinates x, y by the ratios x^1/x^3, x^2/x^3, in which x^3 was not allowed to be zero. A different approach to homogeneous point coordinates in the plane is now to be explained.

Instead of two axes of reference, choose three lines to form the *triangle of reference*. Let P_i (Fig. 15) designate the vertices of this triangle, and a_i the sides

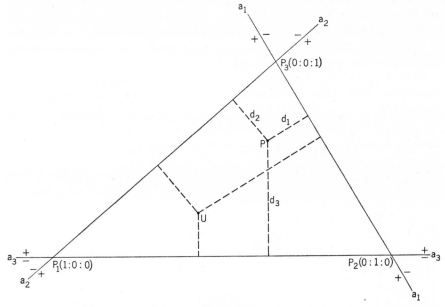

Figure 15

respectively opposite P_i. From any point P in the plane drop perpendiculars of lengths d_i (in some common unit) to the sides a_i. Select some unit of measure e_i relative to each side a_i, and assign an algebraic sign to each side of a_i. (The choice of signs in Fig. 15 has the consequence that any point inside the triangle is on the positive side of all three side lines.) If $p_i = \pm d_i/e_i$, then the p_i are the distances of point P from the sides a_i, each distance being measured in its arbitrary unit e_i, and endowed with the appropriate sign.

DEFINITION: *The homogeneous coordinates x^i of any point P in the plane are three real numbers (not all zero) which are proportional to p_i; that is,*

$$kx^i = p_i = \pm\frac{d_i}{e_i}.$$

It is evident that the coordinates of the vertices of the triangle in Fig. 15 are $P_1(1:0:0)$, $P_2(0:1:0)$, $P_3(0:0:1)$, and that the equations of the sides opposite P_i are $x^i = 0$, for $i = 1, 2, 3$.

A fourth point U can be selected arbitrarily (not on a side of the triangle of reference) to have the coordinates $(1:1:1)$. This choice determines uniquely the signs (up to a factor of -1) and the ratios of the units e_i. One has for U (called the *unit point*)

$$(11) \qquad x^1:x^2:x^3 = 1:1:1 = \pm\frac{1}{k}\frac{d_1}{e_1} : \pm\frac{1}{k}\frac{d_2}{e_2} : \pm\frac{1}{k}\frac{d_3}{e_3}.$$

One may suppose here that all signs are positive or all negative. Let the positive sign be chosen for a coordinate if P and U are on the same side of a side line. It follows from (11) that $d_i = ke_i$ or $e_i = d_i/k$, so that the ratios of the e_i are determined by the distances of U from the sides a_i. Two points are coincident if their homogeneous coordinates are proportional. The coordinates $(0:0:0)$ are meaningless, so they are excluded.

Observe that homogeneous point coordinates were defined by means of ratios of lengths. That these coordinates are actually projective will be shown in Section 6·2.

Relating Cartesian and Homogeneous Point Coordinates

Let Δ denote the triangle of reference $P_1P_2P_3$ in Fig. 16, and use $a_ix + b_iy + c_i =$

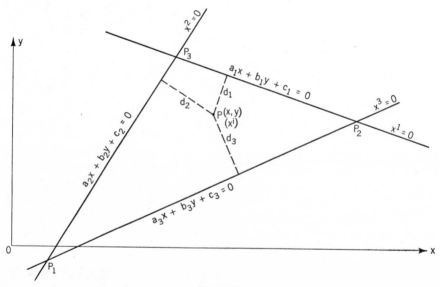

Figure 16

0 as the equations (in cartesian coordinates) of the sides of Δ. From the formula for the distance of a point from a line, one has

$$d_i = \frac{a_ix + b_iy + c_i}{\pm\sqrt{a_i^2 + b_i^2}},$$

from which

$$kx^i = p_i = \pm\frac{d_i}{e_i} = \frac{a_ix + b_iy + c_i}{e_i\sqrt{a_i^2 + b_i^2}},$$

where the index i is not summed. Because the e_i may be chosen arbitrarily, the transformation between the homogeneous point coordinates x^i and the cartesian coordinates x, y can be written as

(12) $$kx^i = a_ix + b_iy + c_i,$$

for which the inverse is given by

(13) $$x = \frac{A_ix^i}{C_ix^i}, \quad y = \frac{B_ix^i}{C_ix^i}.$$

Observe that the equation of the y axis relative to the reference triangle in Fig. 16 is $A_ix^i = 0$, and that the line $y = 0$ in cartesian coordinates is $B_ix^i = 0$ in homogeneous coordinates. For points with coordinates x^i which satisfy $C_ix^i = 0$, the cartesian coordinates x, y do not exist. The line with equation $C_ix^i = 0$ is the "line at infinity."

5-4. Homogeneous line coordinates

The plückerian line coordinates (u, v) in Section 4-3 were given homogeneous form by writing $u = u_1/u_3$ and $v = u_2/u_3$, with $u_3 \neq 0$. The definition of homogeneous line coordinates given next is effected as the dual of the discussion in Section 5-3.

Again, select a reference triangle Δ with vertices P_i and side lines a_i. Drop perpendiculars from P_i to the line l for which the homogeneous line coordinates are desired, the lengths of the perpendiculars being d_i as measured in some common unit. Select arbitrary units e_i relative to the three vertices P_i, and assign arbitrary signs to the sides of line l. Write $p_i = \pm d_i/e_i$, which means that p_i is the distance from line l to the vertex P_i measured in its unit e_i and given a proper sign.

DEFINITION: *The real homogeneous coordinates u_i of any line l in the plane are three numbers (not all zero) proportional to p_i; that is,*

(14) $$ku_i = p_i = \pm\frac{d_i}{e_i}, \qquad\qquad i = 1, 2, 3.$$

A unit line u is selected arbitrarily (not through a vertex of the reference triangle) and given the coordinates $[1:1:1]$. This determines the signs (up to a factor -1) and the ratios of the units e_i. One has

$$u_1:u_2:u_3 = 1:1:1 = \pm d_1/e_1 : \pm d_2/e_2 : \pm d_3/e_3,$$

or $ke_i = d_i$, from which the units e_i are the distances from the unit line u to the vertices P_i measured in a common unit k. See Section 6-2 for the projective character of the line coordinates here defined in a metric manner. It is evident

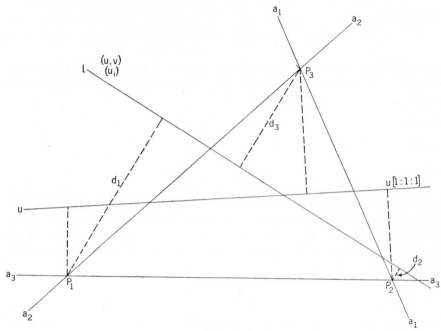

Figure 17

that the lines a_1, a_2, a_3 in Fig. 17 have the respective line coordinates $[1:0:0]$, $[0:1:0]$, $[0:0:1]$, and that the equations of the vertices opposite a_i are $u_i = 0$, for $i = 1, 2, 3$.

Relating Plückerian and Homogeneous Line Coordinates

The equations of the lines a_i opposite P_i in Fig. 18 are $a_i x + b_i y + c_i = 0$. Solve these equations in pairs for the cartesian coordinates of the vertices P_i to obtain

(15) $$P_1 \left(\frac{A_1}{C_1}, \frac{B_1}{C_1}\right), \quad P_2 \left(\frac{A_2}{C_2}, \frac{B_2}{C_2}\right), \quad P_3 \left(\frac{A_3}{C_3}, \frac{B_3}{C_3}\right),$$

where A_1, B_1, $\cdots$ are the usual cofactors, as in equation (13). Recall that (u, v) are the plückerian coordinates of the line l with equation $ux + vy + 1 = 0$. Let u_i be the homogeneous line coordinates of l. From analytical geometry, the distances d_i from P_i to l are given by

$$d_i = \frac{u\dfrac{A_i}{C_i} + v\dfrac{B_i}{C_i} + 1}{\pm\sqrt{u^2 + v^2}} = \frac{uA_i + vB_i + C_i}{\pm C_i\sqrt{u^2 + v^2}}.$$

It follows, by the definition of homogeneous line coordinates, that

$$k'u_i = \frac{A_iu + B_iv + C_i}{\pm e_iC_i\sqrt{u^2 + v^2}}.$$

Let the common factor $\sqrt{u^2 + v^2}$ be absorbed with the proportionality factor k', and write $\lambda_i = \pm e_iC_i$ to obtain

(16)
$$k\lambda_iu_i = A_iu + B_iv + C_i,$$

with i not summed. The inverse of equations (16) takes the form

(17)
$$u = \frac{\sum_i a_i\lambda_iu_i}{\sum_i c_i\lambda_iu_i}, \quad v = \frac{\sum_i b_i\lambda_iu_i}{\sum_i c_i\lambda_iu_i}.$$

Observe that if the unit line is chosen so that $\lambda_1 = \lambda_2 = \lambda_3$—which means that the ratios of the e_i are chosen so that $\pm e_1C_1 = \pm e_2C_2 = \pm e_3C_3$—then equations (16) take the form

(18)
$$\sigma u_i = A_iu + B_iv + C_i,$$

with the inverse

(19)
$$u = \frac{a_iu_i}{c_iu_i}, \quad v = \frac{b_iu_i}{c_iu_i},$$

in which the index i is summed. Equations (18) and (19) should be compared with equations (12) and (13). A line for which $u = 0$ in plückerian coordinates has the equation $a_iu_i = 0$ in homogeneous line coordinates. For lines with

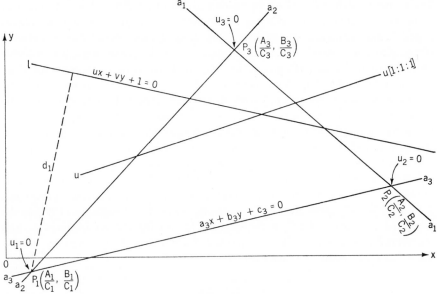

Figure 18

coordinates u_i which satisfy $c_i u_i = 0$, the (u, v) line coordinates do not exist. The equation $c_i u_i = 0$ is the line equation of the origin. (See Section 4-2.)

Incidence Relation

The condition under which the point (x, y) and line (u, v) are incident is $ux + vy + 1 = 0$. By use of equations (13) and (19), which relate (x, y) and (u, v) to homogeneous coordinates, the equation $ux + vy + 1 = 0$ of united position is

$$\frac{a_i u_i}{c_i u_i} \frac{A_j x^j}{C_j x^j} + \frac{b_i u_i}{c_i u_i} \frac{B_j x^j}{C_j x^j} + 1 = 0,$$

which, on rearrangement, becomes

$$(a_i A_j + b_i B_j + c_i C_j) u_i x^j = 0,$$

or

$$D \delta_{ij} u_i x^j = 0.$$

Therefore, the condition of united position in homogeneous point and line coordinates x^i and u_i is

$$u_i x^i = 0.$$

5-5. Two aspects of mapping equations

The correspondence described by equations (6) in Section 5-1 was thought of as between points x^i in a plane π and points $\bar{x}^i$ in a plane $\bar{\pi}$. But the planes π and $\bar{\pi}$ may coincide, in which case the homography establishes a mapping of the plane into itself. In general, a point x^i in the plane maps into another point $\bar{x}^i$ in the plane. (Points which remain fixed under a homography are studied in Chapter 7.) This aspect by which points are transported to new positions has been referred to earlier as the alibi aspect. Equations (6) may be interpreted in a different way, however, namely, that of the alias aspect by which the points remain fixed but their names change—that is, the reference system changes. It will be seen next that equations (6) appear as describing a transformation of coordinates instead of a mapping of points.

Let any point P have cartesian coordinates (x, y), homogeneous coordinates x^i relative to the "old" reference triangle $P_1 P_2 P_3$, and homogeneous coordinates $\bar{x}^i$ relative to the "new" triangle of reference (Fig. 19). Equations (12) give the relation $kx^i = a_i x + b_i y + c_i$ between (x, y) and the old coordinates x^i, and the relation between (x, y) and the new coordinates $\bar{x}^i$ is given by $k' \bar{x}^i = \bar{a}_i x + \bar{b}_i y + \bar{c}_i$. Solve the latter for

$$x = \frac{\overline{A}_i \bar{x}^i}{\overline{C}_i \bar{x}^i}, \quad y = \frac{\overline{B}_i \bar{x}^i}{\overline{C}_i \bar{x}^i},$$

and substitute these expressions for x and y into $kx^i = a_i x + b_i y + c_i$ to obtain equations of the form

(20) $$\rho x^i = a_{i1}\bar{x}^1 + a_{i2}\bar{x}^2 + a_{i3}\bar{x}^3 \equiv a_{ij}\bar{x}^j,$$

where

$$a_{ij} \equiv a_i\bar{A}_j + b_i\bar{B}_j + c_i\bar{C}_j.$$

Note that equations (20) are of the form of equations (6) with a change in notation. The inverse of (20) may be written as

(21) $$k\bar{x}^i = A_{ji}x^j,$$

in which A_{ji} is the cofactor of a_{ij} in the matrix (a_{ij}).

The significance of the transformation (20) of coordinates from the new to the old triangle of reference is shown by writing below the coordinates of a number of points in Fig. 19.

Point	Old	New
P_1	$(1:0:0)$	$(A_{11}:A_{12}:A_{13})$
P_2	$(0:1:0)$	$(A_{21}:A_{22}:A_{23})$
P_3	$(0:0:1)$	$(A_{31}:A_{32}:A_{33})$
U	$(1:1:1)$	$(A_{11} + A_{21} + A_{31}$
		$:A_{12} + A_{22} + A_{32}$
		$:A_{13} + A_{23} + A_{33})$
P_1	$(a_{11}:a_{21}:a_{31})$	$(1:0:0)$
P_2	$(a_{12}:a_{22}:a_{32})$	$(0:1:0)$
P_3	$(a_{13}:a_{23}:a_{33})$	$(0:0:1)$
U	$(a_{11} + a_{12} + a_{13}$	$(1:1:1)$
	$:a_{21} + a_{22} + a_{23}$	
	$:a_{31} + a_{32} + a_{33})$	

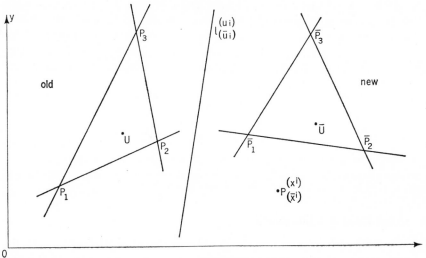

Figure 19

Transformation of Line Coordinates

Let the homogeneous line coordinates of line l in Fig. 19 be u_i (old) and $\bar{u}_i$ (new). The equations of l are then $u_i x^i = 0$ (old) and $\bar{u}_i \bar{x}^i = 0$ (new). In order to arrive at the relation connecting the u_i and $\bar{u}_i$, substitute x^i from (20) into $u_i x^i = 0$ to obtain $u_i a_{ij} \bar{x}^j = 0$, which is $\bar{u}_j \bar{x}^j = 0$. Hence, $k\bar{u}_j = a_{ij} u_i$, so that the equation of transformation of line coordinates is

$$(22) \qquad\qquad k\bar{u}_i = a_{ji} u_j,$$

which has the inverse

$$(23) \qquad\qquad k' u_i = A_{ij} \bar{u}_j.$$

It is convenient to change the notation slightly to conform to the notation introduced in equations (6) and (8). Replacement of a_{ji} in (20) by a_i^j, and A_{ij} in (23) by A_j^i allows the point and line coordinate transformations and their inverses in equations (20), (21), (23) to be exhibited as follows.

	Transformation	Inverse
Point	$\rho x^i = a_j^i \bar{x}^j$	$\rho' \bar{x}^i = A_j^i x^j$
Line	$k u_i = A_i^j \bar{u}_j$	$k' \bar{u}_i = a_i^j u_j$

Recall that A_j^i is the cofactor of a_i^j in the matrix (a_j^i), where superscripts are used for the point variables and subscripts for the line variables. The x^i and u_i coordinates are said to transform contragrediently. Note that

$$u_i x^i = a_j^i \bar{x}^j A_i^k \bar{u}_k = a_j^i A_i^k \bar{x}^j \bar{u}_k = a \delta_j^k \bar{x}^j \bar{u}_k = a \bar{u}_k \bar{x}^k,$$

where a is the determinant $|a_i^j|$. This means that the form $u_i x^i$ remains invariant (except for an unimportant nonzero factor) under the transformation of the contragredient point and line coordinates. The vanishing of the invariant gives the incidence relation of point and line in any coordinate system.

The condition of united position can be used as follows to determine the equation of the line determined by the points $Q_1(x_1^i)$ and $Q_2(x_2^i)$. The conditions that Q_1 and Q_2 be on the line $u_i x^i = 0$ are $u_i x_1^i = 0$ and $u_i x_2^i = 0$. Eliminate u_i from the last three equations to find

$$(24) \qquad\qquad \begin{vmatrix} x^1 & x^2 & x^3 \\ x_1^1 & x_1^2 & x_1^3 \\ x_2^1 & x_2^2 & x_2^3 \end{vmatrix} = 0$$

as the equation of the line $Q_1 Q_2$, the line coordinates of which are

$$u_i = e_{ijk} x_1^j x_2^k.$$

5-6. Cross ratio in a line pencil

The cross ratio of four points on a line was introduced in Section 1-7. Dually, one needs to consider the cross ratio of four lines through a point. In the case of points on a line, the simple ratio into which a point C divides the pair of points A and B was considered first. Analogously, in the case of lines through a point, one may consider first the simple ratio into which a line c (Fig. 20) separates the pair of lines a and b through S. Intersect the rays a, b, c, d of the pencil by a line l in the respective points A, B, C, D. From C draw the perpendiculars of lengths h and k to the rays a and b. Denote angle ASC by (ac) and angle BSC by (bc). Define the simple ratio into

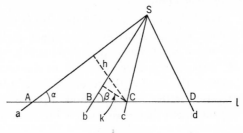

Figure 20

which c separates a and b as h/k and write it as (abc). One has then from Fig. 20

$$(abc) \equiv \frac{h}{k} = \frac{h/SC}{k/SC} = \frac{\sin (ac)}{\sin (bc)}.$$

In a similar way it is seen that for a fourth line d of the pencil

$$(abd) = \frac{\sin (ad)}{\sin (bd)}.$$

The cross ratio of the four lines a, b, c, d, denoted by $(abcd)$, is defined as the ratio of the simple ratios in which c and d separate a and b. Thus,

(25) $$(abcd) = \frac{(abc)}{(abd)} = \frac{\sin (ac)}{\sin (bc)} \div \frac{\sin (ad)}{\sin (bd)}.$$

From Fig. 20 it is also seen that the simple ratio (ABC) in which C divides A and B takes the form

(26) $$(ABC) = \frac{AC}{BC} = \frac{h \csc \alpha}{k \csc \beta} = (abc) \frac{\sin \beta}{\sin \alpha},$$

from which

(27) $$(abc) = (ABC) \frac{\sin \alpha}{\sin \beta}.$$

Similarly, one has

(28) $$(abd) = (ABD) \frac{\sin \alpha}{\sin \beta}.$$

Using (27) and (28) in (25) yields

(29) $$(abcd) = \frac{(abc)}{(abd)} = \frac{(ABC)(\sin \alpha/\sin \beta)}{(ABD)(\sin \alpha/\sin \beta)} = \frac{(ABC)}{(ABD)} = (ABCD),$$

which proves the

THEOREM OF PAPPUS: *The cross ratio of any four lines in a pencil is the same as the cross ratio of the four points in which any transversal intersects the four lines.*

Another statement of the theorem is that cross ratio is invariant under projection. Pappus stated his theorem in the following way. If three lines c, d, b through a point S are cut by two lines through a point A in C, D, B and C', D', B', respectively, then the ratio of the rectangles $(AC)(DB)$ and $(CB)(AD)$ is equal to the ratio of the rectangles $(AC')(D'B')$ and $(C'B')(AD')$. It is left as an exercise for the reader to show that the statement by Pappus is equivalent to the statement that cross ratio is invariant under projection.

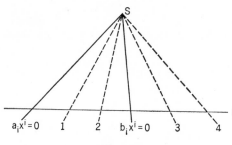

It will be found convenient to use the fact stated in the

THEOREM: *If $(a_i x^i) + \lambda_k(b_i x^i) = 0$, for $k = 1, 2, 3, 4$, are four lines of the pencil of lines determined by the two fixed lines $a_i x^i = 0$ and $b_i x^i = 0$, then the cross ratio of these four lines is the cross ratio of the four parameters λ_k.*

Figure 21

Proof: Take the line l (Fig. 21) as the x^1 axis in cartesian coordinates ($x^3 \equiv 1$), and write the cross ratio $(x_1^1 x_2^1 x_3^1 x_4^1)$ of the intercepts x_k^1 of the four lines with l. With $x^3 = 1$ and $x^2 = 0$ the equation of the pencil yields $(a_1 x^1 + a_3) + \lambda_k(b_1 x^1 + b_3) = 0$, from which the four intercepts x_k^1 are given by

$$(30) \qquad x_k^1 = -\frac{b_3 \lambda_k + a_3}{b_1 \lambda_k + a_1}.$$

Because the λ_k and x_k^1 are related by a homography it follows that

$$(x_1^1 x_2^1 x_3^1 x_4^1) = (\lambda_1 \lambda_2 \lambda_3 \lambda_4),$$

which completes the proof.

An important consequence of the last theorem is that the sum of the parameters for any two lines which separate the base lines l: $a_i x^i = 0$ and m: $b_i x^i = 0$ harmonically is zero. That is, the harmonic conjugate of the line $\lambda l + \mu m = 0$ with respect to $l = 0$ and $m = 0$ is the line $\lambda l - \mu m = 0$. In order to see this, write the four lines as $1l + 0m = 0$, $0l + 1m = 0$, $\lambda l + \mu m = 0$, $l + km = 0$. The cross ratio $(0/1, 1/0, \mu/\lambda, k)$ of the four parameters is -1 if and only if $k = -\mu/\lambda$.

The cross ratio of the four lines $y - y_1 = m_i(x - x_1)$, for $i = 1, 2, 3, 4$, through the point (x_1, y_1) is the cross ratio of the four slopes m_i. This is evident if one takes the lines $y - y_1 = 0$ and $x - x_1 = 0$ as the base lines of the pencil in the theorem. The slopes m_i are the respective parameters.

In the notation of homogeneous point coordinates, each of the four lines $x^2 + \lambda_i x^3 = 0$, for $i = 1, 2, 3, 4$, contains the vertex $P_1(1:0:0)$ of the triangle of reference. The base lines are $x^2 = 0$ and $x^3 = 0$. Hence, the cross ratio of the four lines is $(\lambda_1 \lambda_2 \lambda_3 \lambda_4)$. Note also that the harmonic conjugate of $\lambda x^2 + \mu x^3 = 0$ with respect to $x^2 = 0$ and $x^3 = 0$ is the line $\lambda x^2 - \mu x^3 = 0$.

The intersection of the line $\lambda x^2 + \mu x^3 = 0$ with the line $x^1 = 0$ opposite P_1 in the triangle of reference is the point $(0: -(\mu/\lambda)x^3 : x^3) = (0: -\mu : \lambda)$. Thus, the four lines $x^2 = 0$, $x^3 = 0$, $\lambda x^2 + \mu x^3 = 0$, and $\lambda x^2 - \mu x^3 = 0$ intersect $x^1 = 0$ in the points $(0:0:1)$, $(0:1:0)$, $(0: -\mu : \lambda)$, $(0: \mu : \lambda)$, the cross ratio of which is -1.

Harmonic Construction

If three lines a, b, c of a pencil are given, it is desired to draw the fourth line d which is the harmonic conjugate of c with respect to a and b. Intersect a, b, c by a line l in the points A, B, C.
The problem is solved if one can locate the point D on l which is the harmonic conjugate of C with respect to A and B. *Construction:* Draw any two lines p and q through A (Fig. 22) and an arbitrary line r through B. Draw the join s of C and the intersection H of r and p. Line s intersects q at K. The join of B and K intersects p at R. Line r intersects q at S. Draw the line RS to intersect l in the required point D.

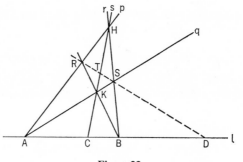

Figure 22

Analytic proof of the construction: Choose the points A, B, H as the vertices of the triangle of reference. That is, assign the coordinates $A(1:0:0)$, $B(0:1:0)$, $H(0:0:1)$, and let K be the unit point $(1:1:1)$. The equation of line HK is

$$\begin{vmatrix} x^1 & x^2 & x^3 \\ 0 & 0 & 1 \\ 1 & 1 & 1 \end{vmatrix} \equiv x^2 - x^1 = 0,$$

so that HK has line coordinates $[-1:1:0]$. Following the explanation in Section 4-4, this can be expressed briefly in the form

$$HK: \qquad \begin{pmatrix} 0 & 0 & 1 \\ 1 & 1 & 1 \end{pmatrix} \rightarrow [-1:1:0].$$

The point C is the intersection of lines $HK[-1:1:0]$ and $AB[0:0:1]$. Thus, write

$$C: \qquad \begin{bmatrix} -1 & 1 & 0 \\ 0 & 0 & 1 \end{bmatrix} \rightarrow (1:1:0).$$

The remainder of the work to find the coordinates of D proceeds as follows:

$$AK: \quad \begin{pmatrix} 1 & 0 & 0 \\ 1 & 1 & 1 \end{pmatrix} \rightarrow [0:-1:1],$$

$$S: \quad \begin{bmatrix} 1 & 0 & 0 \\ 0 & -1 & 1 \end{bmatrix} \rightarrow (0:-1:-1) = (0:1:1),$$

$$BK: \quad \begin{pmatrix} 0 & 1 & 0 \\ 1 & 1 & 1 \end{pmatrix} \rightarrow [1:0:-1],$$

$$R: \quad \begin{bmatrix} 0 & 1 & 0 \\ 1 & 0 & -1 \end{bmatrix} \rightarrow (-1:0:-1) = (1:0:1),$$

$$RS: \quad \begin{pmatrix} 1 & 0 & 1 \\ 0 & 1 & 1 \end{pmatrix} \rightarrow [-1:-1:1],$$

$$D: \quad \begin{bmatrix} -1 & -1 & 1 \\ 0 & 0 & 1 \end{bmatrix} \rightarrow (-1:1:0).$$

Thus, the coordinates of A, B, C, D are found to be respectively

$$(1:0:0), \quad (0:1:0), \quad (1:1:0), \quad (-1:1:0),$$

which means that D is the harmonic conjugate of C.

Remark: The cross ratio of any four concurrent lines can be calculated by finding the cross ratio of the points in which the lines intersect a side of the triangle of reference.

Synthetic proof of the construction: In Fig. 22, the four points A, B, C, D are perspective through the center H with the points R, S, T, D. This is expressed by

$$A, B, C, D \overset{H}{\barwedge} R, S, T, D.$$

Also, one has

$$R, S, T, D \overset{K}{\barwedge} B, A, C, D.$$

Hence,

$$(ABCD) = (BACD) = \frac{1}{(ABCD)},$$

from which $(ABCD)^2 = 1$. Because A, B, C, D are distinct, it follows that the cross ratio $(ABCD) = -1$.

Remark: Here is an instance in which the synthetic proof is much shorter than the analytic proof. The analytic proof was exhibited, however, to give the reader some suggestions for the solution of subsequent exercises.

EXERCISES

1. Find the coordinates of the points in which the unit line $[1:1:1]$ meets the sides of the triangle of reference.

2. Write the line coordinates of the lines joining the unit point to the vertices of the triangle of reference, and then find the coordinates of the points where these lines meet the opposite sides of the reference triangle.

3. Show that the points x_1^i, x_2^i, x_3^i are collinear if and only if $e_{ijk}x_1^i x_2^j x_3^k = 0$. (See Exercise 6 on p. 89.)

4. Show that any point on the line l through the two points x_1^i and x_2^i has coordinates of the form $x^i = \lambda x_1^i + \mu x_2^i$. (See Section 3-8.)

5. Let the unit line intersect the sides opposite the vertices P_i of the triangle of reference in the points Q_i. Let lines P_2Q_2 and P_3Q_3 intersect in H_1; P_3Q_3 and P_1Q_1 in H_2; and P_1Q_1 and P_2Q_2 in H_3. Show that the lines H_iP_i, for $i = 1, 2, 3$, are concurrent. What are the coordinates of the common point?

Ans. $(1:1:1)$.

6. Find the cross ratio of the four lines

$$3x - y + 2 = 0, \quad 8x - y + 7 = 0, \quad 7x - 4y + 3 = 0, \quad x + 3y + 4 = 0.$$

Ans. $\frac{1}{2}$.

7. What is the modulus of the homography in equation (30) of Section 5-6? What is the meaning of its nonvanishing?

8. Let the unit line meet the sides opposite P_i in the triangle of reference in the points Q_i. Find the locus of a point $H(\alpha:\beta:1)$ such that the lines HQ_3, HQ_2, HP_1, HQ_1 always form a harmonic set.

Ans. $(\alpha:1:1)$.

9. Dualize Exercise 8.

10. Lines P_iH through the vertices P_i of a triangle and a common point H intersect the sides opposite P_i in the points Q_i. Any line u intersects the sides opposite P_i in the points R_i. Show that

$$(P_2P_3Q_1R_1)(P_3P_1Q_2R_2)(P_1P_2Q_3R_3) = -1.$$

Suggestion: Let P_i be the vertices of the triangle of reference and H the unit point $(1:1:1)$. Find Q_i to have coordinates $Q_1(0:1:1)$, $Q_2(1:0:1)$, $Q_3(1:1:0)$. Take u as the line $u_i x^i = 0$. Then find $R_1(0:u_3:-u_2)$, $R_2(-u_3:0:u_1)$, $R_3(u_2:-u_1:0)$. The three cross ratios are $-u_3/u_2$, $-u_1/u_3$, $-u_2/u_1$.

11. Show that a consequence of the result in Exercise 10 is that

$$\frac{P_2Q_1}{Q_2P_1}\frac{P_3Q_2}{Q_3P_2}\frac{P_1Q_3}{Q_1P_3} = -\frac{P_2R_1}{R_2P_1}\frac{P_3R_2}{R_3P_2}\frac{P_1R_3}{R_1P_3}.$$

12. *Polar of a point relative to a triangle.* In Exercise 10 let p_i denote the sides of the triangle which are opposite P_i. Let R_1 be the intersection of Q_2Q_3 with p_1, R_2 that of Q_3Q_1 with p_2, and R_3 that of Q_1Q_2 with p_3. Show that the R_i are collinear. (The line $R_1R_2R_3$ is called the *polar line* of H relative to the triangle $P_1P_2P_3$, and H is the *pole* of its polar line.) *Suggestion:* Take H as the unit point, and find the coordinates of R_i.

Ans. The unit line.

13. Verify that the points P_1, P_2, Q_3, R_3 in Exercise 12 form a harmonic set.

5-7. Trilinear coordinates*

The general homogeneous point coordinates used heretofore in this chapter may be specialized to obtain particular kinds of coordinates which are especially adapted to the solution of certain types of problems. One specialization—that of setting the third coordinate x^3 equal to 1 and considering x^1 and x^2 as cartesian coordinates—has been mentioned. The specialization to obtain such coordinates from *projective* coordinates will be examined in detail in Chapter 6.

All homogeneous coordinates of points and lines in the plane are defined relative to a triangle of reference, and they are therefore in a sense trilinear coordinates. However, this name is usually reserved to apply to the particular kind of homogeneous coordinates for which the units e_i are all the same. This means that the trilinear coordinates x^i of a point P are proportional to the distances d_i of P from the sides p_i of the triangle of reference Δ (Fig. 23). It follows that the unit point $(1:1:1)$ cannot be chosen arbitrarily as heretofore, but must be taken as the incenter I of Δ.

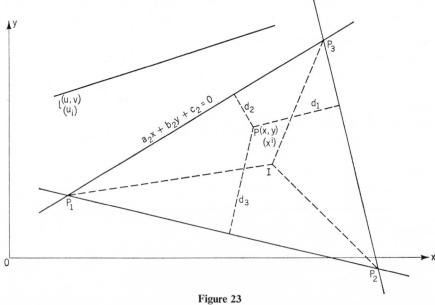

Figure 23

Relating Cartesian and Trilinear Coordinates

Let the sides of Δ have the equations in cartesian coordinates x, y, as indicated in Fig. 23. Assume that these equations are normalized; that is, $\sqrt{a_i^2 + b_i^2} = 1$ for $i = 1, 2, 3$. One has

$$d_i = \pm(a_ix + b_iy + c_i).$$

---

* For additional treatment of trilinear coordinates, see W. A. Whitworth, *Trilinear Coordinates* (Cambridge, 1866) and C. Smith, *Conic Sections* (London, 1882, revised 1910).

The sign is chosen as $+$ or $-$ according as P and the incenter (unit point) are on the same or opposite side of the side p_i of Δ. Because the x^i are proportional to d_i, the equations relating cartesian and trilinear coordinates are

$$(31) \qquad\qquad kx^i = a_ix + b_iy + c_i,$$

which have the inverse

$$(32) \qquad\qquad x = \frac{A_ix^i}{C_ix^i}, \quad y = \frac{B_ix^i}{C_ix^i},$$

as in equations (12) and (13).

From the fact that the sum $p_id_i = 2K$, where K is the area of Δ, one has $kp_ix^i = 2K$, or

$$(33) \qquad\qquad \frac{k}{2K}(p_1x^1 + p_2x^2 + p_3x^3) = 1,$$

a relation which may be employed to render equations homogeneous in x^i. The proportionality factor k may be set equal to 1.

Equation of Unit Line

It is to be shown next that the unit line has the equation $p_ix^i = 0$. From Exercise 13 in the last section it is seen that the harmonic conjugate of the line P_1I relative to the sides p_2 and p_3 of Δ is the line through P_1 parallel to side $p_1 \equiv P_2P_3$. Similarly, the harmonic conjugates of P_2I and P_3I relative to their adjacent sides are lines through P_2 and P_3 parallel to the respectively opposite sides. Hence, the unit line is the so-called line at infinity. From (32) it is observed that this line has the equation $C_ix^i = 0$. Note that the altitude h_i from P_i to side p_i is obtained by substituting the coordinates $(A_i/C_i, B_i/C_i)$ of P_i into the normalized function $a_ix + b_iy + c_i$:

$$h_i = \frac{a_iA_i + b_iB_i + c_iC_i}{C_i} \equiv \frac{M}{C_i}, \qquad i = 1, 2, 3.$$

Also, one has $2K = h_ip_i$. Hence, $C_i = Mp_i/2K$. Because the C_i are proportional to the p_i, the equation $C_ix^i = 0$ of the line at infinity becomes

$$(34) \qquad\qquad p_1x^1 + p_2x^2 + p_3x^3 = 0,$$

which is the equation of the unit line in trilinear coordinates.

Relating Trilinear Line Coordinates and Plückerian Coordinates

Any line l (Fig. 23) with plückerian coordinates (u, v) has an equation of the form $ux + vy + 1 = 0$. The distances D_i from the vertices P_i of Δ to line l are given by

$$D_i = \frac{u\dfrac{A_i}{C_i} + v\dfrac{B_i}{C_i} + 1}{\sqrt{u^2 + v^2}} = \frac{uA_i + vB_i + C_i}{C_i\sqrt{u^2 + v^2}}.$$

Since the D_i are proportional to the line coordinates u_i of l, one may absorb $\sqrt{u^2 + v^2}$ into the proportionality factor, and write

(35)
$$ku_i = \frac{A_i u + B_i v + C_i}{C_i},$$

the inverse of which has the form

(36)
$$u = \frac{\sum_i a_i(C_i u_i)}{\sum_i c_i(C_i u_i)}, \quad v = \frac{\sum_i b_i(C_i u_i)}{\sum_i c_i(C_i u_i)}.$$

Incidence Relation

In nonhomogeneous coordinates the condition under which the point (x, y) and the line (u, v) are in united position is $ux + vy + 1 = 0$. Substitute for (x, y) from (32) and for (u, v) from (36) to obtain the condition

$$\sum_i a_i C_i u_i \sum_j A_j x^i + \sum_i b_i C_i u_i \sum_j B_j x^i + \sum_i c_i C_i u_i \sum_j C_j x^i = 0,$$

which can be simplified to yield

$$\left(\sum_{i,j} C_i u_i x^i\right)(a_i A_j + b_i B_j + c_i C_j) = 0.$$

The second expression on the left is zero if $i \neq j$, and is $M (\neq 0)$ if $i = j$. Hence, the equation of united position takes the form

(37)
$$C_1 u_1 x^1 + C_2 u_2 x^2 + C_3 u_3 x^3 = 0.$$

It will be seen next that $C_i = \sin \alpha_i$, where α_i is the angle in Δ at the vertex P_i.

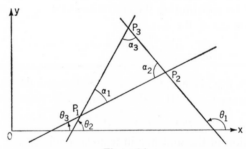

Figure 24

Let the lines $l_i \equiv a_i x + b_i y + c_i = 0$ make angles θ_i with the x-axis (Fig. 24), so that

$$\tan \theta_i = -\frac{a_i}{b_i}.$$

Note that because $a_i^2 + b_i^2 = 1$

$$\sin \alpha_1 = \sin(\theta_2 - \theta_3) = \sin \theta_2 \cos \theta_3 - \cos \theta_2 \sin \theta_3$$
$$= a_2 b_3 - a_3 b_2 = C_1.$$

In a similar way one finds $\sin \alpha_2 = C_2$ and $\sin \alpha_3 = C_3$. Hence, the condition of incidence for point x^i and line u_i in trilinear coordinates is

(38) $$u_1x^1 \sin \alpha_1 + u_2x^2 \sin \alpha_2 + u_3x^3 \sin \alpha_3 = 0.$$

The unit line (i.e., the line at infinity) therefore has the equation

$$x^1 \sin \alpha_1 + x^2 \sin \alpha_2 + x^3 \sin \alpha_3 = 0,$$

which is an alternative form for $p_ix^i = 0$ or $C_ix^i = 0$.

Remark: Because the C_i were shown to be proportional to the p_i, and the p_i are proportional to $\sin \alpha_i$ by the Law of Sines, it follows that the C_i are proportional to $\sin \alpha_i$.

EXAMPLE

Find the trilinear coordinates of the centroid G (intersection of the medians) of the triangle of reference (Fig. 25).

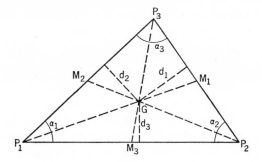

Figure 25

Solution: Because the centroid G satisfies $\overline{GP_3} = 2\overline{GM_3}$, it follows that $3d_3 = p_2 \sin \alpha_1 = p_1 \sin \alpha_2$, and, similarly, $3d_1 = p_3 \sin \alpha_2 = p_2 \sin \alpha_3$ and $3d_2 = p_1 \sin \alpha_3 = p_3 \sin \alpha_1$. Hence,

$$d_1:d_2:d_3 = p_3 \sin \alpha_2 : p_1 \sin \alpha_3 : p_2 \sin \alpha_1$$
$$= \sin \alpha_2 \sin \alpha_3 : \sin \alpha_3 \sin \alpha_1 : \sin \alpha_1 \sin \alpha_2.$$

Therefore, the trilinear coordinates of the centroid G are

(39) $$(\csc \alpha_1 : \csc \alpha_2 : \csc \alpha_3).$$

EXERCISES

1. Show that the trilinear coordinates of the orthocenter H (intersection of the altitudes of Δ) are

   (40) $$(\sec \alpha_1 : \sec \alpha_2 : \sec \alpha_3).$$

2. Show that the trilinear coordinates of the circumcenter C of Δ are

   (41) $$(\cos \alpha_1 : \cos \alpha_2 : \cos \alpha_3).$$

The usual condition for collinearity of three points with coordinates x_1^i, x_2^i, x_3^i—that the determinant $|x_j^i| = 0$—obtains for trilinear coordinates. For instance, note that the centroid G, the orthocenter H, and the circumcenter C are collinear, because the determinant of the coordinates in (39), (40), (41) vanishes. That is,

(42)
$$\begin{vmatrix} \csc \alpha_1 & \csc \alpha_2 & \csc \alpha_3 \\ \sec \alpha_1 & \sec \alpha_2 & \sec \alpha_3 \\ \cos \alpha_1 & \cos \alpha_2 & \cos \alpha_3 \end{vmatrix} = 0.$$

(See Exercise 1 on p. 118.) The line of the points G, H, C is called the line of Euler (1707–1783). It will be seen next that another interesting point lies on the Euler line. This is the point of Feuerbach (1800–1834).

Feuerbach Circle

The Feuerbach circle (also called the *nine-point circle*) of any triangle Δ is known to contain the midpoints of the sides, the feet of the altitudes, and the midpoints of the segments from the orthocenter H to the vertices of Δ. (The proof of this is omitted here.) The center of this circle is the Feuerbach center F. It will be shown next that the trilinear coordinates of F are

(43)
$$\cos (\alpha_2 - \alpha_3) : \cos (\alpha_3 - \alpha_1) : \cos (\alpha_1 - \alpha_2).$$

Although the coordinates (43) may be found by means of the geometry of the triangle, an analytic method will be employed to illustrate a useful technique.

Because the Feuerbach circle contains the feet M_i of the medians of the triangle $P_1P_2P_3$, the Feuerbach center of triangle $P_1P_2P_3$ is the circumcenter of the triangle $M_1M_2M_3$. Note that the angles at M_i in the triangle $M_1M_2M_3$ are equal to the angles α_i, respectively. The point coordinates of F relative to $M_1M_2M_3$ are, from (41), $\cos \alpha_i$. Hence, with $x^i = \cos \alpha_i$, the incidence condition (38) gives

$$\sum_i \bar{u}_i \sin \alpha_i \cos \alpha_i = 0$$

or

(44)
$$\sum_i \bar{u}_i \sin 2\alpha_i = 0,$$

where the $\bar{u}_i$ are the line coordinates of F relative to $M_1M_2M_3$. Relative to $P_1P_2P_3$, the incidence condition for F with line coordinates u_i and a point x^i is

(45)
$$\sum_i u_i x^i \sin \alpha_i = 0.$$

The relation between the $\bar{u}_i$ in (44) and the u_i in (45) will now be determined. The point coordinates of M_1, M_2, M_3 relative to $P_1P_2P_3$ are readily found to be

$$M_1(0 : \csc \alpha_2 : \csc \alpha_3), \quad M_2(\csc \alpha_1 : 0 : \csc \alpha_3), \quad M_3(\csc \alpha_1 : \csc \alpha_2 : 0).$$

If the coordinates of M_i are used in turn for x^i in the incidence relation (38), there results

$$u_2 + u_3 = 0, \quad u_3 + u_1 = 0, \quad u_1 + u_2 = 0.$$

Relative to $M_1M_2M_3$, these equations have the respective forms $\bar{u}_1 = 0$, $\bar{u}_2 = 0$, $\bar{u}_3 = 0$. Hence,

$$k\bar{u}_1 = u_2 + u_3, \quad k\bar{u}_2 = u_3 + u_1, \quad k\bar{u}_3 = u_1 + u_2.$$

Now substitute the $\bar{u}_i$ values into equation (44) to obtain

$$(u_2 + u_3) \sin 2\alpha_1 + (u_3 + u_1) \sin 2\alpha_2 + (u_1 + u_2) \sin 2\alpha_3 = 0$$

or

$$\sum u_1(\sin 2\alpha_1 + \sin 2\alpha_3) = \sum 2u_1 \sin (\alpha_2 + \alpha_3) \cos (\alpha_2 - \alpha_3) = 0,$$

from which

$$\sum u_1 \sin \alpha_1 \cos (\alpha_2 - \alpha_3) = 0.$$

Comparison of the last equation with (45) shows that the trilinear coordinates of F relative to $P_1P_2P_3$ are given by (43).

A proof can now be given for the

THEOREM: *The Feuerbach point F is on the Euler line.*

Proof: It is only necessary to show that the centroid G, the orthocenter H, and the Feuerbach center F are collinear—that is, that the determinant

(46)
$$\begin{vmatrix} \csc \alpha_1 & \csc \alpha_2 & \csc \alpha_3 \\ \sec \alpha_1 & \sec \alpha_2 & \sec \alpha_3 \\ \cos (\alpha_2 - \alpha_3) & \cos (\alpha_3 - \alpha_1) & \cos (\alpha_1 - \alpha_2) \end{vmatrix}$$

vanishes. This is equivalent to the vanishing of the determinant

$$\begin{vmatrix} \sin \alpha_2 \sin \alpha_3 & \sin \alpha_3 \sin \alpha_1 & \sin \alpha_1 \sin \alpha_2 \\ \cos \alpha_2 \cos \alpha_3 & \cos \alpha_3 \cos \alpha_1 & \cos \alpha_1 \cos \alpha_2 \\ \cos (\alpha_2 - \alpha_3) & \cos (\alpha_3 - \alpha_1) & \cos (\alpha_1 - \alpha_2) \end{vmatrix}.$$

Add the first row to the second to see that the last determinant is indeed zero. Another interesting fact in the geometry of the triangle is stated in the

THEOREM: *The four collinear points H (orthocenter), G (centroid), F (Feuerbach center), and C (circumcenter) constitute a harmonic set.*

Proof: In order to show that $(HGFC) = -1$, the cross ratio of the four lines P_1H, P_1G, P_1F, P_1C will be determined. The equation of P_1H is

$$\begin{vmatrix} x^1 & x^2 & x^3 \\ 1 & 0 & 0 \\ \sec \alpha_1 & \sec \alpha_2 & \sec \alpha_3 \end{vmatrix} = 0,$$

or

$$x^2 \cos \alpha_2 - x^3 \cos \alpha_3 = 0.$$

Similarly, the respective equations of P_1G, P_1F, P_1C are obtained as

$$x^2 \sin \alpha_2 - x^3 \sin \alpha_3 = 0,$$

$$x^2 \cos (\alpha_1 - \alpha_2) - x^3 \cos (\alpha_3 - \alpha_1) = 0,$$

$$x^2 \cos \alpha_3 - x^3 \cos \alpha_2 = 0.$$

On dividing the last four equations by the respective coefficient of x^2 in each case, the cross ratio of the four lines is seen to be the cross ratio of the four coefficients of x^3:

(47)
$$\left(\frac{\cos \alpha_3}{\cos \alpha_2}, \frac{\sin \alpha_3}{\sin \alpha_2}, \frac{\cos (\alpha_3 - \alpha_1)}{\cos (\alpha_1 - \alpha_2)}, \frac{\cos \alpha_2}{\cos \alpha_3}\right).$$

The rather involved trigonometry required to show that the cross ratio in (47) is indeed -1 is left as an exercise (see Exercise 5).

EXERCISES

1. Verify that the determinant in (42) vanishes.

2. Write the equations in trilinear line coordinates of the centroid, orthocenter, circumcenter, incenter, and the midpoints of the sides of the triangle of reference.

3. Use the centroid and the orthocenter to show that the Euler line has the equation
$$x^1 \sin 2\alpha_1 \sin (\alpha_2 - \alpha_3) + x^2 \sin 2\alpha_2 \sin (\alpha_3 - \alpha_1) + x^3 \sin 2\alpha_3 \sin (\alpha_1 - \alpha_2) = 0.$$

4. Show that the line joining the circumcenter and the incenter has the equation
$$x^1(\cos \alpha_2 - \cos \alpha_3) + x^2(\cos \alpha_3 - \cos \alpha_1) + x^3(\cos \alpha_1 - \cos \alpha_2) = 0.$$

5. Verify that the cross ratio in (47) is -1.

6. Find the condition under which the lines $l_i x^i = 0$ and $l_i' x^i = 0$ are perpendicular. *Hint:* Use equations (31) to transform to cartesian coordinates in which the orthogonality condition is known.

   Ans. $(a_i a_j + b_i b_j) l_i l_j' = 0.$

7. Show that the lines $l_i x^i = 0$ and $l_i' x^i = 0$ are parallel if and only if
$$\begin{vmatrix} l_1 & l_2 & l_3 \\ l_1' & l_2' & l_3' \\ p_1 & p_2 & p_3 \end{vmatrix} = 0.$$

8. Find the equation of the line through the point y^i and parallel to the line $l_i x^i = 0$. *Suggestion:* The required line meets the given line where $p_i x^i = 0$. Hence, the required line is a member of the pencil $l_i x^i + \lambda p_i x^i = 0$. Hence, eliminate λ from this equation and $l_i y^i + \lambda p_i y^i = 0$ to find the required line given by $y^i(p_j l_i - l_j p_i)x^i = 0$, in which a sum takes place on both i and j.

9. Show that coordinates can be chosen such that any four points in the plane can be assigned the coordinates $A(p:q:-r)$, $B(p:-q:r)$, $C(-p:q:r)$, $D(-p:-q:-r)$. Equivalently, show that for any four points (x^i), (y^i), (z^i), (w^i), coordinates can be chosen such that $x^i + y^i + z^i + w^i = 0$ for $i = 1, 2, 3, 4$. *Hint:* Select the diagonal triangle of the complete quadrangle determined by the four points as the triangle of reference $P_1 P_2 P_3$. If A, B, C, D are the four given points, let AC and BD intersect in P_2, AB and CD in P_1, and AD and BC in P_3. Add the coordinates of A and B to obtain $(1:0:0)$. Also, add the coordinates of D and C to obtain $(1:0:0)$.

10. Given two triangles with vertices P_i and $\bar{P}_i$, show that if from a point S the vertices P_1, P_2, P_3 project into three collinear points on the sides $\bar{P}_2\bar{P}_3$, $\bar{P}_3\bar{P}_1$, $\bar{P}_1\bar{P}_2$, then from S the vertices $\bar{P}_1$, $\bar{P}_2$, $\bar{P}_3$ project into three collinear points on the sides P_2P_3, P_3P_1, P_1P_2. Find the locus of the point S in the plane.

5-8. Areal coordinates*

A. F. Möbius (1790–1868) introduced *barycentric coordinates* x^i of a point P, relative to a triangle Δ, defined by

$$x^1 : x^2 : x^3 = \frac{d_1}{h_1} : \frac{d_2}{h_2} : \frac{d_3}{h_3},$$

where the d_i are the distances of P from the sides, and the h_i are the corresponding altitudes of Δ to the same sides. Barycentric coordinates become *areal coordinates* if the relation $x^1 + x^2 + x^3 = 1$ obtains. Areal coordinates may be defined as ratios of areas as follows. Denote the area of the triangle of reference $P_1P_2P_3$ (Fig. 26) by $(P_1P_2P_3)$, in which the positive orientation of the triangle Δ

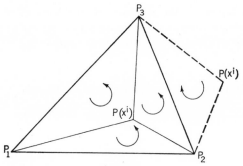

Figure 26

is given by the order P_1, P_2, P_3. It is to be observed that the order P_2, P_1, P_3, for instance, gives the opposite or negative orientation. Hence, the symbol $(P_2P_1P_3)$ is used for the negative of the area of Δ. If a fourth point $P(x^i)$ is inside Δ, the orientation PP_2P_3, for instance, is positive, but if P is on the opposite side of P_2P_3 from P_1 the orientation of PP_2P_3 is negative. The areal coordinates x^i of any point P in the plane are defined by

$$(48) \qquad x^1 = \frac{(PP_2P_3)}{(P_1P_2P_3)}, \quad x^2 = \frac{(P_1PP_3)}{(P_1P_2P_3)}, \quad x^3 = \frac{(P_1P_2P)}{(P_1P_2P_3)},$$

where the sign of x^i is positive or negative according as the orientation of the numerator is positive or negative. Note that if point P is inside the triangle Δ, then all three coordinates are positive, and one has the relation

$$(49) \qquad x^1 + x^2 + x^3 = 1.$$

The relation (49) holds for all points in the plane if the proper sign is used according to the orientation of the numerators in (48). Observe that x^1, for instance, is positive or negative according as P_1 and P are on the same or oppo-

---

* For additional treatment of areal coordinates, see E. H. Askwith, *Analytical Geometry of the Conic Sections* (Black, London, 1918).

site sides of P_2P_3. Similar statements hold for x^2 and x^3. Note that any equation in areal coordinates can be rendered homogeneous by replacing 1 by the sum $x^1 + x^2 + x^3$.

It is readily seen that the areal coordinates of the vertices P_i of the triangle Δ are $P_1(1, 0, 0)$, $P_2(0, 1, 0)$, $P_3(0, 0, 1)$. Also, the midpoints M_i of the sides of Δ are $M_1(0, \frac{1}{2}, \frac{1}{2})$, $M_2(\frac{1}{2}, 0, \frac{1}{2})$, $M_3(\frac{1}{2}, \frac{1}{2}, 0)$, and the centroid of Δ has areal coordinates $(\frac{1}{3}, \frac{1}{3}, \frac{1}{3})$. The latter coordinates have the ratios $1:1:1$, so the centroid is the unit point for areal coordinates. In a manner similar to that used in the last section for finding the unit line in trilinear coordinates, it can be shown that the unit line in areal coordinates is the line at infinity with the equation $x^1 + x^2 + x^3 = 0$.

Problems involving ratios of areas, for instance, can be solved efficaciously by means of areal coordinates (see the Exercises to follow). Although areal coordinates are defined by means of metric notions, these coordinates are not, in general, well adapted to the solution of problems involving distance and angle. (See the distance formula in Exercise 9.) For many problems it is immaterial whether areal or trilinear coordinates are employed.

EXAMPLE

Find the areal coordinates of the orthocenter of the triangle of reference.

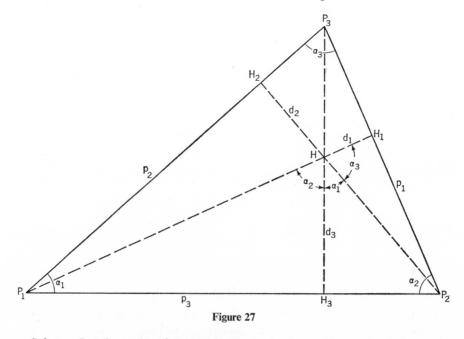

Figure 27

Solution: Let the angles of Δ at P_i in Fig. 27 be denoted by α_i, let d_i denote the distances from the orthocenter H to the sides of lengths p_i, and let h_i be the altitudes of Δ. The areal coordinates of H are in the ratios

$$d_1p_1 : d_2p_2 : d_3p_3.$$

The angles about point H are as indicated in Fig. 27. From the relations $d_1 \sec \alpha_2 = d_2 \sec \alpha_1$, $d_2 \sec \alpha_3 = d_3 \sec \alpha_2$, one has

$$d_1 : d_2 : d_3 = \sec \alpha_1 : \sec \alpha_2 : \sec \alpha_3.$$

Also, one has

$$p_1 : p_2 : p_3 = \sin \alpha_1 : \sin \alpha_2 : \sin \alpha_3.$$

Hence, the ratios of the areal coordinates are

$$d_1 p_1 : d_2 p_2 : d_3 p_3 = \tan \alpha_1 : \tan \alpha_2 : \tan \alpha_3.$$

Now divide by $\tan \alpha_1 + \tan \alpha_2 + \tan \alpha_3 \equiv \tan \alpha_1 \tan \alpha_2 \tan \alpha_3$ to obtain the required coordinates of H:

$$(\cot \alpha_2 \cot \alpha_3, \cot \alpha_3 \cot \alpha_1, \cot \alpha_1 \cot \alpha_2).$$

Relating Cartesian and Areal Coordinates

Let the vertices P_i of the triangle of reference in Fig. 26 have cartesian coordinates $(\bar{x}_i, \bar{y}_i)$, and take the cartesian coordinates of any point P as $(\bar{x}, \bar{y})$. Because the area of a triangle with orthogonal cartesian coordinates $(\bar{x}_i, \bar{y}_i)$ for vertices is given by

$$K \equiv \frac{1}{2} \begin{vmatrix} \bar{x}_1 & \bar{x}_2 & \bar{x}_3 \\ \bar{y}_1 & \bar{y}_2 & \bar{y}_3 \\ 1 & 1 & 1 \end{vmatrix},$$

it follows that the first areal coordinate x^1 of P is obtained as

$$x^1 = \frac{(PP_2P_3)}{(P_1P_2P_3)} = \frac{1}{K} \begin{vmatrix} \bar{x} & \bar{x}_2 & \bar{x}_3 \\ \bar{y} & \bar{y}_2 & \bar{y}_3 \\ 1 & 1 & 1 \end{vmatrix},$$

from which

$$x^1 K = \bar{x}(\bar{y}_2 - \bar{y}_3) + \bar{y}(\bar{x}_3 - \bar{x}_2) + (\bar{x}_2 \bar{y}_3 - \bar{x}_3 \bar{y}_2).$$

Similarly,

$$x^2 K = \bar{x}(\bar{y}_3 - \bar{y}_1) + \bar{y}(\bar{x}_1 - \bar{x}_3) + (\bar{x}_3 \bar{y}_1 - \bar{x}_1 \bar{y}_3),$$
$$x^3 K = \bar{x}(\bar{y}_1 - \bar{y}_2) + \bar{y}(\bar{x}_2 - \bar{x}_1) + (\bar{x}_1 \bar{y}_2 - \bar{x}_2 \bar{y}_1).$$

Multiply the last three equations by $\bar{x}_1$, $\bar{x}_2$, $\bar{x}_3$, respectively, and add to find

$$\bar{x} = \bar{x}_1 x^1 + \bar{x}_2 x^2 + \bar{x}_3 x^3 = \bar{x}_i x^i.$$

Similarly, use the multipliers $\bar{y}_1$, $\bar{y}_2$, $\bar{y}_3$ to obtain

$$\bar{y} = \bar{y}_i x^i.$$

Note that use of the multipliers 1, 1, 1 gives

$$1 = x^1 + x^2 + x^3.$$

Hence, the equations relating areal coordinates x^i and cartesian coordinates $(\bar{x}, \bar{y})$ are

(50) $$\bar{x} = \bar{x}_i x^i, \quad \bar{y} = \bar{y}_i x^i, \quad 1 = x^1 + x^2 + x^3.$$

Remark: Equations (50) hold for oblique as well as for orthogonal cartesian coordinates.

Areal coordinates in the plane relative to a triangle of reference can be extended to *volume* coordinates in space relative to a tetrahedron of reference.*

EXERCISES

1. Show that the equation of the line at infinity is $x^1 + x^2 + x^3 = 0$ in areal coordinates.

2. Find the condition under which the lines $l_i x^i = 0$ and $l'_i x^i = 0$ in areal coordinates are parallel.

3. Define areal line coordinates.

4. Define coordinates of points in space relative to a tetrahedron of reference as a generalization of areal coordinates in the plane.

5. Show that areal coordinates may be generalized to n-space by referring the $n + 1$ coordinates x^i of a point P to a *simplex* of reference determined by $n + 1$ linearly independent points $P_1, P_2, \cdots, P_{n+1}$, where the kth coordinate of x^k is given by the ratio

$$x^k = \frac{(P_1 P_2 \cdots P_{k-1} P P_{k+1} \cdots P_{n+1})}{(P_1 P_2 \cdots P_k \cdots P_{n+1})},$$

in which the parenthetical expressions denote hypervolumes of simplexes.

6. Consider the particular case of equations (50) in which the vertex P_3 is at the origin of the $\bar{x}, \bar{y}$ oblique cartesian axes, with P_1 on the $\bar{x}$-axis and P_2 on the $\bar{y}$-axis. Show that the areal coordinates x^i and the cartesian coordinates are related by

$$x^1 = \frac{\bar{x}}{p_2}, \quad x^2 = \frac{\bar{y}}{p_1}, \quad x^3 = 1 - \frac{\bar{x}}{p_2} - \frac{\bar{y}}{p_1},$$

and verify that the equation

$$p_1^2 x^2 x^3 + p_2^2 x^3 x^1 + p_3^2 x^1 x^2 = 0$$

represents a circle. Find the form of the equation of the circle if the angle at P_3 is $\pi/2$.

$$Ans. \quad \bar{x}^2 + \bar{y}^2 = p_2 \bar{x} + p_1 \bar{y}.$$

7. Find the equation of the line through the intersection of $l_i x^i = 0$, $l'_i x^i = 0$ and parallel to the side $P_2 P_3$ of the triangle of reference.

8. If K is the area of the triangle of reference and the ξ^i_j are the areal coordinates of any three points (the subscript denotes the point and the superscript the coordinates), the area of the triangle determined by the three points ξ^i_j is given by $K|\xi^i_j|$— that is, by K times the determinant of the nine coordinates ξ^i_j.

9. Show that the distance d between the points with areal coordinates x^i_1 and x^i_2 is given by the quadratic form

$$(d)^2 = -\tfrac{1}{2}(p_{ij})^2(x^i_1 - x^i_2)(x^j_1 - x^j_2),$$

---

* In this connection, see a paper by the author on "Volume Coordinates," *Am. Math. Monthly*, Vol. 53, No. 7, pp. 377–383.

where p_{ij} is the length of the side P_iP_j of the triangle of reference. Note that $p_{ij} = 0$ when $i = j$.

10. Consider the triangle $P_1P_2P_3$ and the trisectors of the interior angles of it. Let the trisectors neighboring the sides P_2P_3, P_3P_1, P_1P_2 intersect in the points B_1, B_2, B_3, respectively. Prove that the triangle $B_1B_2B_3$ is always equilateral. (This is Morley's theorem.)*

Solutions for the following four exercises appear in the *American Mathematical Monthly*. The reference for each problem is stated.

11. Given a triangle with angles α, β, γ, show that the ratio of the area of the Morley triangle (see Exercise 10) of the given triangle to the area of the given triangle is

$$\frac{\left(\prod \sin^2 \frac{\alpha}{3}\right)\left(1 - 4 \sum \cos^2 \frac{\alpha}{3} + 16 \prod \cos \frac{\alpha}{3}\right)}{\left(\prod \sin \alpha\right)\left(\prod \sin \frac{\pi - \alpha}{3}\right)},$$

where $\prod$ indicates a product and $\sum$ a sum extended over α, β, γ.†

12. Let P be a point on the circumcircle of a triangle ABC; A_0, B_0, C_0 are the points where AP, BP, CP meet BC, CA, AB; A_1, B_1, C_1 are the points dividing AA_0, BB_0, CC_0 in the same ratio so that

$$AA_1:A_1A_0 = BB_1:B_1B_0 = CC_1:C_1C_0 = k;$$

and finally, A_2, B_2, C_2 are the points where the altitudes meet the perpendiculars at P to AP, BP, CP. Prove that the ratio of the areas $A_1B_1C_1$ and ABC equals

$$\frac{1 - k}{(1 + k)^2} + \frac{k^2}{4(1 + k)^2} \frac{AA_2:BB_2:CC_2}{R^3},$$

where R is the circumradius. (This problem was proposed by R. Goormaghtigh, Bruges, Belgium.)‡

13. If in triangle ABC, $\sin^2 A + \sin^2 B + \sin^2 C = 1$, prove that the circumcircle cuts the nine-point circle orthogonally. (This problem was proposed by D. L. MacKay, Evander Childs High School, New York.)§

14. On the sides A_0B_0, B_0C_0, C_0A_0 of a triangle $A_0B_0C_0$, the points A_1, B_1, C_1 are taken respectively such that $A_0A_1/A_0B_0 = B_0B_1/B_0C_0 = C_0C_1/C_0A_0 = 1/n$, where n is a positive integer. A triangle $A_2B_2C_2$ is now obtained from triangle $A_1B_1C_1$ in the same manner that $A_1B_1C_1$ was obtained from $A_0B_0C_0$. Consider the sequence of triangles T_0, T_1, T_2, $\cdots$, T_n formed in this manner. Let R_n be the ratio of the area of T_n to T_0, and determine the limit of R_n as n increases through integer values without limit. (This problem was proposed by J. Rosenbaum, Hartford Federal College.)‖

---

* For a generalization of this exercise, see H. Lebesgue, *L'Enseignement Mathematique, Sur les n-Sectrices d'un Triangle*, 1939–1940, p. 39.

† "Problem 4477," *Am. Math. Monthly*, Vol. 60, No. 5, p. 337.

‡ "Problem 3795," *Am. Math. Monthly*, Vol. 45, No. 10, p. 697.

§ "Problem E285," Vol. 45, No. 2, p. 119.

‖ "Problem E241," *Am. Math. Monthly*, Vol. 44, No. 6, p. 386.

CHAPTER 6

Geometry in the Projective Plane

6-1. Central projection

The homography between lines l and $\bar{l}$ defined in Chapter 1 was seen in Chapter 2 to represent a projectivity between the lines. The homography between planes π and $\bar{\pi}$ defined by equations (1) in Section 5-1, or

(1) $$\bar{x} = \frac{a_1 x + b_1 y + c_1}{a_3 x + b_3 y + c_3}, \quad \bar{y} = \frac{a_2 x + b_2 y + c_2}{a_3 x + b_3 y + c_3},$$

will now be shown to have a projective interpretation in three-space. Project points of plane $\bar{\pi}$ with equation $z = my$ from the center $S(h, k, l)$ onto plane π with equation $z = 0$. The coordinates in plane π are x, y. A coordinate system with coordinates $\bar{x}$, $\bar{y}$ will be established in plane $\bar{\pi}$. This particular type of mapping—in which the corresponding points on π and $\bar{\pi}$ are collinear with a point S—is called a *perspectivity*. The line SP (Fig. 28) has the symmetric equations

$$\frac{X - x}{h - x} = \frac{Y - y}{k - y} = \frac{Z - 0}{l - 0}.$$

Let this line intersect plane $\bar{\pi}$ in $P'(x', y', z')$. Because P' is on the plane $\bar{\pi}$, so that $z' = my'$, it follows that

(2) $$\frac{x' - x}{h - x} = \frac{y' - y}{k - y} = \frac{my'}{l}.$$

Solve equations (2) for x' and y':

(3) $$x' = \frac{(l - mk)x + mhy}{my + (l - mk)}, \quad y' = \frac{ly}{my + (l - mk)}.$$

In plane π, take $\bar{x} = x'$ and $\bar{y} = \sqrt{y'^2 + z'^2} = y'\sqrt{1 + m^2}$. Then, from (3), one obtains

(4) $$\bar{x} = \frac{(l - mk)x + mhy}{my + (l - mk)}, \quad \bar{y} = \frac{l\sqrt{1 + m^2}\, y}{my + (l - mk)}$$

for the perspectivity between π and $\bar{\pi}$ relative to the center of projection $S(h, k, l)$. Observe that equations (4) are of the type of equations (1), with some of the terms missing. Thus, a perspectivity is a particular kind of homography—that is, the particular case in which lines joining corresponding points are concurrent. A projectivity was defined earlier as a sequence of perspectivities. It can be shown that if the perspectivity (4), which projects points of $\bar{\pi}$ into points of π through the center S, is followed by a second perspectivity with center $S'(p, q, r)$ which projects points of π into points of another plane π', then the product of the two perspectivities, which is a mapping from $\bar{\pi}$ to π', is expressed by equations of the form of (1). It is readily verified that the product of any number of perspectivities is represented by equations of the form of (1). Thus, a homography between two planes may be interpreted as a projectivity—that is, a sequence of perspectivities—so that hereafter the terms homography and projectivity will be considered as synonymous.

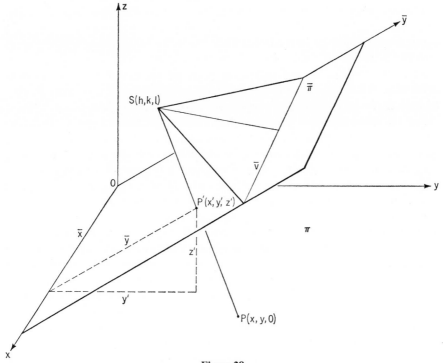

Figure 28

Any nonhorizontal plane through S (Fig. 28) meets $\bar{\pi}$ in a line $\bar{l}$, and π in a corresponding line l. The *horizontal plane* through S is an exceptional plane. It intersects $\bar{\pi}$ in a line $\bar{v}$ which has no correspondent in π (from the point of view of euclidean geometry). The line $\bar{v}$ in $\bar{\pi}$ is called the *vanishing line* of $\bar{\pi}$ under the perspectivity. However, just as the euclidean plane was augmented by an ideal line to obtain the projective plane, three-dimensional euclidean space is augmented by an ideal plane to obtain three-dimensional projective space.

In this space, the correspondent of line $\bar{v}$ in $\bar{\pi}$ is the line in π in which π intersects the ideal plane. Observe that the plane through S which is parallel to $\bar{\pi}$ intersects π in its vanishing line v. The correspondent of v in $\bar{\pi}$ is the intersection of $\bar{\pi}$ and the ideal plane. Any two lines $\bar{l}$ and $\bar{l}'$ in $\bar{\pi}$ which meet on $\bar{v}$ project into parallel lines in π (see Exercise 2).

If $a_3 = b_3 = 0$ in equations (1), the resulting specialized projectivity is an affine mapping under which the ideal line is the vanishing line in each of planes π and $\bar{\pi}$ (see Exercise 4). An affine mapping is effected by a parallel projection between π and $\bar{\pi}$, which means that the lines joining corresponding points in π and $\bar{\pi}$ are parallel. In particular, if the planes π and $\bar{\pi}$ are parallel, a parallel projection maps configurations in π into congruent configurations in $\bar{\pi}$. Under the general affinity (mapping by parallel projection between two nonparallel planes) the metric invariants angle and distance are lost, but many aspects of configurations remain invariant. Straight lines map into straight lines, the order of points on a line is unchanged, a tangent to a curve goes into a tangent to a curve, parallel lines go into parallel lines, the midpoint of a line segment maps into the midpoint of the projected segment, and the ratio of two areas is the same as the ratio of the corresponding projected areas. All of these are affine invariants. Affine geometry may be defined as the study of invariants of configurations under the group of mappings by parallel projection.

Just as affine geometry is a generalization of euclidean geometry, projective geometry is a generalization of affine geometry. Under the general projectivity described by equations (1), some of the affine invariants are lost, but interesting projective invariants remain to be investigated. A tangent to a curve remains a tangent to a curve under projection, the order of points on a line (or a curve) is unchanged, and the cross ratio of four elements (say, four planes through a line) remains invariant under a projectivity. Any conic section can be projected into any other conic section (see Exercise 3). For this reason, all conics may be said to be projectively equivalent. One should note that as the type of mapping is made more general, the number of invariants decreases. The English mathematician A. Cayley (1821–1895) remarked that projective geometry is "all" geometry, which may mean that he did not realize the possibility of significant invariants under a more general mapping than that in equations (1). In the hierarchy of geometry a projectivity becomes a particular case of the more general *topological mapping* (or *homeomorphism*) described by $\bar{x} = f(x, y)$, $\bar{y} = g(x, y)$, which mapping is one-to-one and continuous with a continuous inverse.

For some purposes equations (1) are useful to represent a projectivity, but for much that follows the homogeneous form developed in Section 5-1 is preferred. In the next section the homogeneous coordinates used in the projectivity

(5) $$k\bar{x}^i = a^i_j x^j$$

will be given projective significance.

EXERCISES

1. Show that the line $\bar{v}$ in $\bar{\pi}$ in Fig. 28 has the equations $my = l$ and $z = l$, and that line v in π is represented by $my = mk - l$ and $z = 0$.

2. Show that the two lines with symmetric equations

$$\frac{x-a}{c} = \frac{my-l}{m} = \frac{z-l}{m}, \quad \frac{x-a}{1+m^2} = \frac{my-l}{mc} = \frac{z-l}{mc}$$

are in plane $\bar{\pi}$ (Fig. 28), that they intersect in a point on the vanishing line $\bar{v}$ in $\bar{\pi}$, and that they project into parallel lines in plane π.

3. Show that the circle $z = 0$, $(x - c)^2 + y^2 = a^2$, with $c > a$, projects from $S(c, o, -b)$ into the hyperbola $x = 0$, $a^2(z + b)^2 = b^2(c^2 + y^2)$ in the yz plane.

4. Project points of $\bar{\pi}$, with equation $z = ky$, into π (Fig. 28) by a set of parallel lines with direction $(l:m:n)$ to obtain the affine mapping

$$(n - mk)\bar{x} = (n - mk)x + lky, \quad (n - mk)\bar{y} = n\sqrt{1 + k^2}\, y.$$

5. Find the equation of the conical surface which is the locus of the projecting rays of points of the circle $y = b$, $x^2 + (z - a)^2 = a^2$ from the center $S(o, o, 2a)$. Show that the intersection of this surface with the plane $z = 0$ is the parabola $z = 0$, $4a^2y = b(x^2 + 4a^2)$. From the projective point of view, the point $A(o, b, 2a)$ on the circle maps into the ideal point on the parabola, thus making the mapping of the circle into the parabola both one-to-one and continuous.

6-2. Projective nature of homogeneous coordinates

The homogeneous point and line coordinates defined in Sections 3 and 4 of Chapter 5 in terms of distance—a metric invariant—will now be shown to have projective significance. This is done by proving the

THEOREM: *The ratios of homogeneous coordinates can be expressed as cross ratios.*

Proof: Consider point coordinates first. In Fig. 29 the lines joining $P(x^i)$ to the vertices P_i of the triangle of reference are denoted by l_i, and the lines joining the unit point U to the vertices P_i are identified by m_i. The cross ratio of the four lines through P_1 is

(6) $$(a_2a_3l_1m_1) = \frac{(a_2a_3l_1)}{(a_2a_3m_1)}$$

by equation 5-25. The simple ratio $(a_2a_3l_1)$ is expressed by

$$(a_2a_3l_1) = \frac{\sin{(a_2l_1)}}{\sin{(a_3l_1)}} = \frac{d_2}{d_3},$$

and the simple ratio $(a_2a_3m_1)$ is

$$(a_2a_3m_1) = \frac{\sin{(a_2m_1)}}{\sin{(a_3m_1)}} = \frac{e_2}{e_3}.$$

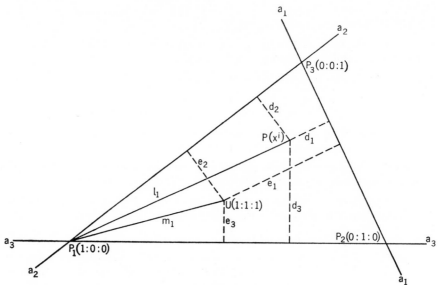

Figure 29

Hence, from (6),

(7)
$$(a_2 a_3 l_1 m_1) = \frac{d_2/d_3}{e_2/e_3} = \frac{d_2/e_2}{d_3/e_3} = \frac{x^2}{x^3},$$

which shows that the ratio $x^2:x^3$ of homogeneous point coordinates is expressed by a cross ratio which is known to be invariant under a projectivity. Similarly, it follows from (7) that

(8)
$$\frac{x^1}{x^3} = (a_1 a_3 l_2 m_2), \quad \frac{x^2}{x^1} = (a_2 a_1 l_3 m_3).$$

The proof for line coordinates is similar. Let the line l with coordinates u_i intersect the sides a_i of the triangle of reference in the points L_i (Fig. 30), and let the unit line $u[1:1:1]$ intersect a_i in the points M_i. Write the cross ratio of the four points on side a_1 as

(9)
$$(P_2 P_3 L_1 M_1) = \frac{(P_2 P_3 L_1)}{(P_2 P_3 M_1)} = \frac{P_2 L_1}{P_3 L_1} \div \frac{P_2 M_1}{P_3 M_1}.$$

From Fig. 30, one has

$$\frac{P_2 L_1}{P_3 L_1} = \frac{d_2}{d_3}, \quad \frac{P_2 M_1}{P_3 M_1} = \frac{e_2}{e_3}$$

Hence, from (9),

(10)
$$(P_2 P_3 L_1 M_1) = \frac{d_2/d_3}{e_2/e_3} = \frac{d_2/e_2}{d_3/e_3} = \frac{u_2}{u_3}.$$

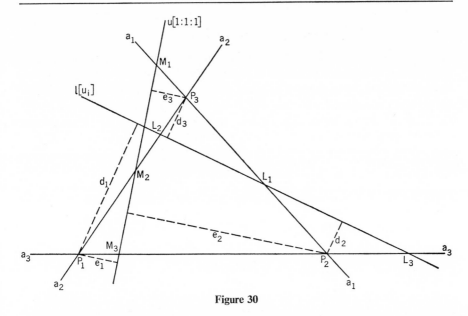

Figure 30

which shows that the ratio $u_2:u_3$ of homogeneous line coordinates is expressed as a cross ratio and is therefore invariant under projection. In a similar manner, it follows that

$$\frac{u_1}{u_3} = (P_1P_3L_2M_2), \quad \frac{u_2}{u_1} = (P_2P_1L_3M_3).$$

This completes the proof of the theorem.

Note that projective point and line coordinates could have been defined initially, as in this section. However, the approach by use of the distance concept was deemed more meaningful for the reader.

Relation of Unit Point to Unit Line

It has been seen that the unit point $U(1:1:1)$, or the unit line $u[1:1:1]$, can be chosen arbitrarily. However, as soon as one of these is selected the other is determined uniquely. The construction of the unit line, given the unit point, will now be explained. In Fig. 29 construct the harmonic conjugate of the line P_1U relative to the sides a_2 and a_3 through vertex P_1, and let its intersection with a_1 be denoted by Q_1. Analogously, construct the points Q_2, Q_3 on sides a_2, a_3. The points Q_i lie on the unit line. Conversely, if the unit line is selected first, the unit point is readily constructed. For a proof of this construction, see Exercise 12 on p. 111. The unit point and unit line are in the pole and polar relation with respect to the triangle of reference.

6-3. Theorem of G. Desargues (1593–1662)

There are two famous theorems of Desargues in projective geometry. One of them relates to a pencil of conics (Chapter 8) and the other to perspective triangles in a plane or in space. The latter theorem is to be proved in this section. Let the two triangles $P_1P_2P_3$ and $\overline{P}_1\overline{P}_2\overline{P}_3$ be in the same plane, and let P_1, $\overline{P}_1$; P_2, $\overline{P}_2$; P_3, $\overline{P}_3$ be corresponding vertices. It is to be shown that if lines joining corresponding vertices are concurrent, then the points of intersection of corresponding sides of the triangles are collinear. This is stated more succinctly in the

THEOREM: *If two triangles are perspective from a point, they are perspective from a line, and conversely.*

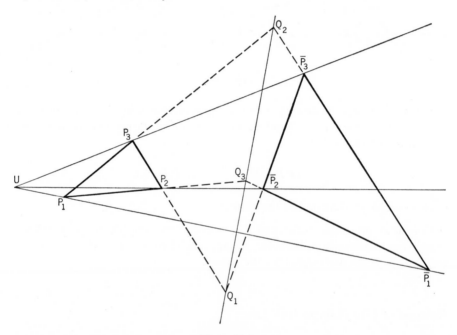

Figure 31 A

Proof: Select triangle $P_1P_2P_3$ as the triangle of reference (Fig. 31a), and let the lines $P_1\overline{P}_1$, $P_2\overline{P}_2$, $P_3\overline{P}_3$ intersect in a point U which is taken as the unit point $(1:1:1)$. Because $\overline{P}_1$ is on line P_1U, the coordinates of $\overline{P}_1$ are a linear combination of those of P_1 and U and hence can be taken as $(\alpha:1:1)$, where α is a parameter. Likewise, the coordinates of $\overline{P}_2$ and $\overline{P}_3$ are taken as $(1:\beta:1)$ and $(1:1:\gamma)$, respectively, where β and γ are parameters. In order to emphasize the fact that the vertices of the given triangles may be paired in more than one way, a second figure (Fig. 31b) is provided.

The coordinates of the required points and lines are found as follows:

$$P_2P_3: \quad \begin{pmatrix} 0 & 1 & 0 \\ 0 & 0 & 1 \end{pmatrix} \rightarrow [1:0:0]$$

$$\overline{P_2P_3}: \quad \begin{pmatrix} 1 & \beta & 1 \\ 1 & 1 & \gamma \end{pmatrix} \rightarrow [\beta\gamma - 1:1 - \gamma:1 - \beta]$$

$$Q_1: \quad \begin{bmatrix} 1 & 0 & 0 \\ \beta\gamma - 1 & 1 - \gamma & 1 - \beta \end{bmatrix} \rightarrow (0:\beta - 1:1 - \gamma).$$

In a similar manner, the coordinates of Q_2, Q_3 are found to be $(1 - \alpha:0:\gamma - 1)$ and $(\alpha - 1:1 - \beta:0)$. The determinant

$$\begin{vmatrix} 0 & \beta - 1 & 1 - \gamma \\ 1 - \alpha & 0 & \gamma - 1 \\ \alpha - 1 & 1 - \beta & 0 \end{vmatrix}$$

is zero. Hence, the points Q_i are collinear. This proves the theorem.

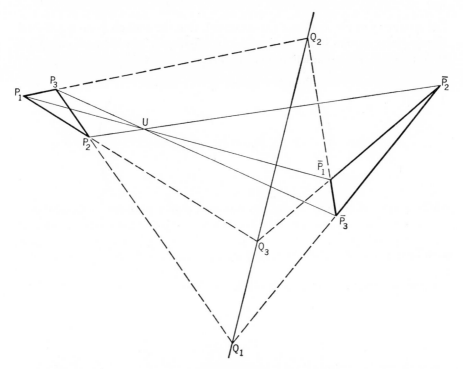

Figure 31 B

The converse can be proved readily, in a similar manner, by employing line coordinates with the line $Q_1Q_2Q_3$ as the unit line. Note, however, that the converse is the dual of the theorem in the present case, in which the two triangles are coplanar, so that no proof is required. This last remark does not hold for noncoplanar triangles. The proof of the theorem of Desargues with the triangles noncoplanar is left as an exercise.

The point U and the line $Q_1Q_2Q_3$ (Figs. 31a and 31b) are called the *center* and *axis* respectively of the perspectivity. Both the Desargues configuration in the plane and the theorem of Pappus (see Exercise 10) are important in the axiomatic development of projective geometry. (See Section 9-9.)

Configuration Symbols

The Desargues configuration (Fig. 31a) has ten points and ten lines. Three lines pass through each point, and three points lie on each line. Hence, the configuration symbol (incidence matrix) is

$$
\begin{array}{cc}
 & \text{Points} \quad \text{Lines} \\
\begin{array}{c} \text{Points} \\ \text{Lines} \end{array} & \left(\begin{array}{cc} 10 & 3 \\ 3 & 10 \end{array} \right)
\end{array}
$$

The symmetry of the incidence matrix reveals that the configuration is self-dual. The complete n-point in the plane and its configuration symbol were introduced in Section 4-1. The complete n-point in three-space has the symbol

$$
\begin{array}{cccc}
 & \text{Points} & \text{Lines} & \text{Planes} \\
\text{Points} & \left(\begin{array}{ccc} n & n-1 & \frac{1}{2}(n-1)(n-2) \\[2mm] \text{Lines} \quad 2 & \frac{n}{2}(n-1) & n-2 \\[2mm] \text{Planes} \quad 3 & 3 & \frac{n}{6}(n-1)(n-2) \end{array} \right)
\end{array},
$$

which is read as follows. There are n points, and each point is incident with $n-1$ lines, and $_{n-1}C_2 = \frac{1}{2}(n-1)(n-2)$ planes. Two of the points are on each line. There are $_nC_2 = (n/2)(n-1)$ lines, and $n-2$ planes are incident with each line. Three of the points are on each plane, three of the lines are on each plane, and there are $_nC_3 = (n/6)(n-1)(n-2)$ planes.

It follows that the complete five-point in three-space has the symbol

$$
\begin{array}{cccc}
 & \text{Points} & \text{Lines} & \text{Planes} \\
\text{Points} & 5 & 4 & 6 \\
\text{Lines} & 2 & 10 & 3 \\
\text{Planes} & 3 & 3 & 10
\end{array},
$$

for which the configuration is determined by five points with no four of them coplanar. Any plane section of the complete five-point by a plane which does not contain any one of the five points is a plane Desargues configuration.

There are important applications of the Desargues theorem. Two of them are exhibited in the following examples.

EXAMPLE 1

Given two lines *l* and *m* and a point P_1 (Fig. 32), construct the line through P_1 and the inaccessible point of intersection of *l* and *m*.

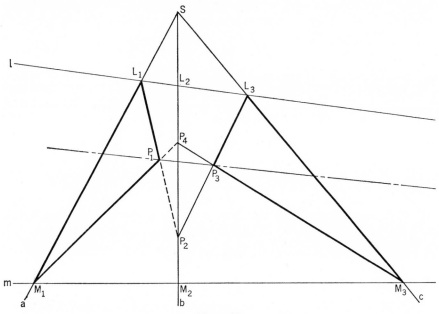

Figure 32

Solution: Select any point *S* and draw lines *a*, *b*, *c* through *S* to intersect *l* and *m* in L_1, M_1; L_2, M_2; L_3, M_3, respectively. Line L_1P_1 intersects *b* in point P_2, and M_1P_1 meets *b* at P_4. Next draw the lines M_3P_4 and L_3P_2 to intersect at P_3. The line P_1P_3 is the required line which passes through the intersection of *l* and *m*. A proof by pure geometry is supplied immediately by noticing that line *b* is the axis of perspectivity of the triangles $L_1M_1P_1$ and $L_3M_3P_3$. Hence, the lines *l* and *m* (and P_1P_3) intersect in the center of perspectivity by the theorem of Desargues.

EXAMPLE 2

Consider a complete quadrangle determined by the points P_i, where $i = 1, 2, 3, 4$, and the six lines P_1P_3, P_2P_4, P_3P_4, P_1P_2, P_1P_4, P_2P_3. On the line P_2P_4 select an arbitrary point *S*, and draw through it two arbitrary lines *a* and *c* (Fig. 33). Denote the intersections of line *a* with P_1P_2 and P_1P_4 by L_1 and M_1, respectively, and the intersections of *c* with P_3P_2 and P_3P_4 by L_3 and M_3, respectively. Prove that the lines L_1L_3, M_1M_3, P_1P_3 are concurrent.

Solution: The proof is immediate as soon as one realizes that the statement in Example 2 is another way to describe the Desargues configuration in Fig. 33.

The third example illustrates the use of coordinates in establishing a geometric fact.

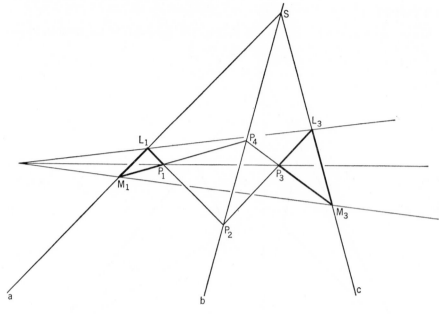

Figure 33

EXAMPLE 3

Prove that the diagonal triangle of a complete quadrangle is perspective with each of the four triangles determined by the four points, the fourth point in each instance being the center of perspectivity.

Solution: This can be done by observing the concurrence of certain lines. However, an analytic proof will be given. With $P_1P_2P_3$ as the triangle of reference and P_4 as the unit point, the coordinates of the intersection Q of P_1P_4 and P_2P_3 (Fig. 33) are found to be $(0:1:1)$. Point M (the intersection of P_1P_3 and P_2P_4) has coordinates $(1:0:1)$, and point H (the intersection of P_1P_2 and P_3P_4) has coordinates $(1:1:0)$. Let P_2P_3 intersect MH at R, P_1P_2 intersect QM at S', and P_1P_3 intersect QH at T. The coordinates of the last three points are given by $R(0:-1:1)$, $S'(-1:1:0)$, $T(-1:0:1)$. The points R, S', T all lie on the unit line $[1:1:1]$, which is the polar of P_4 with respect to the triangle $P_1P_2P_3$. In a similar manner, it can be shown that the polar of P_1 with respect to the triangle $P_2P_3P_4$ is the axis of the perspectivity between the triangle $P_2P_3P_4$ and the diagonal triangle QMH. The equation of this axis is $3x^1 - x^2 - x^3 = 0$. Likewise, the polars of P_2 and P_3 may be considered (see Exercise 6).

Linkages

A model for Fig. 31 can be constructed by using three fixed straight wires through a fixed ring at U, and three straight wires P_2P_3, P_3P_1, P_1P_2 through fixed rings at P_1, P_2, P_3. Use sliding rings at $\overline{P}_1$, $\overline{P}_2$, $\overline{P}_3$ with wires $\overline{P}_2\overline{P}_3$, $\overline{P}_3\overline{P}_1$, $\overline{P}_1\overline{P}_2$

through them. As the rings at $\bar{P}_1$, $\bar{P}_2$, $\bar{P}_3$ move independently, the straight wire $Q_1Q_2Q_3$ through variable rings Q_1, Q_2, Q_3 moves in the plane. The model thus constructed is an instance of a *linkage*.

From Fig. 31 it is evident that if $\bar{P}_2$ and $\bar{P}_3$ are held fixed and $\bar{P}_1$ is allowed to move, the line $Q_1Q_2Q_3$ rotates about the point Q_1. This is seen analytically as follows. In the proof of the theorem of Desargues, the points Q_1 and Q_2 had coordinates given by $Q_1(0:\beta - 1:1 - \gamma)$ and $Q_2(1 - \alpha:0:\gamma - 1)$. Hence, the equation of the axis $Q_1Q_2Q_3$ may be written in the form

$$\frac{x^1}{\alpha - 1} + \frac{x^2}{\beta - 1} + \frac{x^3}{\gamma - 1} = 0,$$

from which it follows that, as α varies, the line $Q_1Q_2Q_3$ passes through the fixed point of intersection of the lines $x^1 = 0$ and $(\gamma - 1)x^2 + (\beta - 1)x^3 = 0$. Similarly, varying $\bar{P}_2$ causes the axes to revolve about Q_2, and if only $\bar{P}_3$ is allowed to move, the axis turns about Q_3. The axis assumes a doubly infinite set of positions as the parameters α, β, γ vary independently. If β and γ are functions of α, the equation of the axis has the form $u_i(\alpha)x^i = 0$, and the point coordinates x^i of the locus to which the variable line is tangent are given by

$$x^i = e^{ijk}u_j(\alpha)u'_k(\alpha).$$

(See Section 4-4.)

It can be shown that if three triangles are perspective from a point, the three axes of the three pairs of triangles are concurrent. The reader may wish to verify this, say, for the particular case of the triangles $P_1P_2P_3$ (Fig. 32); $\bar{P}_1\bar{P}_2\bar{P}_3$ with vertices $(2:1:1)$, $(1:2:1)$, $(1:1:2)$; and $\bar{\bar{P}}_1\bar{\bar{P}}_2\bar{\bar{P}}_3$ with vertices $(2:1:1)$, $(1:3:1)$, $(1:1:4)$. Show that the point of concurrence of the three axes is $(1:-4:3)$.

Figures of projective geometry may be visualized as linkages, with some elements fixed and others movable.

EXERCISES

1. In Fig. 32 take P_1, P_2, P_3 as vertices of the triangle of reference, and P_4 as the unit point. Find the equations of the sides of the diagonal triangle of the complete quadrangle determined by P_i, with $i = 1, \cdots, 4$.

2. In Fig. 32, with the triangle of reference and unit point chosen as in Exercise 1, assign suitable coordinates to S and L_1, and find the equation of line M_1M_3. *Hint:* Take S as $(1:\beta:1)$ and L_1 as $(1:\alpha:0)$, where α and β are parameters.

3. Construct a line through a point and parallel to two given parallel lines.

4. Write the configuration symbols for (a) the section of a complete n-point in three-space by a plane not through any one of the n given points, (b) a tetrahedron determined by four points in space, and (c) a complete n-point in four-dimensional space.

5. Show that the totality of pairs of points on a line l given by the totality of binary quadratic forms $a_{ij}x^ix^j$, with $i, j = 1, 2$, are in one-to-one correspondence with the lines of the projective plane. Show that a necessary condition for three lines

in the projective plane to be concurrent is that the corresponding pairs of points on l be in involution. What is the line envelope in the projective plane whose lines correspond to pairs of coincident points on line l?

6. In Example 3 of this section, find the equations of the polar lines of P_2 and P_3 with respect to the triangles $P_3P_4P_1$ and $P_1P_2P_4$, respectively.

7. Prove the theorem of Desargues on perspective triangles if (a) the two triangles lie in parallel planes, and (b) the two triangles lie in nonparallel planes.

8. Find the equation of the locus of a point P for which the cross ratio of the lines joining P to four fixed points A, B, C, D is a constant k.

9. The lines joining the vertices P_i of a given triangle to an arbitrary point P meet the sides p_i opposite P_i in the points F_i. The lines F_2F_3, F_3F_1, F_1F_2 meet p_1, p_2, p_3 in H_1, H_2, H_3, respectively. Show that if $P_1P_2P_3$ is the triangle of reference, and P has coordinates a^i, the points H_i lie on the line $(x^1/a^1) + (x^2/a^2) + (x^3/a^3) = 0$. The line $H_1H_2H_3$ is called the *polar line* of $P(a^i)$ relative to the triangle. Deduce that the polar line of the unit point is the unit line. (See Section 6-2.)

10. *Theorem of Pappus.* Select three arbitrary points P_1, P_2, P_3 on a line l and three arbitrary points $\bar{P}_1$, $\bar{P}_2$, $\bar{P}_3$ on a line $\bar{l}$ (Fig. 34). If Q_1, Q_2, Q_3 are the intersections of the joins of $P_2\bar{P}_3$, $\bar{P}_2P_3$; $P_3\bar{P}_1$, $\bar{P}_3P_1$; $P_1\bar{P}_2$, $\bar{P}_1P_2$, respectively, then Q_1, Q_2, Q_3 are collinear. Prove the theorem. *Suggestion:* Take $P_1P_2\bar{P}_1$ as the triangle of reference, and $\bar{P}_2$ as the unit point.

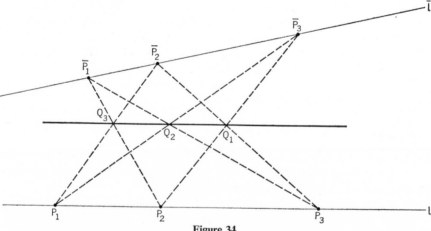

Figure 34

Note: The reader will recall from plane analytical geometry that a conic is represented by an equation of the second degree in cartesian coordinates, say, $f(x, y) = 0$. If f is the product of two linear factors in the variables x, y, the conic is called *degenerate, reducible,* or *composite* (see Section 8-3). If the lines l and $\bar{l}$ are considered together as a composite conic, the points P_1, $\bar{P}_2$, P_3, $\bar{P}_1$, P_2, $\bar{P}_3$, P_1 are the vertices of a hexagon which is inscribed in the conic. The lines $P_1\bar{P}_2$, $\bar{P}_1P_2$; $P_2\bar{P}_3$, $\bar{P}_2P_3$; $P_3\bar{P}_1$, $\bar{P}_3P_1$ are pairs of opposite sides of the hexagon. Hence, the intersections of pairs of opposite sides of the inscribed hexagon are collinear. Pascal's theorem on the inscribed hexagon of a general conic appears in Section 8-5.

11. Consider Fig. 34 as a linkage, with fixed rings at P_1, P_2, $\overline{P}_1$, $\overline{P}_2$, and sliding rings at P_3 and $\overline{P}_3$. Show that the variable straight wire $Q_1Q_2Q_3$ always passes through a fixed ring at the point $(0:1:1)$.

12. Show that the line $Q_1Q_2Q_3$ in Fig. 34 passes through the intersection of l and $\bar{l}$ if and only if the lines $P_1\overline{P}_1$, $P_2\overline{P}_2$, $P_3\overline{P}_3$ are concurrent.

13. The vertices V_i of a variable triangle move on three respective fixed lines p_i in such a manner that the line V_2V_3 contains a fixed point F_1 and the line V_3V_1 contains a fixed point F_2. Show that the line coordinates u_i of the third side V_1V_2 satisfy a second-degree equation, which means that the envelope of the third side is a curve of class two. Show that, in a special case, the envelope may be a point. *Suggestion:* Choose the three fixed lines as the triangle of reference, F_1 as $(1, 1, 1)$, and F_2 as $(1, r, s)$, where r and s are constants. Assign variable coordinates to V_1, V_2, V_3, and demand collinearity for V_2, V_3, F_1, as well as for V_3, V_1, F_2.

14. State and prove the dual of Exercise 13.

15. State and prove the dual of Exercise 10.

16. Write the symbol for the configuration of Pappus in Fig. 34.

17. Two fixed lines l and l' intersect at H. Two fixed points M and M' are collinear with H and lie in the plane of l and l'. A line revolves about a fixed point F and intersects l and l' in Q and Q', respectively. Prove that the locus of P, the intersection of MQ and $M'Q'$, is a straight line, and find its equation.
    Ans. If coordinates are assigned as $M(1, 0, 0)$, $F(0, 1, 0)$, $H(0, 0, 1)$, $M'(1, 0, h)$, $U(1, 1, 1)$ taken on line l, and $l[1, -1, 0]$, $l'[1, \alpha, 0]$, the locus of P is the line $hx^1 + \alpha h x^2 - (1 + \alpha)x^3 = 0$.

18. Find the equation of the locus of the point P in Exercise 17 if M, H, M' are not collinear.

19. Take any two points S and T on a fixed line p, and join each of them to each of two fixed points P_1 and P_2 in the plane. The line SP_2 intersects TP_1 in the point Q_2, and TP_2 intersects SP_1 in Q_1. Show that the line Q_1Q_2 contains a fixed point on line P_1P_2.

20. State and prove the dual of Exercise 19.

6-4. Specialization of projective coordinates

Homogeneous cartesian point coordinates in the plane were defined in Section 4-4 as any three numbers x^1, x^2, x^3, where $x^3 \neq 0$, such that $x = x^1/x^3$ and $y = x^2/x^3$, where x and y are nonhomogeneous cartesian point coordinates. It will be seen that projective point and line coordinates (see Section 6-2) can be specialized to obtain cartesian point and line coordinates. This means that the ordinary metric geometry studied by cartesian methods is a particular case of projective geometry. Projective geometry is the study of invariants of configurations under the group of projective mappings. Euclidean geometry is the study of invariants under the particular kinds of projective mappings called rotations and translations. The latter constitute a subset of the group of projective mappings. The euclidean mappings can be shown to form a group which

is therefore a subgroup of the group of projectivities. Two modes of interpretation by specialization are possible. One may start with the projective plane and
single out one particular line as the ideal line and endow it with special properties
in order to obtain projective interpretations of metric geometry. Or one may
start with metric geometry and attempt to relate it to a more general situation
through the use of projective concepts. More details on the specialization of
projective mappings will be seen in the chapter on collineations. In this section,
some projective concepts are employed to obtain an enlarged view of metric
geometry.

In order to show that projective point coordinates can be specialized to
homogeneous cartesian coordinates, let one side of the triangle of reference be
the ideal line, let the other two sides become perpendicular to each other, and,

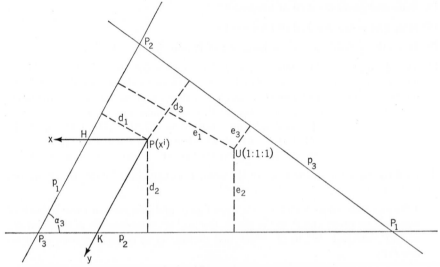

Figure 35

finally, let the units of measure for these two sides be the same. Recall that if x^i
are projective coordinates of a point P (Fig. 35), then

$$kx^i = \frac{d_i}{e_i}.$$

As the side p_3 takes the position of the ideal line (so-called line at infinity in the
euclidean plane), the ratio d_3/e_3 approaches unity, and $kx^1 = d_1/e_1$, $kx^2 = d_2/e_2$,
$kx^3 = 1$. Draw lines through P parallel to sides p_1 and p_2 and intersecting P_3P_1
and P_3P_2 at K and H, respectively. Note that $PH \sin \alpha_3 = d_1$ and $PK \sin \alpha_3 = d_2$,
so that

$$\frac{x^1}{x^3} = \frac{PH \sin \alpha_3}{e_1}, \quad \frac{x^2}{x^3} = \frac{PK \sin \alpha_3}{e_2}.$$

If *PH* and *PK* are denoted by x and y, if $\alpha_3 = \pi/2$, and, finally, if $e_1 = e_2 = 1$, it follows that

$$x = \frac{x^1}{x^3}, \quad y = \frac{x^2}{x^3},$$

which means that the x^i are now homogeneous cartesian point coordinates where $x^3 = 1$.

Homogeneous Line Coordinates

A similar procedure is now employed to show that projective line coordinates can be specialized to obtain homogeneous line coordinates which are related to nonhomogeneous line coordinates u, v by

$$u = \frac{u_1}{u_3}, \quad v = \frac{u_2}{u_3}.$$

Let one side p_3 of the triangle of reference be the ideal line, let the other two sides be perpendicular, let the units of measure relative to these two sides be

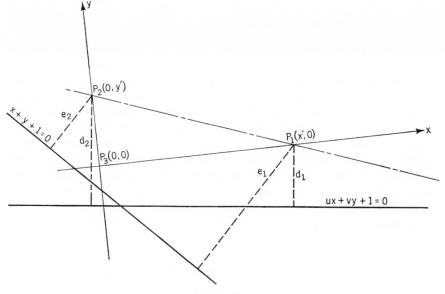

Figure 36

equal, and, finally, let the unit line have equation $x + y + 1 = 0$. From Fig. 36, it is observed that, by use of the formula for the distance from a line to a point,

$$e_1 = \frac{x' + 1}{\sqrt{2}}, \quad e_2 = \frac{y' + 1}{\sqrt{2}}, \quad e_3 = \frac{1}{\sqrt{2}},$$

and that the distances d_i from any line $ux + vy + 1 = 0$ to the vertices of the triangle of reference are given by

$$d_1 = \frac{ux' + 1}{\sqrt{u^2 + v^2}}, \quad d_2 = \frac{vy' + 1}{\sqrt{u^2 + v^2}}, \quad d_3 = \frac{1}{\sqrt{u^2 + v^2}}.$$

Note that

$$\lim_{x' \to \infty} \frac{u_1}{u_3} = \lim_{x' \to \infty} \frac{d_1/e_1}{d_3/e_3} = \lim_{x' \to \infty} \frac{ux' + 1}{x' + 1} = u.$$

In a similar way, $\lim_{y' \to \infty} (u_2/u_3) = v$. Hence, the u_i, with $u_3 \neq 0$, are specialized to the plückerian coordinates u, v.

The equation $ux + vy + 1 = 0$ of united position becomes $u_1 x^1 + u_2 x^2 + u_3 x^3 = 0$, or $u_i x^i = 0$, in homogeneous coordinates. The particular line with equation $x^3 = 0$, and line coordinates $[0, 0, 1]$, is actually not in the euclidean plane, but it may be used to afford an interpretation of certain metric results by means of projective concepts. Dually, the point with equation $u_3 = 0$ and point coordinates $(0, 0, 1)$ is the origin. Lines through the origin cannot be represented by use of the nonhomogeneous coordinates u, v, but all lines through the origin are represented by the coordinates $[u_1, u_2, 0]$. All points on the ideal line have coordinates of the form $(x^1, x^2, 0)$.

6-5. Ideal and imaginary elements

Several theorems will now be proved to depict the roles of the ideal line and complex numbers in analytical geometry. Some prefatory remarks are necessary. One considers the complex projective plane which is the set of all triples $(kx^1 : kx^2 : kx^3)$, with $k \neq 0$, and with x^i complex numbers. If the x^i are restricted to real numbers, the set of all real triples constitutes the real projective plane, which is a subspace of the complex projective plane. As has been seen, the real projective plane can be specialized to the euclidean plane. In the preceding development, and also in subsequent chapters, the projective transformations considered are those transformations of the complex projective plane which carry the real subplane into itself. One studies then the invariants (in the entire complex plane) under these transformations. Further, in the theorems to follow, one considers the points common to the curves in the complex plane whose intersections with the real euclidean plane are circles and other conics. The reader must realize, of course, that the complex projective plane is not to be confused with the complex plane used in the theory of functions of complex variables. Indeed, a point in the complex projective plane contains four real independent variables.

THEOREM 1: *All lines of a family of parallel lines have a point in common on the ideal line.*

Proof: Let the family of parallel lines have the equation $y = mx + b$, where m is a constant and b is a parameter. In homogeneous coordinates, the equation becomes $x_2 = mx_1 + bx_3$. The intersection of this line with the line $x_3 = 0$ is given by

$$\begin{bmatrix} m & -1 & b \\ 0 & 0 & 1 \end{bmatrix} \rightarrow (-1, -m, 0) \equiv (1, m, 0),$$

which is a single point on the ideal line.

THEOREM 2: *All circles in the plane contain the same two fixed complex points on the ideal line.*

Proof: Let the equation of all circles be $x^2 + y^2 + Ax + By + C = 0$, where A, B, C are parameters. In homogeneous coordinates, the equation becomes $(x^1)^2 + (x^2)^2 + Ax^1x^3 + Bx^2x^3 + C(x^3)^2 = 0$. Solve the latter equation with the ideal line $x^3 = 0$ to obtain $(x^1)^2 + (x^2)^2 = 0$, from which $x^2 = \pm ix^1$. Thus, the two points $(x^1, x^2, 0) \equiv (x^1, \pm ix^1, 0) \equiv (1, \pm i, 0)$ are obtained on the ideal line. These points, designated by $I(1, i, 0)$ and $J(1, -i, 0)$, are called the *circular points at infinity* because they lie on all circles in the plane.

DEFINITION: *The lines through a point $P(a^i)$ and the circular points are called the* isotropic lines *through P.*

The equations of the isotropic lines are

$$\begin{vmatrix} x^1 & x^2 & x^3 \\ a^1 & a^2 & a^3 \\ 1 & \pm i & 0 \end{vmatrix} = 0,$$

or

$$a^3(x^2 \pm ix^1) = (a^2 \pm ia^1)x^3.$$

In particular, the isotropic lines through the origin have the equations $x^2 = \pm ix^1$. Isotropic lines are also called *minimal lines*, for the following reason. Take two points $P_1(x_1, y_1)$ and $P_2(x_2, y_2)$ on an isotropic line $y = ix$ through the origin. If the pythagorean distance formula of the real euclidean plane is applied to the two complex points P_1 and P_2, one has

$$\sqrt{(x_1 - x_2)^2 + (y_1 - y_2)^2} = \sqrt{(x_1 - x_2)^2(1 + i^2)} = 0.$$

Similarly, the pythagorean measure of length between any two points on any isotropic line can be shown to be zero. Hence, the name *minimal lines* for isotropic lines.

THEOREM 3: *The isotropic lines through a point are fixed under a rotation about the point.*

Proof: For simplicity, choose the origin at the point, so that the isotropic lines through the point are $y = \pm ix$. Under the rotation

$$x = \bar{x} \cos \theta + \bar{y} \sin \theta,$$

$$y = -\bar{x} \sin \theta + \bar{y} \cos \theta,$$

the equations $y = \pm ix$ go into

$$-\bar{x} \sin \theta + \bar{y} \cos \theta = \pm i(\bar{x} \cos \theta + \bar{y} \sin \theta),$$

which can be solved for $\bar{y}$ to obtain

$$\bar{y} = \frac{\sin\theta \pm i\cos\theta}{\cos\theta \pm i\sin\theta}\bar{x} = \pm i\bar{x}.$$

This completes the proof.

THEOREM 4: *A real conic is (1) an ellipse, (2) a parabola, or (3) a hyperbola, if it has in common with the ideal line (1) two complex points, (2) two real and coincident points, or (3) two real and distinct points.*

Proof: Let the conic have the equation $ax^2 + 2hxy + by^2 + 2gx + 2fy + c = 0$. In homogeneous coordinates, this becomes

$$a(x^1)^2 + 2hx^1x^2 + b(x^2)^2 + 2gx^1x^3 + 2fx^2x^3 + c(x^3)^2 = 0,$$

which is known to represent an ellipse, parabola, or hyperbola according as $h^2 - ab < 0, = 0$, or > 0.

Solve the equation of the conic with the line $x^3 = 0$ to obtain

$$x^3 = 0, \quad a(x^1)^2 + 2hx^1x^2 + b(x^2)^2 = 0,$$

which represent two points on the line $x^3 = 0$. The equation $a(x^1)^2 + 2hx^1x^2 + b(x^2)^2 = 0$ alone represents two lines through the origin. If $h^2 - ab < 0$, the conic is an ellipse, the lines through the origin are complex, and the two points on the ideal line are complex. If $h^2 - ab = 0$, the conic is a parabola, and the points on the ideal line are real and coincident. Finally, if $h^2 - ab > 0$, the conic is a hyperbola, and the intersection points with the ideal line are real and distinct. This completes the proof.

THEOREM 5: *If a real noncomposite conic contains either one of the circular points, it contains the other also, and is a circle.*

Proof: If the point $I(1, i, 0)$ satisfies the equation

$$a(x^1)^2 + 2hx^1x^2 + b(x^2)^2 + 2gx^1x^3 + 2fx^2x^3 + c(x^3)^2 = 0$$

of the conic, then $(a - b) + 2hi = 0$, which implies that $a = b$ and $h = 0$. Hence, the conic is a circle which also contains $J(1, -i, 0)$.

Foci and Asymptotes

DEFINITION: *The* foci *of a curve are the intersections of the tangent lines to the curve from the circular points.*

A curve of class n has n tangents from a point. Hence, such a curve has n^2 foci. A conic, for instance, has four foci.

EXAMPLE 1

Find the foci of the ellipse $b^2x^2 + a^2y^2 = a^2b^2$.

Solution: It is readily shown that the tangent line to the ellipse at the point $(\bar{x}, \bar{y})$ is $b^2x\bar{x} + a^2y\bar{y} = a^2b^2$, or $b^2x^1\bar{x}^1 + a^2x^2\bar{x}^2 - a^2b^2x^3\bar{x}^3 = 0$ in homogeneous coordinates. Demand that this tangent line contain the point $I(1, i, 0)$ to find $b^2\bar{x}^1 + ia^2\bar{x}^2 = 0$. Solve the latter equation with $b^2(\bar{x}^1)^2 + a^2(\bar{x}^2)^2 - a^2b^2(\bar{x}^3)^2 = 0$, to find the coordinates of the points of tangency:

$$\bar{x}^1 : \bar{x}^2 : \bar{x}^3 = a^2 : ib^2 : \pm\sqrt{a^2 - b^2}.$$

Hence, the tangents from $I(1, i, 0)$ to the ellipse have the equations

$$x^2 = ix^1 \pm i\sqrt{a^2 - b^2}\, x^3,$$

and the tangents from $J(1, -i, 0)$ are $x^2 = -ix^1 \pm i\sqrt{a^2 - b^2}\, x^3$. The four equations of the tangents can be solved in pairs to obtain the four foci of the ellipse:

$$(\pm\sqrt{a^2 - b^2}, 0, 1), \quad (0, \pm i\sqrt{a^2 - b^2}, 1).$$

DEFINITION: *The tangent line to a curve at an intersection with the ideal line is called an* asymptote *to the curve.*

A curve of degree n intersects a line in n points. Hence, such a curve has n asymptotes.

EXAMPLE 2

Find the asymptotes of the hyperbola $b^2x^2 - a^2y^2 = a^2b^2$.

Solution: Write the equation in the form $\phi \equiv b^2(x^1)^2 - a^2(x^2)^2 - a^2b^2(x^3)^2 = 0$, and solve with the line $x^3 = 0$ to obtain the points $(x^1, \pm(b/a)x^1, 0) \equiv (a, \pm b, 0)$. Recall that the equation of the tangent line to $\phi(x^1, x^2, x^3) = 0$ at the point y^i is $x^i(\partial\phi/\partial y^i) = 0$, to have the tangent at $(a, b, 0)$ to the hyperbola in the form

$$a(2b^2x^1) + b(-2a^2x^2) + (0)(-2a^2b^2x^3) = 0,$$

or $bx^1 - ax^2 = 0$. Thus, the tangent lines at $(a, \pm b, 0)$ are $y = \pm(b/a)x$—the required asymptotes.

EXERCISES

1. Find the foci for the parabola $y^2 = 4px$ and for the hyperbola $b^2x^2 - a^2y^2 = a^2b^2$.
   Ans. $(p, 0, 1); (\pm\sqrt{a^2 + b^2}, 0, 1), (0, \pm i\sqrt{a^2 + b^2}, 1)$.

2. Show that (a) the asymptotes of the circle $x^2 + y^2 = a^2$ are the minimal lines through the center of the circle, (b) the asymptotes of the ellipse $b^2x^2 + a^2y^2 = a^2b^2$ are $y = \pm i(b/a)x$, and (c) the asymptotes of the parabola $y^2 = 4px$ are given by the ideal line counted twice.

3. A line intersects an algebraic curve of degree n in n points, some of which may have complex coordinates. Explain why only one solution is obtained when the equations $4x^2 - 9y^2 = 36$ and $2x + 3y = 4$ are solved for the intersections.

4. It is shown in books on algebra that, if complex numbers are admitted, a curve of degree m intersects a curve of degree n in mn points.* Explain why no more than two points are obtained when the equations of two circles are solved for the intersections.

---

* See, for instance, H. H. Hilton, *Plane Algebraic Curves* (Oxford, 1920), p. 10.

5. Deduce from Theorem 3 that the circular points are invariant under a rotation about a point in the plane. They are also fixed under a translation.

6. Find the points where the curve $2x^2 - xy - y^2 + x + y + 2 = 0$ intersects the ideal line, and thus identify the conic section.

7. Prove that two lines l and l' through a point P in the plane are perpendicular if and only if they separate the isotropic lines through P harmonically. Deduce that as the perpendicular lines l and l' revolve about P, they intersect the ideal line in points of an involution for which the circular points are the fixed points. Note that perpendicularity of two lines in the plane can therefore be defined projectively in terms of cross ratio.

8. Let ϕ_1 and ϕ_2 be the angles of inclination of two lines l_1 and l_2 to a fixed direction in the plane, and let $m_1 \equiv \tan \phi_1$ and $m_2 \equiv \tan \phi_2$ denote the slopes of l_1, l_2. Show that the cross ratio of m_1, m_2 and the parameters i, $-i$ for the isotropic lines—i.e. $(m_1, m_2, i, -i)$—can be expressed as

$$[\cos (\phi_1 - \phi_2) + i \sin (\phi_1 - \phi_2)]^2,$$

which, by the Euler formula $e^{i\theta} = \cos \theta + i \sin \theta$, can be written as $\exp [2i(\phi_1 - \phi_2)]$. Hence, conclude that the angle $\phi_1 - \phi_2$ between l_1 and l_2 can be expressed as

$$\phi_1 - \phi_2 = \frac{1}{2i} \log (m_1, m_2, i, -i).$$

(This is Laguerre's projective definition of angle.)

9. Deduce from the result in Exercise 8 that two perpendicular lines separate the isotropic lines through their intersection point harmonically.

10. Consider two isotropic lines l_1 and l_2 with the same "slope"; that is, say, $m_1 = m_2 = i$. Use the formula

$$\tan \theta = \frac{m_2 - m_1}{1 + m_1 m_2}$$

to conclude that θ is undefined. From $m_1 = m_2$ and $1 + m_1 m_2 = 0$, the conclusion could be drawn that l_1 and l_2 are both parallel and perpendicular! But it has already been agreed that l_1 and l_2 are parallel because they meet on the ideal line. Show that an isotropic line fails to make an angle with any finite line.*

11. Draw a line parallel to side PQ of a triangle PQR intersecting PR in A and QR in B; PB and AQ intersect in S. Show that RS meets PQ in the midpoint M of PQ. *Hint:* One vertex of a diagonal triangle is an ideal point of intersection of AB and PQ.

6-6. Models for the projective plane

In Section 1-3 models for the euclidean and projective lines were described. It was seen that a mapping can be established under which a complete circle has its points in one-to-one correspondence with the points of the projective line.

---

*See W. C. Graustein, *Introduction to Higher Geometry* (Macmillan, New York, 1930), p. 123.

This is described by saying that the circle is a *model* of the projective line. By deleting a point of the circle a model was obtained for the euclidean line. It is desired to find a model for the projective plane.

One such model arises from the following observation. The real projective plane was defined in Section 6-2 as the totality of ordered real number triples (x^1, x^2, x^3), with the provision that (kx^1, kx^2, kx^3) is equivalent to (x^1, x^2, x^3), where $k \neq 0$. Now regard the numbers x^i as the direction numbers of a line through the origin of a rectangular cartesian system of coordinates in three-space

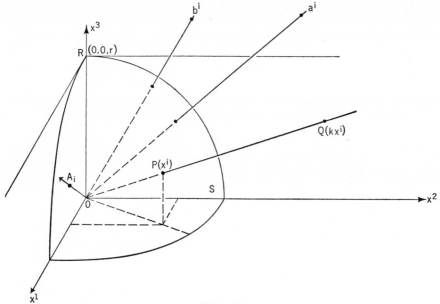

Figure 37

(Fig. 37). To every point $P(x^i)$ in the doubly infinite set of points in the projective plane there corresponds a unique line OP in the doubly infinite set of lines (called a *bundle* of lines) through the origin O. Note that the points O and $Q(kx^i)$ determine the same line as do O and $P(x^i)$. A bundle of lines through a point is therefore a model of the projective plane.

Two distinct points a^i and b^i in the projective plane π determine a line with line coordinates given by

(11) $\qquad \begin{pmatrix} a^1 & a^2 & a^3 \\ b^1 & b^2 & b^3 \end{pmatrix} \rightarrow [a^2b^3 - a^3b^2, a^3b^1 - a^1b^3, a^1b^2 - a^2b^1].$

The two corresponding lines through O in Fig. 37 determine a plane with an equation in the form

(12) $\qquad\qquad\qquad A_1x^1 + A_2x^2 + A_3x^3 = 0.$

The numbers A_i are direction numbers of the normal to the plane with equation (12). Because line A_i is orthogonal to both a^i and b^i, it follows that

(13) $$A_i a^i = 0, \quad A_i b^i = 0,$$

from which the numbers A_i are proportional to the line coordinates in (11). Thus, if lines through O correspond to points in the projective plane π, then planes through O correspond to lines in π. Linearly dependent points are on a line in π, and they correspond to linearly dependent lines in a plane in the bundle. The geometry of lines and planes in a bundle is completely equivalent to the geometry of the projective plane. Note that the condition for incidence of the line u_i and the point x^i in π, that is, $u_i x^i = 0$, means that the line x^i in the bundle is in a plane which is normal to the direction u_i. A point locus in π gives a line locus (conical surface) in the bundle, and a line envelope in π gives a conical surface which is the envelope of planes in the bundle.

A sphere of radius r and center at O (Fig. 37) may be used as a model for the projective plane. However, each line of the bundle in the foregoing model intersects the sphere in two points; in order to render the correspondence one-to-one between the points of the sphere and the points of the projective plane, it is necessary to identify diametrically opposite points on the sphere.

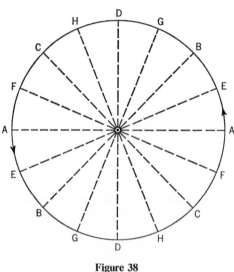

Figure 38

For a second type of model, consider the tangent plane to the sphere S at the point $R(0, 0, r)$ as the projective plane π, and take as the correspondent of point $P(x^i)$ in π the point P on the sphere S where the line OP intersects S. This mapping of π to S is rendered one-to-one by considering only the surface of the sphere above the plane x^1Ox^2. The point $R(0, 0, r)$ maps into itself, and the ideal line in π maps into the circle $x^3 = 0$, $(x^1)^2 + (x^2)^2 = r^2$. A line from O to a point on the ideal line in π should intersect the equator circle in the x^1x^2-plane in only one point. Hence, pairs of diametrically opposite points on this equator circle are identified as one point. Thus, the hemisphere, with opposite points on the equator identified, has its points in one-to-one correspondence with the points of the projective plane. Then, if all points on the half sphere are projected into the circle $x^3 = 0$, $(x^1)^2 + (x^2)^2 = r^2$ by lines parallel to the x^3-axis, the circular region (Fig. 38), with diametrically opposite points considered as coincident, is also a model for the projective plane. The circular model may be deformed, by a continuous one-to-one mapping, into a rectangular region (Fig. 39), with opposite points identified as indicated. The rectangular region with the pattern of matching boundary points as indicated in Fig. 38 is called the

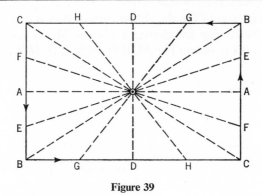

Figure 39

fundamental region for the projective plane. In order to see how this rectangular model of π can be folded into a closed surface, some examples of fundamental regions for simpler closed surfaces will be shown first.

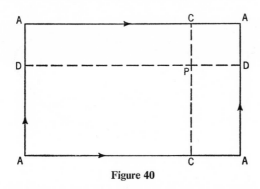

Figure 40

Consider the region in Fig. 40, with boundary points identified as shown. Let the two lines ACA be brought into coincidence to form a tube (Fig. 41),

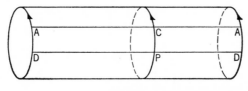

Figure 41

and think of the tube as elastic. Stretching is an acceptable topological mapping. Now bend the tube in order to bring the circular ends ADA into coincidence. The resulting closed surface is the torus (Fig. 42). Fig. 40 exhibits the fundamental region for the torus in Fig. 42.

The fundamental region for the closed surface that is called a Klein bottle can be obtained by making one change in Fig. 40. Merely reverse the direction of the right side ADA to obtain Fig. 43. If the right side ADA is twisted through

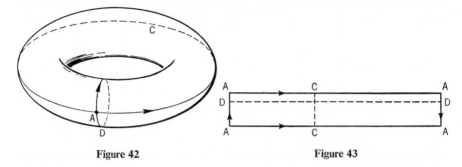

Figure 42   Figure 43

an angle of 180° and then brought into coincidence with the left side ADA, the resulting surface is the Möbius band, shown in Fig. 44. From this figure it can

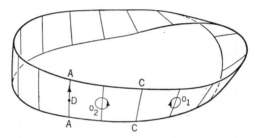

Figure 44

be seen that the Möbius band is not only one-sided (unilateral) but also non-orientable. To realize this, take a small circle with center at O_1 to the right of

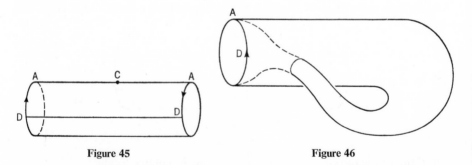

Figure 45   Figure 46

line CC. Orient the circle as indicated by the arrow. Now move the circle to the right around the strip without crossing the boundary of the surface. When the small circular indicatrix comes around to the position to the left of CC, the direction arrow is reversed. Thus, the Möbius band is nonorientable. The fact that the center O_1 moves from a position which appears to be on the side of the observer to a position O_2 on the apparent opposite side from the observer, means that the surface has only one side.

One way to close the Möbius band is to bring the sides *ACA* (Fig. 43) into coincidence to form a tube as shown in Fig. 45. Next it is desired to bring the circular ends *ADA* into coincidence. This cannot be done in the manner used for the torus in Fig. 42, because the orientation must be preserved. Instead,

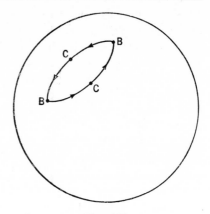

Figure 47

bend the tube but carry the circular right end through the surface of the tube so that as it approaches the circular left end the two circles will have the same orientation. The resulting closed surface (Fig. 46) is called a Klein bottle. A suitable cut along the surface of the Klein bottle renders it into a Möbius band.

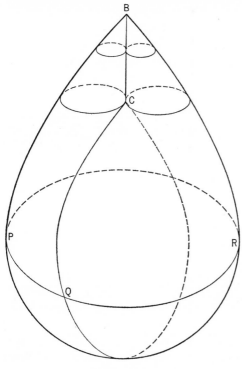

Figure 48

The Klein bottle is a closed surface (no boundary) which is unilateral.

Finally, a closed surface topologically equivalent to the projective plane will be achieved. It is desired to fold the fundamental region in Fig. 39 (or equivalently that in Fig. 38) into a closed surface. Whereas the four points marked *A* in Fig. 40 go into a single point on the torus (Fig. 42), the points indicated by *B* and *C* in Fig. 39 go into two distinct points on the closed surface. First deform the region into a sphere (Fig. 47), with a quadrangular hole having as boundary the edge *BCBCB* of the region in Fig. 39. As *B* is drawn toward *B*, one segment *BC* must be passed through the surface in order to coincide with and have the same orientation as the other segment *BC*. As *C* is drawn into coincidence with *C*, the resulting surface has the appearance of Fig. 48. It is a closed surface which intersects itself along the line segment BC. The part of the surface below the curve PQR may be visualized as a hemisphere. The part above the curve PQR is called a *cross cap*. Thus, a cross cap closed by a hemisphere is topologically equivalent to the projective plane. The same closed surface can be attained by closing the Möbius band by a surface through the boundary.

It should be noted that the region inside a square, with no points on the boundary identified, is a fundamental region for the euclidean plane, whereas the square region with boundary points identified as in Fig. 39 is a fundamental region for the projective plane.

It was mentioned that the Möbius band is nonorientable. The projective plane is also nonorientable. It will be indicated next that a projective space is orientable if the dimensionality of the space is odd and nonorientable if it is even. For instance, the projective line is orientable, but the projective plane is not orientable. On the line the point with coordinates $x_1:x_2$ may be said to be positively or negatively directed from the point $y_1:y_2$ according as the determinant

$$\begin{vmatrix} x_1 & x_2 \\ y_1 & y_2 \end{vmatrix}$$

is positive or negative. The sign of the determinant is not affected by using the coordinates $kx_1:kx_2$ and $ky_1:ky_2$, even if k is negative. Orientation of the euclidean plane may be defined as positive or negative according as the determinant

$$\begin{vmatrix} x_1 & x_2 & 1 \\ y_1 & y_2 & 1 \\ z_1 & z_2 & 1 \end{vmatrix}$$

is positive or negative, where x_1, x_2; y_1, y_2; z_1, z_2 are cartesian coordinates of any three noncollinear points in the plane. An attempt to extend this to the projective plane fails because the determinant

$$\begin{vmatrix} x_1 & x_2 & x_3 \\ y_1 & y_2 & y_3 \\ z_1 & z_2 & z_3 \end{vmatrix},$$

being of odd order, changes sign when the coordinates x_i, y_i, z_i are replaced by kx_i, ky_i, kz_i, with k negative. Extension of the argument to projective spaces of higher dimension is immediate.

Another way to realize the nonorientability of the projective plane is the following. Consider the number of regions (Fig. 49) into which three linearly independent lines divide the plane. If the plane is euclidean, there are seven regions. If the plane is a projective space, and therefore closed, there are only four regions, because 6 and 7 identify a single region, as do also 2 and 3 and 4 and 5. After the three lines are oriented arbitrarily, the induced orientation indicated by the arrow in the region marked 7 does not apply to the other part

(6) of the same region. Hence, the projective plane is nonorientable. In euclidean three-space, four linearly independent planes determine fifteen regions, but this number is reduced to eight for projective three-space. It can be shown that an assigned orientation for four linearly independent points induces a consistent orientation for each of the eight regions of projective three-space.

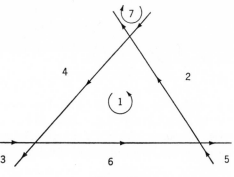

Figure 49

6-7. The infinitesimal projective mapping*

Let the nine coefficients a^i_j in the projective mapping given by equations (6) in Section 5-1,

$$(14) \qquad k\bar{x}^i = a^i_j x^j,$$

be continuous functions of a parameter t. Corresponding to $t = t_0$, one has a particular mapping T_0, but as t varies from t_0, one obtains a variation $T(t)$ of the mapping T_0. By letting $t - t_0$ be sufficiently small, a mapping $T(t)$ can be attained which is as near as one pleases to the mapping T_0. In particular, let T_0 be the identity mapping for which the matrix (a^i_j) is (δ^i_j). Then one can choose for $T(t)$ a mapping by which any point x^i in (14) is arbitrarily near the point $\bar{x}^i$. To do this, let δt be an infinitesimal, and choose for the matrix (a^i_j) the form

$$(15) \qquad (a^i_j) \equiv (\delta^i_j + \alpha^i_j \delta t),$$

in which the α^i_j are constants. Note that if the variable δt takes on its limiting value zero in equations (15), then equations (14) represent the identity mapping. The infinitesimal projective mapping is then of the form

$$(16) \qquad \bar{x}^i = (\delta^i_j + \alpha^i_j \delta t)x^j = x^i + \alpha^i_j x^j \delta t,$$

in which the k of equations (14) is taken as unity for simplicity. Write $\delta x^i = \bar{x}^i - x^i$ to obtain, from (16),

$$(17) \qquad \delta x^i = \alpha^i_j x^j \delta t.$$

Repeated application of the mapping (17) carries the point x^i to a position $\bar{x}^i$, and another application gives

$$\delta \bar{x}^i = \alpha^i_j \bar{x}^j \delta t,$$

in which the $\bar{x}^i$ are functions of t which satisfy the system of linear differential equations

---

* The reader may find it interesting to compare the development of this section with that of Sophus Lie, *Vorlesungen über Continuierliche Gruppen* (Leipzig, 1893), p. 22.

(18)
$$\frac{d\bar{x}^i}{dt} = \alpha^i_j \bar{x}^j.$$

Note that the $\bar{x}^i$ in (18) reduce to x^i when $t = 0$. Hence, the solutions of (18) are of the form

(19)
$$\bar{x}^i = \bar{x}^i(x^1, x^2, x^3; t),$$

for which $\bar{x}^i(x^1, x^2, x^3; 0) = x^i$. This means that the value of the parameter t for the identity mapping is zero. The solutions (19) of equations (18) may be styled the *path curves* of the infinitesimal projective mapping. A general solution for equations (18) can be obtained as follows. Recall that the solution of the differential equation $d\bar{y} = h\bar{y}dt$ is $\bar{y} = ce^{th}$, where c is an arbitrary constant. Suppose $\bar{y} = y$ when $t = 0$. Then $\bar{y} = e^{th}y$.

Now denote the matrix (α^i_j) in (18) by A, the one-row matrix $(\bar{x}^1, \bar{x}^2, \bar{x}^3)$ by $\bar{X}$, and the one-column matrix (x^1, x^2, x^3) by X; that is,

$$A \equiv (\alpha^i_j), \quad \bar{X} \equiv (\bar{x}^1, \bar{x}^2, \bar{x}^3), \quad X \equiv \begin{pmatrix} x^1 \\ x^2 \\ x^3 \end{pmatrix}.$$

With this notation, equation (18) takes the form

(20)
$$d\bar{X} = A\bar{X}\,dt,$$

where $\bar{X} = X$ at $t = 0$. It can be shown that the solution $\bar{y} = e^{th}y$ shown above for $d\bar{y} = h\bar{y}dt$ also holds when the matrix elements in (20) are involved. That is, the solution for (20) has the form

(21)
$$\bar{X} = e^{tA}X.$$

Because

$$e^{t\theta} = 1 + (t\theta) + \frac{(t\theta)^2}{2!} + \frac{(t\theta)^3}{3!} + \cdots = 1 + \sum_{j=1}^{\infty} \frac{(t\theta)^j}{j!},$$

the matrix expression e^{tA} in (21) has the meaning

$$e^{tA} = I + \sum_{j=1}^{\infty} \frac{(tA)^j}{j!},$$

where I is the identity matrix. With this notation, the solution (21) has the form

(22)
$$\bar{X} = e^{tA}X = IX + \sum_{j=1}^{\infty} \frac{(tA)^j}{j!}X,$$

which exhibits the path curves for all infinitesimal projectivities of the form of (17).

There are actually only seven parameters in (17). One of the nine quantities α^i_j can be absorbed in the proportionality factor for the point coordinates, and another can be divided through each of the equations and absorbed with the δt. Some particular choices for the matrix A are suggested in the Exercises. In order to show how to use equations (22), another choice of A is used in the

EXAMPLE

Find from (22) the equations of the path curves for the particular infinitesimal mapping (17) for which the matrix A has the form

$$A \equiv (\alpha_i^j) = \begin{pmatrix} 0 & 1 & 0 \\ -1 & 0 & 0 \\ 0 & 0 & 0 \end{pmatrix}.$$

First solution: Calculate first several powers of A which are needed in the series (22). One obtains

$$A^2 \equiv AA = \begin{pmatrix} -1 & 0 & 0 \\ 0 & -1 & 0 \\ 0 & 0 & 0 \end{pmatrix}, \quad A^3 = -A, \quad A^4 = -A^2, \quad A^5 = A.$$

Hence, from (22),

$$\overline{X} = X + t\begin{pmatrix} 0 & 1 & 0 \\ -1 & 0 & 0 \\ 0 & 0 & 0 \end{pmatrix}\begin{pmatrix} x^1 \\ x^2 \\ x^3 \end{pmatrix} + \frac{t^2}{2!}\begin{pmatrix} -1 & 0 & 0 \\ 0 & -1 & 0 \\ 0 & 0 & 0 \end{pmatrix}\begin{pmatrix} x^1 \\ x^2 \\ x^3 \end{pmatrix}$$

$$+ \frac{t^3}{3!}\begin{pmatrix} 0 & -1 & 0 \\ 1 & 0 & 0 \\ 0 & 0 & 0 \end{pmatrix}\begin{pmatrix} x^1 \\ x^2 \\ x^3 \end{pmatrix} + \cdots,$$

from which

$$\bar{x}^1 = x^1 + t(x^2) + \frac{t^2}{2!}(-x^1) + \frac{t^3}{3!}(-x^2) + \frac{t^4}{4!}(x^1) + \frac{t^5}{5!}(x^2) + \cdots,$$

$$\bar{x}^2 = x^2 + t(-x^1) + \frac{t^2}{2!}(-x^2) + \frac{t^3}{3!}(x^1) + \frac{t^4}{4!}(x^2) + \frac{t^5}{5!}(-x^1) + \cdots,$$

$$\bar{x}^3 = x^3.$$

Now change the notation to the nonhomogeneous form $x, y, \bar{x}, \bar{y}$ to have from the last three equations the solution

(23)
$$\bar{x} = x\left(1 - \frac{t^2}{2!} + \frac{t^4}{4!} - \cdots\right) + y\left(t - \frac{t^3}{3!} + \frac{t^5}{5!} - \cdots\right) = x\cos t + y\sin t,$$

$$\bar{y} = -x\sin t + y\cos t.$$

Square and add the equations in (23) to obtain $\bar{x}^2 + \bar{y}^2 = x^2 + y^2$, which shows that the path curves for this example are circles. Any point distant r from the origin maps into another point on the circle $x^2 + y^2 = r^2$ under (17). Repeated application of (17) moves the point successively along the circle.

Second solution: Observe that for this particular case the equations (18) may be integrated directly. They are

$$\frac{d\bar{x}^1}{\bar{x}^2} = \frac{d\bar{x}^2}{-\bar{x}^1} = \frac{d\bar{x}^3}{0} = dt,$$

which have the solutions

$$(\bar{x}^1)^2 + (\bar{x}^2)^2 = \text{constant}, \quad \bar{x}^3 = \text{constant}.$$

At $t = 0$, one has $\bar{x}^1 = x^1$, $\bar{x}^2 = x^2$, $\bar{x}^3 = x^3$. Hence,

$$(\bar{x}^1)^2 + (\bar{x}^2)^2 = (x^1)^2 + (x^2)^2, \quad \bar{x}^3 = x^3.$$

Thus, the mapping of this example is a rotation about the origin.

Hamilton-Cayley Theorem

The labor involved in calculating powers of the matrix A in the series (22) is reduced by making use of the Hamilton-Cayley theorem in algebra, according to which every square matrix satisfies its characteristic equation. Although the theorem holds for an $n \times n$ matrix, it will be explained here for the case $n = 3$. The equation $|a_j^i - \delta_j^i \lambda| = 0$ is the *characteristic* equation of the matrix (a_j^i). In expanded form it can be written as

$$f(\lambda) \equiv -\lambda^3 + a_i^i \lambda^2 - A_i^i \lambda + a = 0$$

(see equation 7-59), where a_i^i is the sum of the elements on the principal diagonal of the matrix (a_j^i), A_i^i is the sum of the cofactors of a_i^i, with $i = 1, 2, 3$, and $a \equiv |a_j^i|$. If $A \equiv (a_j^i)$, the Hamilton-Cayley theorem states that

$$f(A) \equiv -A^3 + a_i^i A^2 - A_i^i A + aI = 0,$$

where, of course, the symbol 0 means the zero matrix, and I is the unit matrix. It follows that

$$A^3 = a_i^i A^2 - A_i^i A + aI,$$

from which

$$A^4 = a_i^i A^3 - A_i^i A^2 + aA,$$

and, more generally,

(24) $$A^{3+k} = a_i^i A^{2+k} - A_i^i A^{1+k} + aA^k.$$

It should be noticed here that the one-parameter group of mappings $\bar{x}^i = \bar{x}^i(x^1, x^2, x^3; t)$, where $i = 1, 2, 3$, obtained as solutions of (18), is a particular case of the more general r-parameter set of continuous transformations given by

$$\bar{x}^i = \bar{x}^i(x^1, x^2, \cdots, x^n; t_1, t_2, \cdots, t_r).$$

This set constitutes an r-parameter group of continuous mappings if a set of values of $t_1, \cdots, t_r$ exists for which $\bar{x}^i = x^i$, and if, for every mapping of the set, values $t_1', \cdots, t_r'$ exist for which the inverse

$$x^i = x^i(\bar{x}^1, \bar{x}^2, \cdots, \bar{x}^n; t_1', t_2', \cdots, t_r')$$

is in the set.*

EXERCISES

1. Use the method employed in the Example (first solution) to find the path curves for the infinitesimal mapping for which the matrix A in (17) is

$$A \equiv \begin{pmatrix} 0 & 0 & 1 \\ 0 & 0 & 0 \\ 0 & 0 & 0 \end{pmatrix}.$$

---

* Further information on the general theory of r-parameter groups of continuous transformations can be found in Chapter 7 of T. Y. Thomas, *The Differential Invariants of Generalized Spaces* (Cambridge, 1934).

Show that these curves may be interpreted as lines parallel to the *x*-axis. Check the result by integrating equations (18) directly (second solution).

2. Repeat Exercise 1 with

$$A \equiv \begin{pmatrix} r & 0 & 0 \\ 0 & r & 0 \\ 0 & 0 & r-1 \end{pmatrix}.$$

Show that the path curves may be written as $\bar{x} = xe^t$, $\bar{y} = ye^t$, which define a similarity transformation.

3. Calculate A^3, A^4, A^5 in the Example by use of the Hamilton-Cayley theorem.

4. If the $x^i(t)$ satisfy $a_i x^i = 0$ identically in t, show that $e_{ijk} x^i x^{i\prime} x^{k\prime\prime} = 0$ is a differential equation which represents all lines in a plane.

5. Show that the differential equation in Exercise 4 is invariant under the projectivity (14); that is, show that $e_{ijk} \bar{x}^i \bar{x}^{i\prime} \bar{x}^{k\prime\prime}$ is zero if $e_{ijk} x^i x^{i\prime} x^{k\prime\prime}$ is zero. (The differential equation in Exercise 4 is said to *admit* the projective transformation (14).)

CHAPTER 7

Collineations and Correlations in the Plane

7-1. Mapping between two planes

Consider two distinct planes π and $\bar{\pi}$ with projective point coordinates x^i in π and $\bar{x}^i$ in $\bar{\pi}$. A *collineation* between π and $\bar{\pi}$ is a one-to-one correspondence between points of π and $\bar{\pi}$ defined by the nonsingular projective mapping

$$(1) \qquad \rho\bar{x}^i = a_j^i x^j, \qquad\qquad i, j = 1, 2, 3,$$

which has the inverse

$$(2) \qquad \sigma x^i = A_j^i \bar{x}^j,$$

as was seen in Section 5-1.

It will be shown next that any line in π maps into a line in $\bar{\pi}$ under (1). That is, collinear points in π map into collinear points in $\bar{\pi}$, which reveals the appropriateness of the term *collineation*. Any line in π with projective coordinates u_i has the equation

$$(3) \qquad u_i x^i = 0,$$

and any line in $\bar{\pi}$ with coordinates $\bar{u}_i$ has the equation $\bar{u}_i \bar{x}^i = 0$. By use of (2), equation (3) becomes $u_i A_j^i \bar{x}^j = 0$, which is the equation of a line in $\bar{\pi}$. If this line is $\bar{u}_j \bar{x}^j = 0$, it follows that

$$(4) \qquad k\bar{u}_j = A_j^i u_i$$

or, by a change of indices,

$$(5) \qquad k\bar{u}_i = A_i^j u_j.$$

To find the inverse of (5), multiply by a_k^i to obtain

$$(6) \qquad ka_k^i \bar{u}_i = a_k^i A_i^j u_j = a\delta_k^j u_j = au_k,$$

or

$$(7) \qquad ru_k = a_k^i \bar{u}_i,$$

where $r = a/k$. A change of dummy indices in (7) yields

(8) $$ru_i = a_i^j \bar{u}_j,$$

which should be compared with (5). Equations (5) and (8) exhibit the mapping from π to $\bar{\pi}$, and its inverse, in the dual variables u_i and $\bar{u}_i$. Observe that lines through a point in π map into lines through a point in $\bar{\pi}$. For convenience of reference, the equations of a collineation in point and line coordinates together with their inverses are exhibited:

(9)

	Point Coordinates	Inverse
	$\rho \bar{x}^i = a_j^i x^j$	$\sigma x^i = A_j^i \bar{x}^j$
	Line Coordinates	Inverse
	$k \bar{u}_i = A_i^j u_j$	$r u_i = a_i^j \bar{u}_j$

If the structure of the equations in (9) is realized, it is a relatively simple matter to write the inverse of a given collineation, or to find the dual form of the collineation—that is, to go from point to line coordinates or from line to point coordinates. Note that multiplication of the equations in point and line coordinates in (9) gives

$$k \rho \bar{u}_i \bar{x}^i = A_i^j u_j a_k^i x^k = a \delta_k^j u_j x^k = a u_k x^k$$

or

(10) $$\frac{k\rho}{a} \bar{u}_i \bar{x}^i = u_i x^i,$$

which exhibits the invariance of the form $u_i x^i$ under the mapping from π to $\bar{\pi}$.

EXAMPLE

Write (a) the inverse, and (b) the line coordinate form of the collineation

$$\rho \bar{x}^1 = 3x^1 - 2x^2 + x^3,$$
$$\rho \bar{x}^2 = -x^1 + 10x^2 - x^3,$$
$$\rho \bar{x}^3 = x^1 - 2x^2 + 3x^3.$$

Solution: (a) On comparing the collineation with equations (1), it is seen that

$$(a_j^i) \equiv \begin{pmatrix} 3 & -2 & 1 \\ -1 & 10 & -1 \\ 1 & -2 & 3 \end{pmatrix}.$$

If each element in this matrix is replaced by its cofactor, and the resulting matrix is transposed (rows and columns interchanged) the result is the *adjoint* matrix

$$(A_j^i) \equiv \begin{pmatrix} 28 & 4 & -8 \\ 2 & 8 & 2 \\ -8 & 4 & 28 \end{pmatrix}.$$

Hence, the inverse of the given collineation is

$$\sigma x^1 = 28\bar{x}^1 + 4\bar{x}^2 - 8\bar{x}^3,$$
$$\sigma x^2 = 2\bar{x}^1 + 8\bar{x}^2 + 2\bar{x}^3,$$
$$\sigma x^3 = -8\bar{x}^1 + 4\bar{x}^2 + 28\bar{x}^3.$$

(b) The *contragredient* matrix (A^i_j) in equations (5) is the transpose of the adjoint matrix. Hence, the collineation in line coordinates is

$$k\bar{u}_1 = 28u_1 + 2u_2 - 8u_3,$$

$$k\bar{u}_2 = 4u_1 + 8u_2 + 4u_3,$$

$$k\bar{u}_3 = -8u_1 + 2u_2 + 28u_3.$$

Note: It is permissible to divide *all three* of the equations by 2 to gain simplification.

The matrix (a^i_j) in equations (1) contains nine parameters. However, because of the arbitrariness of the proportionality factor ρ, all three of equations (1) can be divided by any one of the nonzero elements of the matrix (a^i_j). This means that eight essential parameters appear in equations (1). These equations describe an eight-parameter group of collineations. A unique collineation is determined by demanding that four assigned points in π (no three collinear) map into four assigned points in $\bar{\pi}$ (no three collinear). The technique for determining the collineation by assigning four pairs of corresponding points was illustrated in Section 5-2.

It will be shown next that if the reference triangle and the unit point in π correspond respectively to the reference triangle and unit point in $\bar{\pi}$, then every point P in π and its correspondent $\bar{P}$ in $\bar{\pi}$ have the same (proportional) coordinates. In order to do this, write out the equations (1) and demand first that the point $(1:0:0)$ in π map into the point $(1:0:0)$ in $\bar{\pi}$. This gives

$$\rho = a^1_1,$$

$$0 = a^2_1,$$

$$0 = a^3_1,$$

which determines $a^2_1 = a^3_1 = 0$. Similarly, if $(0:1:0)$ in π goes into $(0:1:0)$ in $\bar{\pi}$, then $a^1_2 = a^3_2 = 0$, and if $(0:0:1)$ in π corresponds to $(0:0:1)$ in $\bar{\pi}$, then $a^1_3 = a^2_3 = 0$. The collineation now has the form

$$\rho\bar{x}^1 = a^1_1 x^1,$$

$$\rho\bar{x}^2 = a^2_2 x^2,$$

$$\rho\bar{x}^3 = a^3_3 x^3.$$

Finally, on requiring that the unit point $(1:1:1)$ in π map into the unit point $(1:1:1)$ in $\bar{\pi}$, it follows that

$$\rho = a^1_1, \quad \rho = a^2_2, \quad \rho = a^3_3,$$

so that $a^1_1 = a^2_2 = a^3_3$. Hence, the collineation becomes

$$k\bar{x}^i = x^i,$$

by which all pairs of corresponding points have the same coordinates.

7-2. Collineation of a plane into itself. Fixed points

For the following discussion, let planes π and $\bar{\pi}$ coincide. Equations (1) may be interpreted according to either the alias or the alibi aspect. That is, under the alias aspect, the points P in π and $\bar{P}$ in $\bar{\pi}$ are the same but their respective coordinates x^i and $\bar{x}^i$ are referred to two different reference triangles. In this case, equations (1) describe a transformation of coordinates in the projective plane. Under the alibi aspect, there is a single reference triangle, and equations (1) determine the point $\bar{x}^i$ into which the point x^i is mapped. A collineation in the plane is identified with the alibi aspect. The identity mapping is described by the special collineation $\rho\bar{x}^i = x^i$, by which all points remain fixed.

It is of interest to determine the points, if any, which remain fixed under any collineation which is not the identity mapping. If $P(x^i)$ is fixed under the mapping (1), then $k\bar{x}^i = x^i$ for this point. This requirement on equations (1) gives

$$(11) \qquad \lambda x^i = a_j^i x^j,$$

where $\lambda = \rho/k$. Equations (11) may be written as

$$(12) \qquad (a_j^i - \lambda\delta_j^i)x^j = 0, \qquad\qquad i, j = 1, 2, 3,$$

which are of the form of equations (15) in Section 2-7. If the index j is summed and i takes on its three values, the three homogeneous equations (12) can be written in the form

$$(12') \qquad \begin{aligned} (a_1^1 - \lambda)x^1 + a_2^1 x^2 + a_3^1 x^3 &= 0, \\ a_1^2 x^1 + (a_2^2 - \lambda)x^2 + a_3^2 x^3 &= 0, \\ a_1^3 x^1 + a_2^3 x^2 + (a_3^3 - \lambda)x^3 &= 0. \end{aligned}$$

The equations (12′) have a nontrivial solution if and only if

$$(13) \qquad |a_j^i - \lambda\delta_j^i| = 0,$$

that is,

$$(13') \qquad f(\lambda) \equiv \begin{vmatrix} a_1^1 - \lambda & a_2^1 & a_3^1 \\ a_1^2 & a_2^2 - \lambda & a_3^2 \\ a_1^3 & a_2^3 & a_3^3 - \lambda \end{vmatrix} = 0.$$

Because equation (13′) is a cubic in λ, there are, in general, three fixed points (and consequently three fixed lines) under the collineation (1).

At least one fixed point (and therefore one fixed line) must be real. If two of the roots of (13′) are complex, the corresponding fixed points determine a real fixed line. Points with complex homogeneous coordinates are added to the real projective plane to obtain the complex projective plane. It must be realized, however, that because the real projective plane is the principal object of study here, the geometrical description of homogeneous coordinates in Section 5-3 applied only to the real points of the plane.

Let λ_1, λ_2, λ_3 denote the roots of (13'). Substitute λ_1 for λ in any two of equations (12') which can be solved for the ratios $x^1 : x^2 : x^3$, to have the coordinates of one fixed point P_1. Similarly, by substituting λ_2 and λ_3 successively into (12'), two additional fixed points P_2 and P_3 are obtained. Thus, if the roots of (13') are distinct, three distinct fixed points are to be expected. However, a variety of situations may arise, according to the nature of the roots and the rank of the matrix $(a_j^i - \lambda \delta_j^i)$ in equations (12'). For instance, suppose that for $\lambda = \lambda_1$, the rank of $(a_j^i - \lambda \delta_j^i)$ is 1, which means that all three equations in (12') reduce to a single equation which represents a *line* of fixed points. A line which is determined by two fixed points is a fixed line, but under a general projectivity only the two fixed points which determine the fixed line remain fixed. Note then that one must distinguish between a *fixed line* which is determined by two fixed points, and a *line of fixed points* for which every point of the line is a fixed point. From (13') it is seen that zero is a root of the characteristic equation $f(\lambda) = 0$ if and only if the collineation is singular.

In order to prepare for a general classification of collineations in the next section, a proof will now be given for the

THEOREM: *If m is the multiplicity of a root λ_k of $f(\lambda) = 0$—equation (13')— and if r denotes the rank of the corresponding matrix $(a_j^i - \lambda_k \delta_j^i)$ of the coefficients in* (12') *then* $3 - m \leq r < 3$.

Proof: First, it is clear that $r < 3$ because λ_k is a root of $f(\lambda) = 0$, which means that the determinant of the matrix $(a_j^i - \lambda_k \delta_j^i)$ is zero. It will be shown that only the following cases arise.

$$1^\circ: \quad m = 1, r = 2,$$

$$2^\circ: \quad m = 2, r = 2, \text{ or } r = 1,$$

$$3^\circ: \quad m = 3, r = 2, \text{ or } r = 1, \text{ or } r = 0.$$

Case 1°. Suppose for $m = 1$ that $r < 2$. A contradiction is achieved as follows. If $r < 2$, then all second-order minors of the determinant in (13') are zero. The derivative $f'(\lambda)$ is found from (13') by differentiating one column at a time and adding the resulting three determinants to obtain

(14)

$$f'(\lambda) \equiv \frac{df(\lambda)}{d\lambda} = -\begin{vmatrix} a_2^2 - \lambda & a_3^2 \\ a_2^3 & a_3^3 - \lambda \end{vmatrix} - \begin{vmatrix} a_1^1 - \lambda & a_3^1 \\ a_1^3 & a_3^3 - \lambda \end{vmatrix} - \begin{vmatrix} a_1^1 - \lambda & a_2^1 \\ a_1^2 & a_2^2 - \lambda \end{vmatrix}.$$

For $\lambda = \lambda_k$, the hypothesis that $r < 2$ requires that $f'(\lambda_k) = 0$, which means (by a theorem from the calculus) that λ_k is at least a double root of $f(\lambda) = 0$. Thus, $m \geq 2$, which contradicts the hypothesis that $m = 1$. Hence, r cannot be less than 2.

Case 2°. Suppose for $m = 2$ that $r = 0$. This means that, for $\lambda = \lambda_k$, all elements of the determinant in (13') vanish. But

$$f''(\lambda) = 2(a_1^1 - \lambda + a_2^2 - \lambda + a_3^3 - \lambda),$$

so that $f''(\lambda_k) = 0$, with the consequence that λ_k is a *triple* root of $f(\lambda) = 0$. Hence, m must be 3, which contradicts the assumption that $m = 2$. Therefore, r is 1 or 2.

Case 3°. If $m = 3$, then $r \geq 0$, but $r < 3$ so that r may be 2, or 1, or 0. This completes the proof.

It will be demonstrated next that the fixed points P_1 and P_2 corresponding to *distinct* roots λ_1 and λ_2 of $f(\lambda) = 0$ cannot coincide. In order to see this, assume that P_1 and P_2 do coincide. That is, if x_1^i and x_2^i are the respective co-ordinates of P_1 and P_2, let $x_2^i = kx_1^i$, where $k \neq 0$. Because the coordinates x_1^i are solutions of equations (12′) for $\lambda = \lambda_1$ and x_2^i are solutions for $\lambda = \lambda_2$, it follows from the first of (12′) that

(15)
$$(a_1^1 - \lambda_1)x_1^1 + a_2^1 x_1^2 + a_3^1 x_1^3 = 0,$$
$$(a_1^1 - \lambda_2)x_2^1 + a_2^1 x_2^2 + a_3^1 x_2^3 = 0.$$

Now replace x_2^i by kx_1^i in the second equation of (15), and subtract one equation from the other to find $(\lambda_1 - \lambda_2)x_1^1 = 0$, which requires that $x_1^1 = 0$, since $\lambda_1 \neq \lambda_2$. In a similar manner, use of the second and third equations in (12′) leads, in turn, to $x_1^2 = 0$ and $x_1^3 = 0$. Thus, a contradiction arises because there is no point with coordinates $(0:0:0)$. Hence, the fixed points P_1 and P_2 are distinct.

A similar procedure will be used next to show that if $\lambda_1, \lambda_2, \lambda_3$ are three distinct roots of $f(\lambda) = 0$, then the corresponding points P_1, P_2, P_3 cannot be collinear. In order to show this, a contradiction will be arrived at on the assumption that P_i are collinear. Assume then that

(16) $\qquad\qquad\qquad x_3^i = hx_1^i + kx_2^i,$ $\qquad\qquad\qquad hk \neq 0.$

In addition to equations (15), one has for point P_3

$$(a_1^1 - \lambda_3)x_3^1 + a_2^1 x_3^2 + a_3^1 x_3^3 = 0,$$

which, by (16), can be written as

(17) $\qquad (a_1^1 - \lambda_3)(hx_1^1 + kx_2^1) + a_2^1(hx_1^2 + kx_2^2) + a_3^1(hx_1^3 + kx_2^3) = 0.$

Multiply the first equation of (15) by h, the second by k, and subtract the sum of the resulting equations from (17) to obtain the first of the equations

(18) $\qquad\qquad\qquad h(\lambda_1 - \lambda_3)x_1^i = k(\lambda_3 - \lambda_2)x_2^i.$

The second and third equations in (18) are obtained in a similar manner by use of the second and third equations in (12′). Because the coefficients of x_1^i and x_2^i in (18) do not vanish, these equations imply that P_1 and P_2 have proportional coordinates, and that therefore P_1 and P_2 coincide. But P_1 and P_2 are distinct. Hence, the three fixed points P_i corresponding to distinct values λ_i must form a triangle.

EXAMPLE

Find the fixed points of the collineation

$$k\bar{x}^1 = \quad 5x^1 - 2x^2,$$
$$k\bar{x}^2 = -2x^1 + 6x^2 - 2x^3,$$
$$k\bar{x}^3 = \quad\quad - 2x^2 + 7x^3.$$

Solution: Equation (13′) for this instance is

$$f(\lambda) \equiv \begin{vmatrix} 5 - \lambda & -2 & 0 \\ -2 & 6 - \lambda & -2 \\ 0 & -2 & 7 - \lambda \end{vmatrix} = 0,$$

which expands to

$$f(\lambda) \equiv -\lambda^3 + 18\lambda^2 - 99\lambda + 162 = 0,$$

whose roots are 3, 6, 9. For $\lambda = 3$, the first two equations of (12′) are

$$x^1 - x^2 = 0,$$
$$2x^1 - 3x^2 + 2x^3 = 0,$$

which have the solution $(2:2:1)$ for one of the fixed points. Similarly, corresponding to the roots 6 and 9, one finds the fixed points $(2:-1:-2)$ and $(1:-2:2)$. (See Exercise 4.)

EXERCISES

1. Verify that the product of the mappings (1) and (2) is the identity mapping.

2. Find the collineation which is determined by the four pairs of corresponding points

$$A_1(1:0:0) \leftrightarrow \bar{A}_1(3:-1:1),$$
$$A_2(0:1:0) \leftrightarrow \bar{A}_2(-1:5:-1),$$
$$A_3(0:0:1) \leftrightarrow \bar{A}_3(1:-1:3),$$
$$A_4(1:1:1) \leftrightarrow \bar{A}_4(1:4:1).$$

   Ans. The collineation of the Example in Section 7-1.

3. Find the fixed points of the collineation in the Example of Section 7-1.

   Ans. $(1:0:-1)$, $(2:-3 \pm \sqrt{13}:2)$.

4. Express the collineation in the Example of Section 7-2 in line coordinates, find the coordinates of the fixed lines, and then verify the solution by finding the fixed lines by use of the fixed points arrived at in the Example. (The needed roots are 18, 27, 54.)

5. Show that the derivative of the determinant

$$f(t) \equiv \begin{vmatrix} a_1 & b_1 & c_1 \\ a_2 & b_2 & c_2 \\ a_3 & b_3 & c_3 \end{vmatrix},$$

where a_i, b_i, c_i are functions of t, is given by

$$f'(t) \equiv \begin{vmatrix} a_1' & b_1 & c_1 \\ a_2' & b_2 & c_2 \\ a_3' & b_3 & c_3 \end{vmatrix} + \begin{vmatrix} a_1 & b_1' & c_1 \\ a_2 & b_2' & c_2 \\ a_3 & b_3' & c_3 \end{vmatrix} + \begin{vmatrix} a_1 & b_1 & c_1' \\ a_2 & b_2 & c_2' \\ a_3 & b_3 & c_3' \end{vmatrix}.$$

6. Show that $x = a$ is a triple root of $f(x) = 0$ if $f(a) = f'(a) = f''(a) = 0$.

7. Show that the collineation

$$\begin{aligned}
k\bar{x}^1 &= x^1 + x^2 + x^3, \\
k\bar{x}^2 &= 6x^1 \qquad - 2x^3, \\
k\bar{x}^3 &= \qquad\qquad x^3
\end{aligned}$$

is an affine mapping which leaves the line $x^3 = 0$ fixed. Find the remaining fixed lines.

Ans. $[6:2:1]$, $[-6:3:4]$.

7-3. Classification of collineations

Six types of collineations can be distinguished. This will be done analytically by use of the six cases which appeared in the theorem of Section 7-2. A geometrical classification will also be exhibited by making use of the configurations of fixed points and lines. A characteristic form of each type of collineation will be found by using the points and lines of the reference triangle to simplify the analysis. These simplified representations are called *canonical* forms of the collineations.

Analytical Classification

In Case 1° of the theorem of Section 7-2, the roots λ_i of equation (13′) are distinct ($m = 1$, and for each of λ_i the rank r of the matrix $(a_j^i - \lambda\delta_j^i)$ is 2. This general case is the first type listed below. The next two types arise from Case 2° in the theorem, and the last three types from Case 3°. The analysis here, relative to equations (1) in point coordinates, is unchanged if equations (5) are used. Instead of three fixed *points* under Type 1° below, for instance, one finds three fixed *lines*. For every statement concerning fixed points (and lines) a dual statement holds relative to fixed lines (and points).

1°	$\lambda_1 \begin{pmatrix} m = 1 \\ r = 2 \end{pmatrix}$	$\lambda_2 \begin{pmatrix} m = 1 \\ r = 2 \end{pmatrix}$	$\lambda_3 \begin{pmatrix} m = 1 \\ r = 2 \end{pmatrix}$
2°	$\lambda_1 \begin{pmatrix} m = 1 \\ r = 2 \end{pmatrix}$	$\lambda_2 \begin{pmatrix} m = 2 \\ r = 2 \end{pmatrix}$	
3°	$\lambda_1 \begin{pmatrix} m = 1 \\ r = 2 \end{pmatrix}$	$\lambda_2 \begin{pmatrix} m = 2 \\ r = 1 \end{pmatrix}$	
4°	$\lambda_1 \begin{pmatrix} m = 3 \\ r = 2 \end{pmatrix}$		
5°	$\lambda_1 \begin{pmatrix} m = 3 \\ r = 1 \end{pmatrix}$		
6°	$\lambda_1 \begin{pmatrix} m = 3 \\ r = 0 \end{pmatrix}$		

Geometrical Classification

Each of the six types described analytically above will now be treated geometrically, and a canonical form for each type will be obtained.

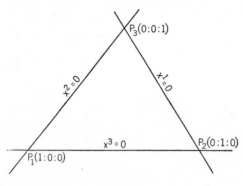

Figure 50

1°. According to the argument given in Section 7-2, the three distinct roots λ_i of equation (13′) are used successively in equations (12′) to find three distinct fixed points which determine a triangle. A canonical form for such a collineation is obtained by choosing the fixed triangle as the triangle of reference. Demand that $P_1(1:0:0) \leftrightarrow \bar{P}_1(1:0:0)$ in equations (1) to obtain

$$\rho = a_1^1, \quad 0 = a_1^2, \quad 0 = a_1^3.$$

Similarly, if $P_2(0:1:0)$ and $P_3(0:0:1)$ are required to be fixed, one finds, in turn, $a_2^1 = a_2^3 = 0$ and $a_3^1 = a_3^2 = 0$. Hence, the equations (1) reduce to

$$(19) \qquad k\bar{x}^1 = a_1^1 x^1, \quad k\bar{x}_2 = a_2^2 x^2, \quad k\bar{x}^3 = a_3^3 x^3,$$

and, for the form (19), the roots λ_i may be taken as $\lambda_1 = a_1^1$, $\lambda_2 = a_2^2$, $\lambda_3 = a_3^3$. Therefore, the canonical form for the general case (Type 1°), as illustrated by Fig. 50, may be written as

$$(20) \qquad k\bar{x}^1 = \lambda_1 x^1, \quad k\bar{x}^2 = \lambda_2 x^2, \quad k\bar{x}^3 = \lambda_3 x^3.$$

Note that there are two fixed points on each fixed line, and two fixed lines through each fixed point.

2°. There are two fixed points, but one is counted twice ($m = 2$). Hence, the two points determine two coincident fixed lines. There is one more fixed line, which may be regarded as the limiting position of line P_2P_3 in Fig. 50 as P_3 approaches coincidence with P_2 (Fig. 51). Choose $P_1(1:0:0)$ again as the fixed point corresponding to $\lambda_1(m = 1)$, and let $P_2(0:1:0)$ be the double fixed point correspond-

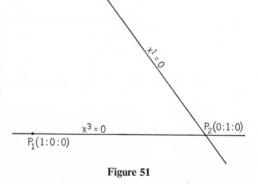

Figure 51

ing to $\lambda_2(m = 2)$. The line $x^3 = 0$ is the double fixed line. Let $x^1 = 0$ be the third fixed line. Because $x^1 = 0$ maps into $\bar{x}^1 = 0$ under equations (1), it follows that $\rho\bar{x}^1 = a_1^1 x^1$. Similarly, one must have $\rho\bar{x}^3 = a_3^3 x^3$. Hence, $a_2^1 =$

$a_3^1 = 0$, $a_1^3 = a_2^3 = 0$. The fact that $(1:0:0)$ is fixed requires that $a_1^2 = 0$. The collineation (1) reduces to

(21) $$\rho \bar{x}^1 = a_1^1 x^1, \quad \rho \bar{x}^2 = a_2^2 x^2 + a_3^2 x^3, \quad \rho \bar{x}^3 = a_3^3 x^3,$$

and, for this collineation, equation (13′) requires that $\lambda_1 = a_1^1$, $\lambda_2 = a_2^2 = a_3^3$. Hence, equations (21) take the canonical form

(22) $$\rho \bar{x}^1 = \lambda_1 x^1, \quad \rho \bar{x}^2 = \lambda_2 x^2 + a_3^2 x^3, \quad \rho \bar{x}^3 = \lambda_2 x^3.$$

Note that a_3^2 remains as an arbitrary parameter.

3°. There is one fixed point and a line of fixed points. In order to see this, observe that for $\lambda = \lambda_1$, $m = 1$ and $r = 2$, which means that two of the equations in (12′) can be solved for a unique point. Let this point be again $P_1(1:0:0)$. For $\lambda = \lambda_2$, $m = 2$ and $r = 1$, which means that no two of the equations (12′) can be solved for a unique point. All three equations in (12′) represent the same line, each point of which is fixed. Take

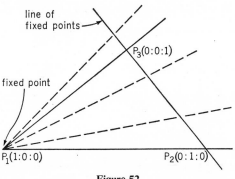

Figure 52

this line as $x^1 = 0$ (Fig. 52). Dually, since there is a line of fixed points, there is a pencil of fixed lines. All lines through P_1 are fixed lines. Two of the fixed points on the line $x^1 = 0$ may be taken as $P_2(0:1:0)$ and $P_3(0:0:1)$. Because P_1, P_2, P_3 are fixed, the collineation has the form of equations (19), but equation (13′) shows that $\lambda_1 = a_1^1$, $\lambda_2 = a_2^2 = a_3^3$. Hence, the canonical form is

(23) $$\rho \bar{x}^1 = \lambda_1 x^1, \quad \rho \bar{x}_2 = \lambda_2 x^2, \quad \rho \bar{x}^3 = \lambda_2 x^3.$$

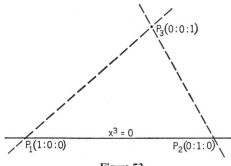

Figure 53

This type of collineation is called a *planar homology* (see Section 7-4). The point P_1 and the line $x^1 = 0$ are called respectively the *center* and *axis* of the homology.

4°. There is a single fixed point counted three times, and a single fixed line counted three times. The fixed line must contain the fixed point, for otherwise more than three fixed points would exist. Choose $P_1(1:0:0)$ as the triple fixed point, and $x^3 = 0$ as the triple fixed line. From equations (1) the consequence is that $a_1^2 = 0$ and $a_1^3 = a_2^3 = 0$, so that the collineation takes the form

$$\rho \bar{x}^1 = a_1^1 x^1 + a_2^1 x^2 + a_3^1 x^3,$$

(24)
$$\rho \bar{x}^2 = \qquad\quad a_2^2 x^2 + a_3^2 x^3,$$

$$\rho \bar{x}^3 = \qquad\qquad\qquad a_3^3 x^3.$$

Because for $\lambda = \lambda_1$, $m = 3$ and $r = 2$, equation (13′) requires that $\lambda_1 = a_1^1 = a_2^2 = a_3^3$. Hence, the canonical form is

$$\rho \bar{x}^1 = \lambda_1 x^1 + a_2^1 x^2 + a_3^1 x^3,$$

(25)
$$\rho \bar{x}^2 = \qquad\quad \lambda_1 x^2 + a_3^2 x^3,$$

$$\rho \bar{x}^3 = \qquad\qquad\qquad \lambda_1 x^3,$$

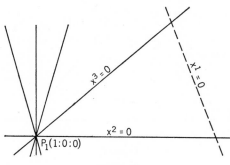

Figure 54

where a_2^1, a_3^1, a_3^2 are left as parameters, with a_2^1 and a_3^2 nonzero.

5°. There is one line of fixed points, and a pencil of fixed lines. The center of the pencil is incident with the line of fixed points. Choose $P_1(1:0:0)$ as the center of the pencil, and $x^2 = 0$ as the line of fixed points (Fig. 54). By the fixity of the lines $x^2 = 0$ and $x^3 = 0$ through P_1, the collineation has the form

$$\rho \bar{x}^1 = a_1^1 x^1 + a_2^1 x^2 + a_3^1 x^3, \quad \rho \bar{x}^2 = a_2^2 x^2, \quad \rho \bar{x}^3 = a_3^3 x^3.$$

Because for $\lambda = \lambda_1$ it is true that $m = 3$ and $r = 1$, it follows that equation (13′) requires $\lambda_1 = a_1^1 = a_2^2 = a_3^3$. Hence, the canonical form is

(26) $$\rho \bar{x}^1 = \lambda_1 x^1 + a_2^1 x^2 + a_3^1 x^3, \quad \rho \bar{x}^2 = \lambda_1 x^2, \quad \rho \bar{x}^3 = \lambda_1 x^3,$$

where a_2^1 and a_3^1 are arbitrary. This type of collineation is called an *elation*.

6°. All points and lines of the plane are fixed. The collineation is the identity mapping $\rho \bar{x}^i = x^i$.

7-4. The characteristic invariant of a homology

It will be shown first that under the homology of equations (23) any point $P(x^i)$ and its correspondent $\bar{P}(\bar{x}^i)$ are collinear with the center $P_1(1:0:0)$ of the homology. This is true because the determinant

$$\begin{vmatrix} 1 & 0 & 0 \\ x^1 & x^2 & x^3 \\ \lambda_1 x^1 & \lambda_2 x^2 & \lambda_2 x^3 \end{vmatrix}$$

vanishes identically.

Let any line through the center P_1 of the homology given by equations (23) intersect the line $x^1 = 0$ in a point P_3 which may be assigned the coordinates

$(0:0:1)$. It will be shown that the cross ratio $(P_1P_3P\overline{P})$ of any two corresponding points P and $\overline{P}$ with P_1 and P_3 is a constant; that is, the cross ratio is independent of the choice of $P(x^i)$. In order to show this, project the four points P_1, P_3, P, $\overline{P}$ from $P_2(0:1:0)$, as indicated in Fig. 55. The respective line coordinates of the lines P_2P_1, P_2P_3, P_2P, and $P_2\overline{P}$ are

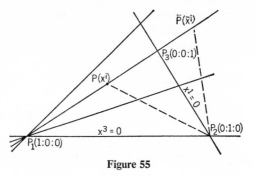

Figure 55

$$[0:0:1], \quad [1:0:0], \quad [-x^3:0:x^1], \quad [-\overline{x}^3:0:\overline{x}^1],$$

and, because the second coordinate is zero for each point, the desired cross ratio is obtained by using the ratio of the first to the third coordinates as the parameter for each point. Thus,

$$(P_1P_3P\overline{P}) = \left(0, \infty, -\frac{x^3}{x^1}, -\frac{\overline{x}^3}{\overline{x}^1}\right) = \frac{x^3\overline{x}^1}{x^1\overline{x}^3} = \frac{x^3\lambda_1x^1}{x^1\lambda_2x^3} = \frac{\lambda_1}{\lambda_2}.$$

The constant λ_1/λ_2 is called the *characteristic invariant* of the homology (23). A special kind of homology, called a *harmonic homology*, is that for which the characteristic invariant λ_1/λ_2 is -1—that is, $\lambda_1 + \lambda_2 = 0$. In this case, equations (23) reduce to

(27) $$\rho\overline{x}^1 = -x^1, \quad \rho\overline{x}^2 = x^2, \quad \rho\overline{x}^3 = x^3.$$

It is evident that a harmonic homology is of period two, because the square of the matrix of the collineation (27) is the identity matrix. One may inquire: Is a collineation of period two necessarily a harmonic homology? The answer to this is given by the

THEOREM: *A collineation of period two is a harmonic homology.*

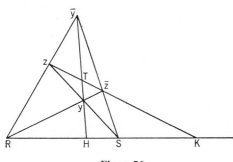

Figure 56

Proof: An attempt by an analytic method to gain the desired conclusion from the hypothesis that the square of the collineation in equations (1) is the identity mapping appears rather forbidding. Therefore, a synthetic type of argument will be used.

Let the collineation be of period two. Choose y, $\overline{y}$ and z, $\overline{z}$ as two pairs of corresponding points, with no three of the four points collinear. Because a collineation is uniquely determined by four pairs of corresponding points, there is only one collineation which maps the four points

y, $\bar{y}$, z, $\bar{z}$ into $\bar{y}$, y, $\bar{z}$, z. In Fig. 56, lines $y\bar{z}$ and $\bar{y}z$ intersect at R, yz and $\bar{y}\bar{z}$ at S, $y\bar{y}$ and $z\bar{z}$ at T, $y\bar{y}$ and RS at H, and $z\bar{z}$ and RS at K. From a previous result the point sets y, $\bar{y}$, H, T and z, $\bar{z}$, K, T are harmonic. The harmonic homology with T as center and line RS as axis makes y correspond to $\bar{y}$ and z to $\bar{z}$. It is a unique collineation of period two. This completes the proof.

7-5. Metric properties of collineations in homogeneous coordinates

If one line of the projective plane is singled out as a fixed line, a subgroup of projective mappings is obtained. This is the group of *affine* mappings. In particular, the line $x^3 = 0$ may be required to be fixed. In this case, the general collineation (1) reduces to the affine collineation given by

$$\rho\bar{x}^1 = a_i^1 x^i,$$
(28)
$$\rho\bar{x}^2 = a_i^2 x^i,$$
$$\rho\bar{x}^3 = a_3^3 x^3,$$

which contains six essential parameters. (There are apparently seven parameters, besides ρ, but all three equations may be divided by the nonzero coefficient a_3^3.) If, in addition, two particular points are singled out on the fixed line as fixed points, a subgroup of the affine group is obtained. It is proposed now to demand that the circular points $I(1:i:0)$ and $J(1:-i:0)$ be fixed under the collineation (28). Let λ_1 and λ_2 denote the roots of (13'), which correspond to I and J, respectively, relative to (28). For $\lambda = \lambda_1$, the coordinates $(1:i:0)$ must satisfy equations (12') with $a_1^3 = a_2^3 = 0$. Hence,

(29) $$(a_1^1 - \lambda_1) + a_2^1 i = 0, \quad a_1^2 + (a_2^2 - \lambda_1)i = 0.$$

Similarly, for $\lambda = \lambda_2$ and the coordinates $(1:-i:0)$, one requires that

(30) $$(a_1^1 - \lambda_2) - a_2^1 i = 0, \quad a_1^2 - (a_2^2 - \lambda_2)i = 0.$$

Eliminate λ_1 from equations (29) to obtain

(31) $$(a_1^2 + a_2^1) + (a_2^2 - a_1^1)i = 0,$$

from which $a_1^2 = -a_2^1$ and $a_2^2 = a_1^1$ because a_j^i are real. (The same result follows by eliminating λ_2 from (30).) Thus, the collineation (28) takes the form

$$\rho\bar{x}^1 = \quad a_1^1 x^1 + a_2^1 x^2 + a_3^1 x^3,$$
(32)
$$\rho\bar{x}^2 = -a_2^1 x^1 + a_1^1 x^2 + a_3^2 x^3,$$
$$\rho\bar{x}^3 = \quad\quad\quad\quad\quad a_3^3 x^3,$$

and the roots of (13') for this collineation are

$$\lambda_1 = a_1^1 + a_2^1 i, \quad \lambda_2 = a_1^1 - a_2^1 i, \quad \lambda_3 = a_3^3.$$

(It can be verified that λ_1 and λ_2 correspond to I and J, respectively.) The fixed point corresponding to $\lambda_3 = a_3^3$ for the collineation (32) is found, by use of (12'), to have the coordinates

(33) $$a_2^1 a_3^2 - a_3^1(a_1^1 - a_3^3): -a_2^1 a_3^1 - a_3^2(a_1^1 - a_3^3):(a_1^1 - a_3^3)^2 + (a_2^1)^2.$$

Suppose that $(a_1^1 - a_3^3)^2 + (a_2^1)^2 \neq 0$ and $a_2^2 \neq 0$. Let the point (33) be $(0:0:1)$. The vanishing of the first two coordinates in (33) is expressed by the homogeneous equations

(34)
$$(a_1^1 - a_3^3)[a_3^1] - a_2^1[a_3^2] = 0,$$
$$a_2^1[a_3^1] + (a_1^1 - a_3^3)[a_3^2] = 0,$$

which, by the hypothesis that $(a_1^1 - a_3^3)^2 + (a_2^1)^2 \neq 0$ have only the trivial solution $a_3^1 = a_3^2 = 0$. Hence, the collineation (32) takes the form

(35)
$$\rho\bar{x}^1 = \quad a_1^1 x^1 + a_2^1 x^2,$$
$$\rho\bar{x}^2 = -a_2^1 x^1 + a_1^1 x^2,$$
$$\rho\bar{x}^3 = \qquad a_3^3 x^3.$$

Divide the first and second equations of (35) by the third, and write $x = x^1/x^3$, $y = x^2/x^3$ to have (35) in the form

(36)
$$\bar{x} = \quad a_1^1 x + a_2^1 y,$$
$$\bar{y} = -a_2^1 x + a_1^1 y,$$

where, without loss of generality, a_3^3 is set equal to 1. Now multiply and divide the right members in (36) by $s \equiv \sqrt{(a_1^1)^2 + (a_2^1)^2}$ to obtain

(37)
$$\bar{x} = s\left(\frac{a_1^1}{s} x + \frac{a_2^1}{s} y\right),$$
$$\bar{y} = s\left(-\frac{a_2^1}{s} x + \frac{a_1^1}{s} y\right).$$

Further, let $a_1^1 = s \cos \theta$, $a_2^1 = s \sin \theta$, to see that (37) is

(38)
$$x = s(x \cos \theta + y \sin \theta),$$
$$y = s(-x \sin \theta + y \cos \theta).$$

If $s = 1$, (38) is a rotation about the origin. If $s \neq 1$, (38) is the product of the rotation $x' = x \cos \theta + y \sin \theta$, $y' = -x \sin \theta + y \cos \theta$, and the stretching $\bar{x} = sx'$, $\bar{y} = sy'$ from the origin. (If $s < 1$, the mapping is a contraction toward the origin.) The foregoing discussion leads to the

THEOREM: *The most general collineation which has the circular points I and J and the origin as fixed points is a rotation about the origin followed by a stretching from the origin.*

Observe that, with three distinct fixed points, the collineation (38) is of Type 1° in the classification of Section 7-3 (p. 163).

It will be assumed next that $a_2^1 = 0$, which means that $\lambda_1 = \lambda_2 = a_1^1$ and $\lambda_3 = a_3^3$. The collineation (32) reduces to

(39)
$$\rho\bar{x}^1 = \lambda_1 x^1 \qquad\quad + a_3^1 x^3,$$
$$\rho\bar{x}^2 = \qquad \lambda_1 x^2 + a_3^2 x^3,$$
$$\rho\bar{x}^3 = \qquad\qquad \lambda_3 x^3,$$

the characteristic equations for which are

$$(\lambda_1 - \lambda)x^1 \qquad\qquad + a_3^1 x^3 = 0,$$

(40)
$$(\lambda_1 - \lambda)x^2 + a_3^2 x^3 = 0,$$

$$(\lambda_3 - \lambda)x^3 = 0,$$

and the characteristic matrix is

(41)
$$\begin{pmatrix} \lambda_1 - \lambda & 0 & a_3^1 \\ 0 & \lambda_2 - \lambda & a_3^2 \\ 0 & 0 & \lambda_3 - \lambda \end{pmatrix}.$$

Suppose that $\lambda_1 \neq \lambda_3$. Then, for $\lambda = \lambda_1$, the rank r of matrix (41) is 1. Since $m = 2$ and $r = 1$ for $\lambda = \lambda_1$, the collineation (39) is of Type 3° in the classification of Section 7-3; that is, it is a special kind of homology for which the line at infinity has every point fixed. Note that for $\lambda = \lambda_3$ in equations (40), one finds the fixed point $(a_3^1 : a_3^2 : \lambda_3 - \lambda_1)$. If this is taken as the origin, then $a_3^1 = a_3^2 = 0$, in which case equations (39) simplify to

(42)
$$\rho \bar{x}^1 = \lambda_1 x^1, \quad \rho \bar{x}_2 = \lambda_1 x^2, \quad \rho \bar{x}^3 = \lambda_3 x^3.$$

Divide the first two equations by the third and introduce nonhomogeneous coordinates to find the form $\bar{x} = mx$, $\bar{y} = my$, where $m = \lambda_1/\lambda_3$. Thus, the stretching from the origin given by (42) is a planar homology with characteristic invariant $\lambda_3/\lambda_1 = 1/m$. For the case $m = -1$, the homology is harmonic. It is merely a reflection about the origin given by $\bar{x} = -x$, $\bar{y} = -y$.

Next, consider the case $\lambda_1 = \lambda_3$ in equations (39). The characteristic matrix is now

43)
$$\begin{pmatrix} \lambda_1 - \lambda & 0 & a_3^1 \\ 0 & \lambda_1 - \lambda & a_3^2 \\ 0 & 0 & \lambda_1 - \lambda \end{pmatrix}.$$

For $\lambda = \lambda_1$, the rank $r = 1$, provided a_3^1 and a_3^2 are not both zero. This is the Type 5° in Section 7-3; that is, it is a planar elation. Every point on the line at infinity is fixed, and every line through the point $(a_3^1 : a_3^2 : 0)$ is fixed. Put $\lambda_3 = \lambda_1$ in (39), reduce to nonhomogeneous form, and write $a_3^1/\lambda_1 = h$, $a_3^2/\lambda_1 = k$, to see that (39) takes the form $\bar{x} = x + h$, $\bar{y} = y + k$. Thus, the planar elation is a translation in the plane.

Finally, if a_3^1 and a_3^2 are both zero in (43), the collineation is the identity mapping.

The foregoing discussion reveals that the collineation which leaves the circular points $I(1:i:0)$ and $J(1:-i:0)$ fixed is at most the product of a translation, a rotation about a point, and a stretching from the point (which includes a contraction and a reflection about the point).

EXERCISES

1. Verify that the characteristic roots λ_1 and λ_2 which follow equations (32) correspond to the circular points $I(1:i:0)$ and $J(1:-i:0)$, respectively.

2. Find the fixed points and lines of the collineation

$$\bar{x} = \frac{1 + y}{x + y}, \quad \bar{y} = \frac{1 - x}{x + y}.$$

Note that the mapping is singular.

Ans. Fixed line, $x - y = 1$.

3. Express the collineation $\bar{x}^1 = x^3$, $\bar{x}^2 = x^1$, $\bar{x}^3 = x^2$ in line coordinates. Find the fixed points and lines of the collineation.

4. Classify the collineation $\bar{x}^1 = x^1 + \alpha x^3$, $\bar{x}^2 = x^2 + \beta x^3$, $\bar{x}^3 = x^3$, and find its fixed points and lines.

5. Show that the distance between two points with orthogonal cartesian coordinates (x_1, y_1) and (x_2, y_2) is invariant under the group of translations and rotations given by

$$\bar{x} = x \cos \theta + y \sin \theta + h,$$

$$\bar{y} = -x \sin \theta + y \cos \theta + k.$$

6. Find the three fixed points under the collineation

$$\bar{x} = x \cos \theta + y \sin \theta,$$

$$\bar{y} = -x \sin \theta + y \cos \theta.$$

7-6. Correlations

Consider two distinct planes π and $\bar{\pi}$. A *correlation* is defined by the equations

(44)
$$\rho \bar{u}_i = a_{ij} x^j, \qquad |a_{ij}| \equiv a \neq 0,$$

which establish a one-to-one correspondence between points $P(x^i)$ of π and lines $\bar{L}(u_i)$ in $\bar{\pi}$. The inverse of the correlation (44) is given by

(45)
$$\sigma x^i = A^{ji} \bar{u}_j.$$

In order to obtain the correlation which effects a correspondence between *points* of $\bar{\pi}$ and *lines* of π, use the invariant condition of united position to have

$$u_i x^i = u_i A^{ji} \bar{u}_j = \bar{u}_i (A^{ij} u_j) = \bar{u}_i \bar{x}^i,$$

whence

(46)
$$k \bar{x}^i = A^{ij} u_j$$

for the desired mapping of a line in π to a point in $\bar{\pi}$. The inverse of (46) is obtained by multiplying by a_{ik} and summing on the index i. Thus,

$$k a_{ik} \bar{x}^i = a_{ik} A^{ij} u_j = a \delta_k^j u_j = a u_k,$$

from which, after a change of indices,

(47)
$$k u_i = a_{ji} \bar{x}^i$$

for the correspondence which takes a point of $\bar{\pi}$ into a line of π. Observe that if the u_i are variables and the x^i are constants, the equation $u_i x^i = 0$ represents all lines through the point $P(x^i)$ in π. By use of (45) and (47), the equation $u_i x^i = 0$ transforms:

$$u_i x^i = a_{ji} \bar{x}^i A^{ki} \bar{u}_k = (a_{ji} A^{ki}) \bar{u}_k \bar{x}^j = \delta_j^k \bar{u}_k \bar{u}^j = \bar{u}_j \bar{x}^j = 0.$$

By (44), if the x^i are constants the $\bar{u}_i$ are constants. Hence, the equation $\bar{u}_j\bar{x}^j = 0$ represents variable points on a line in $\bar{\pi}$. Thus, to points on a line in either plane, there correspond lines through a point in the other under the correlation determined by equations (44). Thus far in the discussion the planes π and $\bar{\pi}$ have been considered as distinct.

Now consider planes π and $\bar{\pi}$ as coincident, and use the same coordinate system for both. To a point P in π there corresponds, by (44), a line $\bar{L}$ in $\bar{\pi}$. To a point $\bar{P}$ in $\bar{\pi}$ there corresponds, by (47), a line L in π. If P and $\bar{P}$ are taken as coincident, are the corresponding lines $\bar{L}$ and L coincident? To answer this question, let $k\bar{x}^i = x^i$, to make $\bar{P}$ coincide with P. Equations (47) then require that

$$(48) \qquad k'u_i = a_{ji}x^j.$$

The condition that L and $\bar{L}$ coincide is that $k'\bar{u}_i = u_i$. Hence, by (44) and (48),

$$a_{ij}x^j = \lambda a_{ji}x^j,$$

or

$$(49) \qquad (a_{ij} - \lambda a_{ji})x^j = 0.$$

The set of three homogeneous equations in (49) have a nontrivial solution if and only if

$$(50) \qquad |a_{ij} - \lambda a_{ji}| = 0,$$

which is a cubic equation in λ. There are, therefore, in general, three points P_i (and consequently three lines L_i) in the plane such that P_i corresponds to L_i, and L_i corresponds to P_i for $i = 1, 2, 3$. For any other point Q there corresponds a line H, but line H does not have Q as its correspondent.

Polar Correlation

Let it be required next that the equations (49) are identities in the x^i. That is, suppose that the coefficients $a_{ij} - \lambda a_{ji} = 0$ for every i and j. This means that for every point P (whether regarded as in π or $\bar{\pi}$) there corresponds only one line L. Such a correspondence is called a *polar correlation*.

It will be seen next that the matrix (a_{ij}) in (44) is symmetric for a polar correlation; that is, $a_{ij} = a_{ji}$ for every i and j. To show this, note that from

$$(51) \qquad a_{ij} - \lambda a_{ji} = 0,$$

interchange of i and j gives $a_{ji} - \lambda a_{ij} = 0$, or, on multiplying by λ,

$$(52) \qquad \lambda a_{ji} - \lambda^2 a_{ij} = 0.$$

Add equations (51) and (52) to obtain $(\lambda^2 - 1)a_{ij} = 0$, which (because not all the a_{ij} are zero) requires that $\lambda = \pm 1$. Suppose first that $\lambda = -1$. Equation (51) requires then that $a_{ij} = -a_{ji}$, which means that the matrix (a_{ij}) is skew-symmetric. It is a theorem from algebra that the determinant of every skew-symmetric matrix of *odd order* is zero. This would contradict the supposition in (44) that $|a_{ij}| \neq 0$. Hence, $\lambda \neq -1$. The alternative, $\lambda = 1$, requires, by (51), that $a_{ij} = a_{ji}$, which means that the matrix (a_{ij}) in (44) is symmetric for a polar correlation. It follows that the matrix (A^{ij}) is also symmetric.

Now let the distinction between the coincident planes π and $\bar{\pi}$ be dropped, and write the equations of a polar correlation and its inverse, from (44) and (45), in the form

(53)
$$\rho u_i = a_{ij} x^j, \quad a_{ij} = a_{ji}, \qquad |a_{ij}| \neq 0,$$
$$k x^i = A^{ji} u_j, \quad A^{ji} = A^{ij}.$$

Equations (53) establish a correspondence between points and lines of a plane. In general, a point $P(x^i)$ does not lie on its corresponding line $L(u_i)$. One may therefore ask which set of points in the plane enjoy the property of being incident with their corresponding lines under the correlation (53). Use the incidence relation $u_i x^i = 0$ to obtain, by (53),

$$u_i x^i = (a_{ij} x^j) x^i = a_{ij} x^i x^j = 0, \qquad a_{ij} = a_{ji}.$$

The point locus given by $a_{ij} x^i x^j = 0$ is a curve of the second order. It is called a *point conic*. This curve is defined in a different manner (Steiner's definition) in the following chapter.

It is natural to ask for the dual of the point conic—that is, the set of lines in the plane which enjoy the property of being in united position with their corresponding points, under the polar correlation (53). To gain the desired result, use the second set of equations in (53) in $u_i x^i = 0$ to obtain

$$u_i x^i = u_i A^{ji} u_j = A^{ji} u_i u_j = A^{ij} u_i u_j = 0.$$

The lines of the set satisfying $A^{ij} u_i u_j = 0$ are tangent to a curve of the second class. It is called a *line conic*. Observe that a simple way to find the line equation of a given point conic $a_{ij} x^i x^j = 0$ is to calculate the cofactors A^{ji} of a_{ij} in the matrix (a_{ij}) and write $A^{ij} u_i u_j = 0$. This works as well in reverse. That is, given the line equation $A^{ij} u_i u_j = 0$ of a conic, calculate the cofactors α_{ji} of A^{ij} in the matrix (A^{ij}) and write $\alpha_{ij} x^i x^j = 0$ for the point conic. It is shown next that the α_{ij} are proportional to the a_{ij}, so the point equation $a_{ij} x^i x^j = 0$ is recovered from the line equation.

According to the established notation, let $a \equiv |a_{ij}|$, and $A \equiv |A^{ij}|$. Denote the cofactor of A^{ij} by α_{ji}. Then

$$A^{ij} \alpha_{jk} = A \delta_k^i.$$

Multiply by a_{li} and sum on i to obtain

$$a_{li} A^{ij} \alpha_{jk} = A a_{li} \delta_k^i,$$

or

$$a \delta_l^j \alpha_{jk} = A a_{lk},$$

which gives

(54)
$$a \alpha_{lk} = A a_{lk}.$$

Hence, the α_{lk} are indeed proportional to the a_{lk}. Observe that by forming the determinant of both sides of (54) it follows that

$$|\alpha_{lk}| = \left(\frac{A}{a}\right)^3 |a_{lk}| = \frac{A^3}{a^2}.$$

It should be pointed out that the correlations (44) do not constitute a group. By (44), a point maps into a line. If a correlation of the same type as (44) is carried out on the line, the latter goes into a point. Hence, the product of two correlations is a collineation, which takes points into points and lines into lines.

7-7. A metric interpretation in three-space

The reader should be aware of a different interpretation of the analysis used in studying equations (1) of a collineation in the plane. In the projective plane (or in the euclidean plane with homogeneous coordinates) the equation $u_i x^i = 0$ represents a line or a point. But in three-dimensional euclidean space S_3, referred to a system of nonhomogeneous cartesian coordinates x^i, the same equation (with u_i constants) represents a plane through the origin, the u_i being direction numbers of a line normal to the plane. Thus, in S_3, a set of values of u_i determines a plane through the origin—that is, the plane perpendicular to the direction u_i. A set of values x^i determines a line through the origin. To the totality of sets of values of $u_1:u_2:u_3$ correspond not only all lines in the projective plane, but also the totality of planes through the origin in S_3. To the totality of sets of values of $x^1:x^2:x^3$ correspond not only all points in the projective plane, but also the totality of lines through the origin in S_3. The u_i are coordinates of planes through the origin, and the x^i are coordinates of lines through the origin in S_3. The incidence condition $u_i x^i = 0$ of point and line in the projective plane becomes in S_3 the condition that the direction x^i (or line x^i) lie in the plane u_i. Thus, $u_i x^i = 0$ is an orthogonality condition in S_3.

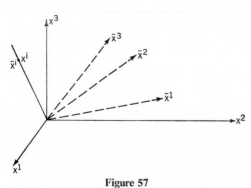

Figure 57

Consider the x^i as coordinates of a point in S_3, referred to a system of orthogonal cartesian axes (Fig. 57). The equations (1), or $\rho \bar{x}^i = a_j^i x^j$, represent a linear transformation of coordinates from x^i to $\bar{x}^i$, where the new $\bar{x}^i$ coordinate axes are not necessarily mutually orthogonal, as are the original x^i coordinate axes. (Note that the alias aspect of equations (1) is in vogue here. These equations represent a change of coordinates rather than, as before, a mapping of points.) Observe that $\bar{x}^1 = 0$, for instance, is the equation of the new $\bar{x}^2\bar{x}^3$ plane. The equation of the same plane in x^i

coordinates is, by (1), $a_j^1 x^j = 0$. From the inverse (5) of (1), it is seen that the equation of the plane $x^1 = 0$, for instance, is $A_j^1 \bar{x}^j = 0$ in the barred coordinate system. The plane coordinates u_i and $\bar{u}_i$ can be introduced as in equations (7) and (9). The fixed point analysis of Section 7-2 can be carried through to show that, in general, there is at least one (real) line through the origin (Fig. 57) for which the x^i and $\bar{x}^i$ have the same coordinates in the two coordinate systems.

The only condition on equations (1) heretofore has been that $|a_j^i| \neq 0$. Further conditions will now be imposed on the matrix (a_j^i) to obtain a *rotation matrix.* In order to introduce this notion, think of a rigid body in space which contains a set of mutually orthogonal axes $\bar{x}^i$, which are initially coincident with a fixed set of cartesian axes x^i in space (Fig. 58). Now rotate the body about the stationary point O to a new position in which the $\bar{x}^i$ directions are as indicated in Fig. 58. Note that a mapping of points takes place here under the

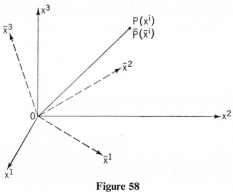

Figure 58

rotation of the body, but that any point P has coordinates x^i referred to the original axes, and the same point $\bar{P}$ has coordinates $\bar{x}^i$ referred to the new $\bar{x}$ system of axes.

It is evident that, under the rotation about O, the length of OP is invariant, which means that

$$(55) \qquad (\bar{x}^1)^2 + (\bar{x}^2)^2 + (\bar{x}^3)^2 \equiv (x^1)^2 + (x^2)^2 + (x^3)^2.$$

If equations (1) are to satisfy the identity (55), then $\rho = 1$, and

$$(56) \quad \text{(a)} \quad \begin{aligned} (a_1^1)^2 + (a_1^2)^2 + (a_1^3)^2 &= 1, \\ (a_2^1)^2 + (a_2^2)^2 + (a_2^3)^2 &= 1, \\ (a_3^1)^2 + (a_3^2)^2 + (a_3^3)^2 &= 1, \end{aligned} \qquad \text{(b)} \quad \begin{aligned} a_2^1 a_3^1 + a_2^2 a_3^2 + a_2^3 a_3^3 &= 0, \\ a_3^1 a_1^1 + a_3^2 a_1^2 + a_3^3 a_1^3 &= 0, \\ a_1^1 a_2^1 + a_1^2 a_2^2 + a_1^3 a_2^3 &= 0. \end{aligned}$$

Equations (56a) and (56b) are the orthogonality conditions for the matrix (a_i^j). It is demonstrated in solid analytical geometry that the six relations in (56) imply that each element of the rotation matrix (a_i^j) is equal to its cofactor, i.e. $a_i^j = A_j^i$, and that the determinant $a \equiv |a_i^j| = +1$ if the $\bar{x}^i$-axes have the same orientation as the original x^i axes, or equals -1 if the $\bar{x}^i$-axes have the opposite orientation. It can be shown (see Exercise 4) that if (a_i^j) is a rotation matrix, then the only real root of its characteristic equation (13') is $\lambda = 1$. For $\lambda = 1$, a fixed line is obtained as the intersection of two of the *planes* in (12'). This line is called the *axis of rotation* of the rigid body The rigid body can be moved to the second position (indicated by the $\bar{x}^i$ axes) by a rotation about the axis of rotation. A method of finding the angle of rotation is shown in Example 2 below.

EXAMPLE 1

Find the axis of the rotation described by

$$3\bar{x}^1 = \quad x^1 - 2x^2 + 2x^3,$$

(57) $\qquad 3\bar{x}^2 = -2x^1 + \quad x^2 + 2x^3,$

$$3\bar{x}^3 = -2x^1 - 2x^2 - \quad x^3.$$

Solution: For a fixed line, the $\bar{x}^i$ are proportional to the x^i. Hence, let $3\bar{x}^i = \lambda x^i$ to obtain

$$(1 - \lambda)x^1 - 2x^2 + 2x^3 = 0,$$

(58) $\qquad -2x^1 + (1 - \lambda)x^2 + 2x^3 = 0,$

$$-2x^1 - 2x^2 + (-1 - \lambda)x^3 = 0.$$

The characteristic equation is

$$\begin{vmatrix} 1 - \lambda & -2 & 2 \\ -2 & 1 - \lambda & 2 \\ -2 & -2 & -1 - \lambda \end{vmatrix} = 0,$$

which has $\lambda = 3$ as the only real root. Place $\lambda = 3$ in the last two equations of (58) to obtain $x^1 : x^2 : x^3 = 1 : -1 : 0$. Hence, the equations of the axis of rotation may be written as $x^1 = t$, $x^2 = -t$, $x^3 = 0$, where t is a parameter.

EXAMPLE 2

Determine the angle of rotation about the axis obtained in Example 1.

Solution: Take any point on a line which is perpendicular to the axis of rotation. The point $(1, 1, 2)$ determines the direction $(1:1:2)$ through the origin, and this direction is orthogonal to the direction $(1:-1:0)$ of the axis. By (57) the point $P : x^i (1, 1, 2)$ is rotated to the position $Q : \bar{x}^i \equiv (1, 1, -2)$. The desired angle θ of rotation from OP to OQ is given by

$$\cos \theta = \frac{(1)(1) + (1)(1) + (2)(-2)}{\sqrt{6} \sqrt{6}} = -\frac{1}{3}.$$

EXERCISES

1. Use the orthogonal conditions to verify that the equations

$$7\bar{x}^1 = 3x^1 - 6x^2 + 2x^3,$$

$$7\bar{x}^2 = 6x^1 + 2x^2 - 3x^3,$$

$$7\bar{x}^3 = 2x^1 + 3x^2 + 6x^3$$

represent either a transformation of orthogonal x^i axes to orthogonal $\bar{x}^i$ axes or a rotation of a rigid body about the origin.

2. Find the equations of the axis of rotation for the mapping in Exercise 1.

3. Calculate the angle of rotation about the axis obtained in Exercise 2.

4. Show that under the collineation $\rho \bar{x}^i = a^i_j x^j$, where (a^i_j) is a rotation matrix, there is only one real root of the characteristic equation for the matrix (a^i_j).

5. Find the fixed line under the rotation in Exercise 4.

6. Find a formula for the angle of rotation about the axis of rotation obtained in Exercise 5.

7-8. Invariants of collineations

The expansion of the characteristic determinant in equation (13′) relative to the matrix (a^i_j) can be effected as follows. Because the result is a polynomial in λ, put $\lambda = 0$ to see that the constant term is the determinant $a \equiv |a^i_j|$. Next, differentiate with respect to λ (see equation (14)) and put $\lambda = 0$ to see that the coefficient of λ in the cubic polynomial $f(\lambda)$ is $-(A^1_1 + A^2_2 + A^3_3)$. A further differentiation (or inspection of (13′)) shows that the coefficient of λ^2 in $f(\lambda)$ is $a^1_1 + a^2_2 + a^3_3$. Hence, the entire expansion is given by

(59) $$f(\lambda) \equiv |a^i_j - \lambda \delta^i_j| \equiv -\lambda^3 + a^i_i \lambda^2 - A^i_i \lambda + a,$$

in which a summation is indicated by the repeated index i. It will be shown that the coefficients in $f(\lambda)$ are invariants in the sense of Section 3-2.

Consider first the collineation (see equations (1))

(60) $$A: \qquad \rho \bar{x}^i = a^i_j x^j,$$

which maps a point x^i to a point $\bar{x}^i$ in the plane. (The symbol A may be used to denote the matrix (a^i_j) as well as the collineation, because the matrix determines the collineation.) Next, effect a transformation of coordinates given by

(61) $$H: \qquad \sigma y^i = h^i_j x^j,$$

for which the inverse is given by

(62) $$H^{-1}: \qquad \tau x^i = H^i_j y^j,$$

where H^i_j is the cofactor of h^j_i in the determinant $h \equiv |h^i_i|$. (Compare equations (5).) Let (62) be carried out first to change the coordinate system from the y's to the x's, and then carry out the mapping (60); finally, perform (61), written as $\sigma \bar{y}^i = h^i_j \bar{x}^j$, to change the coordinate system. Symbolically, the operations just described may be written, in turn, as

(63) $$x = H^{-1} y, \quad \bar{x} = Ax, \quad \bar{y} = H\bar{x},$$

which may be interpreted as matrix equations corresponding to (62), (60), and (61), respectively. The product of the operations in (63) is expressed by

(64) $$\bar{y} = HAH^{-1} y,$$

in which the matrix HAH^{-1} is called the *transform* of A by H. By use of (62), (60), and (61), in turn, equation (64) takes the form

(65) $$r\bar{y}^l = h^l_i a^i_k H^k_j y^j \equiv t^l_j y^j.$$

Equations (64) and (65) state the same fact: the collineation (60) in the x coordinate system is equivalent to the collineation (65) in the y coordinate system.

If the matrix (t_j^i) in (65), with determinant $t \equiv |t_j^i|$, is used instead of (a_j^i) in (59), the result is

$$(66) \qquad |t_j^i - \lambda \delta_j^i| \equiv -\lambda^3 + t_i^i \lambda^2 - T_i^i \lambda + t.$$

Recall that $h_i^l H_j^i = h \delta_j^l$, and use this fact to obtain the characteristic function (66) in the following manner. First, from (65),

$$(67) \qquad t_j^l - \lambda \delta_j^l = h_i^l a_k^i H_j^k - \lambda \delta_j^l = h_i^l a_k^i H_j^k - \frac{\lambda}{h} h_i^l H_j^i$$

$$= h_i^l \left(a_k^i - \frac{\lambda}{h} \delta_k^i \right) H_j^k.$$

Take the determinant of equation (67) to obtain

$$(68) \qquad |t_j^l - \lambda \delta_j^l| = |h_i^l| \, |H_j^k| \left| a_k^i - \frac{\lambda}{h} \delta_k^i \right| = |h_i^l H_j^i| \left| a_k^i - \frac{\lambda}{h} \delta_k^i \right|$$

$$= |h \delta_j^l| \left| a_k^i - \frac{\lambda}{h} \delta_k^i \right| = h^3 \left| a_k^i - \frac{\lambda}{h} \delta_k^i \right|.$$

It follows that the roots of $|t_j^l - \lambda \delta_j^l| = 0$ are the roots of $\left| a_k^i - \frac{\lambda}{h} \delta_k^i \right| = 0$. The latter equation is equivalent to

$$(69) \qquad -\lambda^3 + h a_i^i \lambda^2 - h^2 A_i^i \lambda + h^3 a = 0.$$

Comparison of (69) with (66) shows that

$$(70) \qquad t_i^i = h a_i^i, \quad T_i^i = h^2 A_i^i, \quad t = h^3 a,$$

which means that a_i^i, A_i^i, and a are invariants of weights one, two, and three, respectively, under the transformation (61). (The jacobian of the transformation is denoted by h instead of J, as in Section 3-2.)

It should be realized that both equations (60) and (61) can be interpreted as a transformation of coordinates, and that either one may be a collineation and the other a transformation of coordinates. Therefore, it is seen that the vanishing of an invariant describes a property of a collineation which is maintained under a projectivity or under a change of coordinates. Classification of collineations by means of invariants appears in the following section.

Because the zeros of the characteristic function (59) are changed only by a nonzero factor to produce the zeros of (66), it follows that the fixed points of the collineation (60) are not altered by taking the transform of A by H. That is, the collineation (60) and the collineation (65), which is the transform of (60) by H, being the same mapping, have the same fixed points. The matrices A and HAH^{-1} are said to be *equivalent*. Two given matrices A and B (that is, two given collineations) are equivalent if and only if a matrix H exists such that $B = HAH^{-1}$. It can be shown that two matrices are equivalent if and only if they have the same *invariant factors*, which means that they have the same corresponding *elementary divisors*.*

7-9. Classification by invariants

The collineation (60) was transformed by (61) to obtain the collineation (65), the fixed points of which are determined by the roots of equation (69). These roots determine the fixed elements for (65) according to the classification in Section 7-3. It was seen (equation (70)) that the coefficients in (59) are invariants under the transformation (61). It will be convenient to denote the invariants in (70) by

$$(71) \qquad I_1 = a^i_i, \quad I_2 = A^i_i, \quad I_3 = a,$$

where the subscript on the I indicates the weight of the invariant. With this notation the characteristic equation from (59) takes the form

$$(72) \qquad -\lambda^3 + I_1\lambda^2 - I_2\lambda + I_3 = 0.$$

The symmetric functions of the roots λ_1, λ_2, λ_3 of (72) are given by

$$(73) \qquad I_1 = \lambda_1 + \lambda_2 + \lambda_3, \quad I_2 = \lambda_2\lambda_3 + \lambda_3\lambda_1 + \lambda_1\lambda_2, \quad I_3 = \lambda_1\lambda_2\lambda_3.$$

It will be shown next that the classification of Section 7-3 can be determined by means of the invariants in (71) together with the invariant rank r of the matrix $(a^i_j - \lambda\delta^i_j)$ of the coefficients in (12').

Case 1: If λ_1, λ_2, λ_3 are distinct, it is not possible to eliminate the λ_i from equations (73) to obtain a relation involving I_1, I_2, I_3. Case 1 of the theorem in Section 7-2 shows that the rank of the characteristic matrix $(a^i_j - \lambda\delta^i_j)$ is two for each of the λ_i. All collineations with three distinct fixed points are projectively equivalent to the canonical form (20) in Case 1 of Section 7-3; that is,

$$(74) \qquad k\bar{x}^1 = \lambda_1 x^1, \quad k\bar{x}^2 = \lambda_2 x^2, \quad k\bar{x}^3 = \lambda_3 x^3.$$

Case 2: If two of the roots of (72) coincide, say $\lambda_3 = \lambda_2$, and $r = 2$, then Case 2 of Section 7-3 is characterized as follows. In Section 3-10 it was shown that two roots of

$$(75) \qquad a_0 x^3 + 3a_1 x^2 + 3a_2 x + a_3 = 0$$

coincide if and only if the hessian points of the cubic (75) coincide—that is, if and only if

$$(76) \qquad (a_0 a_3 - a_1 a_2)^2 - 4(a_0 a_2 - a_1^2)(a_1 a_3 - a_2^2) = 0.$$

Comparison of equations (72) and (75) shows that (76) becomes

$$(77) \qquad (I_1 I_2 - 9I_3)^2 - 4(3I_2 - I_1^2)(3I_1 I_3 - I_2^2) = 0$$

relative to (72). If the invariants (73) of a given collineation satisfy (77), and if

---

* For this algebraic theory, which is due to Weierstrass (1868), the reader is referred to M. Bôcher's *Introduction to Higher Algebra* (Macmillan, New York, 1907) and to J. A. Todd's *Projective and Analytical Geometry* (Pitman, London, 1947).

the rank r of the characteristic matrix is two for $\lambda = \lambda_2$, the canonical form (74) must be modified to a form such as that of equation (22) in Case 2 of Section 7-3, with $a_3^2 \neq 0$.

Case 3: Now let the three roots of (72) coincide—that is, let $\lambda_3 = \lambda_2 = \lambda_1$—and require that the rank r of $(a_j^i - \lambda\delta_j^i)$ be two for $\lambda = \lambda_1$. In Section 3-10 it was seen that the three roots of (75) coincide if and only if the hessian points are indeterminate—that is, if and only if

$$(78) \qquad a_0a_2 - a_1^2 = 0, \quad a_0a_3 - a_1a_2 = 0, \quad a_1a_3 - a_2^2 = 0,$$

which become respectively

$$(79) \qquad\qquad 3I_2 = I_1^2, \quad 9I_3 = I_1I_2, \quad 3I_1I_3 = I_2^2$$

relative to equation (72). If the invariants of a collineation satisfy (79), and if $r = 2$, then the canonical form must be of the type of Case 4 in Section 7-3, with a_2^1 and a_3^2 nonzero but with the possibility that a_3^1 may be zero.

(Note that Case 3 of the present classification by invariants corresponds to Case 4 in Section 7-3.)

Case 4: This is equivalent to Case 2 above except that here $r = 1$ for $\lambda = \lambda_2$. This case corresponds to Case 3 in Section 7-3. The canonical form (23) in Section 7-3, or

$$\rho\bar{x}^1 = \lambda_1 x^1, \quad \rho\bar{x}^2 = \lambda_2 x^2, \quad \rho\bar{x}^3 = \lambda_2 x^3,$$

is readily seen to have a characteristic matrix of rank one for $\lambda = \lambda_2$.

Case 5: This is equivalent to Case 3 above except that here $r = 1$ for $\lambda = \lambda_1$. A canonical form such as that in equation (26) in Section 7-3, or

$$\rho\bar{x}^1 = \lambda_1 x^1 + a_2^1 x^2 + a_3^1 x^3, \quad \rho\bar{x}^2 = \lambda_1 x^2, \quad \rho\bar{x}^3 = \lambda_1 x^3,$$

will suffice for this case. Note, however, that a_2^1 and a_3^1 cannot both be zero, because the rank r for $\lambda = \lambda_1$ must be one.

Case 6: This is equivalent to Case 5 above except that the rank is zero, which demands that $a_2^1 = a_3^1 = 0$. Hence, the canonical form is $\rho\bar{x}^i = x^i$, which is the trivial case of the identity mapping.

EXERCISES

1. Investigate the invariants of the mapping

$$\rho\bar{x}^i = a_j^i x^j, \qquad\qquad\qquad i, j = 1, 2,$$

on a line. State the geometric meaning of the vanishing of the invariant $I_1 = a_i^i$ and of $I_2 = a$. Show that $I_1^2 - 4I_2$ is an invariant and state the geometrical meaning of its vanishing.

2. Show that if a collineation on a line is parabolic, then its transform is also parabolic. Show further that an elliptic collineation may be transformed into a hyperbolic collineation. (This means that a canonical form does not distinguish between real and complex fixed points.)

3. Obtain two absolute invariants by use of equations (70).

4. Find the transform of the collineation $k\bar{x}^1 = x^1 + x^2 + x^3$, $k\bar{x}^2 = 6x^1 - 2x^3$, $k\bar{x}^3 = x^3$ by the matrix

$$H \equiv \begin{pmatrix} 1 & -1 & 1 \\ 1 & 1 & -1 \\ -1 & 1 & 1 \end{pmatrix},$$

and verify that the fixed points of the given collineation are the same as those for the transformed collineation.

Ans. The matrix of the transformed collineation is

$$\begin{pmatrix} -1 & -4 & 5 \\ 5 & 8 & -1 \\ 3 & 4 & -3 \end{pmatrix}.$$

5. Classify the collineation $k\bar{x}^1 = 3x^1 - x^2 + x^3$, $k\bar{x}^2 = x^1 + 3x^2 - x^3$, $k\bar{x}^3 = -2x^1 + 6x^3$ by means of the invariants described in Section 7-9.

6. Write the collineation of Exercise 5 in line coordinates and then verify the classification by using an analytical method similar to that in Section 7-3.

7. Show that $(HAH^{-1})^{-1} = HA^{-1}H^{-1}$.

8. If A is the matrix of the collineation $\rho\bar{x}^1 = ax^3$, $\rho\bar{x}^2 = bx^1$, $\rho\bar{x}^3 = cx^2$, find the collineation for which the matrix is A^3.

9. Find, by multiplying matrices, the square of the collineation in Exercise 5.

10. Write the collineation (1) in Section 7-1 in line coordinates, and then find its characteristic equation. By comparing the latter with equation (59), deduce that the configuration of fixed elements under a collineation is self-dual.

11. Find a collineation with fixed points $(0:1:1)$, $(1:0:1)$, $(1:1:0)$ in the following manner. First, obtain the transformation (H^{-1}) of coordinates by which the three points become $(1:0:0)$, $(0:1:0)$, $(0:0:1)$, respectively, and such that a fourth point, say $(1:1:1)$, has new coordinates $(1:-1:1)$. Now perform the collineation (A): $\rho\bar{x}^1 = x^1$, $\rho\bar{x}^2 = 2x^2$, $\rho\bar{x}^3 = 3x^3$, and then change coordinates by H, the inverse of H^{-1}. The result is the collineation $k\bar{x}^1 = 5x^1 + x^2 - x^3$, $k\bar{x}^2 = 2x^1 + 4x^2 - 2x^3$, $k\bar{x}^3 = x^1 - x^2 + 3x^3$. Verify that $(0:1:1)$, $(1:0:1)$, $(1:1:0)$ are fixed under this collineation.

12. Extend equation (59) to the case of the collineations $(i, j = 1, 2, 3, 4)$ in three-space, and thus find the expressions for the invariants I_1, I_2, I_3, I_4.

CHAPTER 8

The Conic

8-1. Intersection of a line and a conic

In Section 7-6 a point conic was defined as the locus of a point which is in united position with its corresponding line under a correlation. Dually, a line conic was seen to be the envelope of a line which is in united position with its corresponding point under a correlation. The equation of a point conic was found to be

$$(1) \qquad f(x) \equiv a_{ij}x^ix^j = 0,$$

for which the matrix (a_{ij}) is symmetric $(a_{ij} = a_{ji})$. The conic will be supposed to be noncomposite, in general. This means that $a \equiv |a_{ij}| \neq 0$ in the general case. The line equation of the conic (1) was found in Section 7-6 to have the form

$$(2) \qquad g(u) \equiv A^{ij}u_iu_j = 0,$$

where A^{ij} (or A^{ji}) is the cofactor of a_{ij} in $|a_{ij}|$. Because the determinant $A \equiv |A^{ij}| = |a_{ij}|^2$, the line conic (2) is noncomposite if the point conic (1) is noncomposite. If x^i is a variable point on the line l determined by two fixed points y^i and z^i (Fig. 59), then

$$(3) \qquad x^i = \lambda y^i + \mu z^i,$$

where λ and μ are parameters. The values of λ and μ corresponding to the points P', P'' where l intersects the conic (1) are obtained by substituting the coordinates (3) into (1) to find

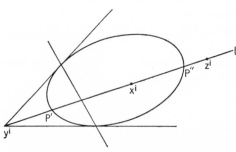

Figure 59

$$a_{ij}(\lambda y^i + \mu z^i)(\lambda y^j + \mu z^j) = 0,$$

or

$$(a_{ij}y^iy^j)\lambda^2 + (a_{ij}z^iy^j + a_{ij}y^iz^j)\lambda\mu + (a_{ij}z^iz^j)\mu^2 = 0,$$

which, by the fact that $a_{ij} = a_{ji}$, can be written as

(4)
$$(a_{ij}y^iy^j)\lambda^2 + 2(a_{ij}y^iz^j)\lambda\mu + (a_{ij}z^iz^j)\mu^2 = 0.$$

To each value of the ratio λ/μ satisfying (4), there corresponds a point given by (3). Hence, the intersections P', P'' of l and the conic (1) are determined. The point conic is a curve of order two.

If l is tangent to the conic, then P' and P'' coincide and equation (4) has equal roots. The condition for this is

(5)
$$(a_{ij}y^iz^j)^2 - (a_{ij}y^iy^j)(a_{kl}z^kz^l) = 0.$$

Let the point y^i be held fixed, and allow z^i to vary. Equation (5) is then the equation of two tangent lines to the conic from the point y^i. Replace z^i by x^i to have the equation of the tangents from the point y^i to the conic in the form

(6)
$$(a_{ij}y^iy^j)(a_{kl}x^kx^l) - (a_{ij}y^ix^j)^2 = 0.$$

Equation (6) is reducible (or composite); that is, its left member can be written as the product of two linear factors in x^1, x^2, x^3. Thus, because two tangents can be drawn to a conic from a point, a conic is of class two.

Next, suppose that the point y^i is on the conic, so that $a_{ij}y^iy^j = 0$. Under this condition, equation (5) gives for the locus of the variable point z^i the tangent line with equation

(7)
$$a_{ij}y^ix^j = 0.$$

Observe that the linear equation (7) represents a line whether the point y^i is on the conic or not. The geometrical interpretation of the line (7) in case $a_{ij}y^iy^j \neq 0$ will now be explained.

DEFINITION: *The points y^i and z^i are conjugate with respect to the conic* (1) *if they separate harmonically the points P', P'' in which the line l (Fig. 59) intersects the conic.*

Again, let y^i be a fixed point, and let it be required to find the locus of points z^i which are conjugate to y^i with respect to the conic (1). Let the ratios λ'/μ' and λ''/μ'', which satisfy (4), correspond to the points P' and P'' as given by (3). The number pairs λ, μ in (3) corresponding to the points y^i and z^i are 1, 0 and 0, 1 respectively. Hence, the cross ratio of the four points y^i, z^i, P', P'' is $(1/0, 0/1, \lambda'/\mu', \lambda''/\mu'')$, which is -1 if $(\lambda'/\mu') + (\lambda''/\mu'') = 0$. This requires that the sum of the roots of equation (4) be zero, that is, $a_{ij}y^iz^j = 0$. Hence, the desired locus of points conjugate to the point y^i is the line $a_{ij}y^ix^j = 0$, which has the same form as the tangent line (7) for the case in which y^i is on the conic. If $a_{ij}y^iy^j \neq 0$, equation (7) represents the *polar* line of y^i relative to the conic (1), and if $a_{ij}y^iy^j = 0$, the polar line is the tangent at y^i The point y^i is the *pole* of its polar line. Note that the correspondence between points and the loci of their conjugate points is a correlation.

8-2. Properties of poles and polars

The polar line $a_{ij}y^ix^j = 0$ of the point y^i relative to the conic $a_{ij}x^ix^j = 0$ passes through the points of contact of the tangents from y^i to the conic (Fig. 59). In order to see this, solve equations (6) and (7) to find $(a_{ij}y^iy^j)(a_{kl}x^kx^l) = 0$, which reduces to $a_{kl}x^kx^l = 0$ because y^i is not on the conic. Hence, the polar of y^i meets the tangents from y^i at points on the conic.

The symmetric property of poles and polars is stated as follows. If the point z^i is on the polar of y^i, then y^i is on the polar of z^i. To show this, note that if z^i is on the polar $a_{ij}y^ix^j = 0$ of y^i, then $a_{ij}y^iz^j = 0$, which is the condition that y^i be on the polar $a_{ij}z^ix^j = 0$ of z^i.

The polar lines relative to a conic C of all points y^i on a line l pass through a point which is the pole of l relative to C. This is shown as follows. If y_1^i and y_2^i are two points on l, any point on l has coordinates $\lambda y_1^i + \mu y_2^i$, whose polar relative to C has the equation $a_{ij}(\lambda y_1^i + \mu y_2^i)x^j = 0$, or

$$(8) \qquad \lambda(a_{ij}y_1^ix^j) + \mu(a_{ij}y_2^ix^j) = 0.$$

As λ and μ vary, equation (8) represents a pencil of lines through the point common to

$$a_{ij}y_1^ix^j = 0, \quad a_{ij}y_2^ix^j = 0.$$

Hence, the polars of points on l are lines of a pencil. In order to show that the center of the pencil is the pole of l, let ξ^i be the center of the pencil. The polar of ξ^i is $a_{ij}\xi^ix^j = 0$. But the conditions $a_{ij}y_1^i\xi^j = 0$, $a_{ij}y_2^i\xi^j = 0$ that ξ^i be the center of the pencil are the conditions that y_1^i and y_2^i be on the polar line of ξ^i, and they insure that $a_{ij}(\lambda y_1^i + \mu y_2^i)\xi^j = 0$, which states that all points on l lie on the polar line of the center ξ^i.

The analysis can often be made simpler by a judicious choice of coordinates. As an instance of this, the last property will be exhibited again in a different manner. There is no loss in generality in taking the line l as $x^3 = 0$. The polar of the point $(y^1:y^2:0)$ on l is then $y^1a_{1j}x^j + y^2a_{2j}x^j = 0$. As the point y^i varies on l, the polar line of y^i varies in the pencil determined by the lines $a_{1j}x^j = 0$ and $a_{2j}x^j = 0$, which intersect in the point $(A^{31}:A^{32}:A^{33})$, the polar of which can readily be shown to be l with equation $x^3 = 0$.

Self-polar Triangle

DEFINITION: *A self-polar triangle relative to a conic C is a triangle for which each vertex is the pole of the opposite side.*

There exists a triply infinite set of self-polar triangles relative to a given conic. This can be seen as follows. One vertex can be chosen as any point (not on the conic) in the plane. There is then a doubly infinite set of choices for the first vertex. The second vertex must be chosen from the singly infinite set of points on the polar line of the first vertex. The polar line of the second vertex intersects the polar line of the first vertex in the third vertex to determine the self-polar triangle.

It will be shown next that if a conic is referred to a self-polar triangle of reference, the equation of the conic is of the form $\alpha(x^1)^2 + \beta(x^2)^2 + \gamma(x^3)^2 = 0$. The polar line of $P_1(1:0:0)$ relative to $a_{ij}x^ix^j = 0$ is $a_{ij}y^ix^j = 0$, where $y^1 = 1$, $y^2 = y^3 = 0$—that is, $a_{1j}x^j = 0$. But this is the line $x^1 = 0$. Hence, $a_{12} = a_{13} = 0$, $a_{11} \neq 0$. The polar of $P_2(0:1:0)$ is $a_{2j}x^j = 0$, which is $x^2 = 0$; hence, $a_{23} = 0$ and $a_{22} \neq 0$. The polar line of $P_3(0:0:1)$ is $a_{3j}x^j = 0$, which is $x^3 = 0$; hence, $a_{33} \neq 0$. The equation of the conic is now $a_{11}(x^1)^2 + a_{22}(x^2)^2 + a_{33}(x^3)^2 = 0$, which may be written as

(9) $$\alpha(x^1)^2 + \beta(x^2)^2 + \gamma(x^3)^2 = 0, \qquad\qquad \alpha\beta\gamma \neq 0.$$

The notion of a self-polar triangle relative to a conic can be generalized to a self-polar tetrahedron relative to a quadric surface in three-space (see Exercise 15).

A Standard Form

The equation of a conic can be given a form which is extremely useful in obtaining projective properties of a conic. This form, $(x^2)^2 = x^1x^3$, is derived as follows. Let the triangle of reference be chosen as shown in Fig. 60. The point $(1:0:0)$ must satisfy the equation $a_{ij}x^ix^j = 0$ of a conic; hence, $a_{11} = 0$. Similarly, because $(0:0:1)$ is on the conic, $a_{33} = 0$. The equation of the tangent to C at P_1 is $a_{1j}x^j = 0$, which is $x^3 = 0$; hence, $a_{12} = 0$. The tangent to C at P_3 is $a_{3j}x^j = 0$, which is $x^1 = 0$; hence, $a_{23} = 0$. Thus, the general equation of C reduces to

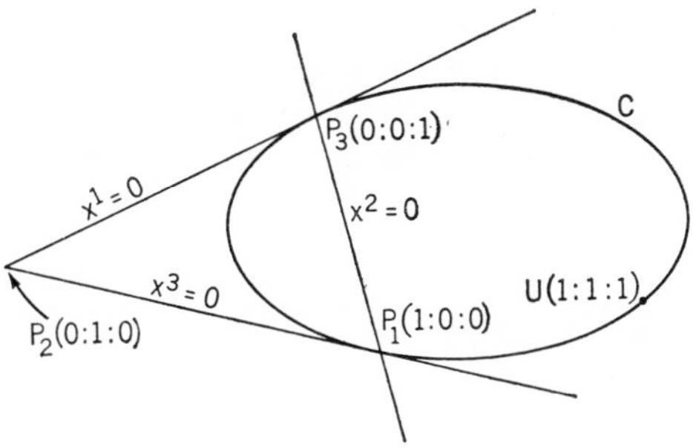

$$2a_{13}x^1x^3 + a_{22}(x^2)^2 = 0.$$

Figure 60

Now choose a point on C as the unit point $U(1:1:1)$, so that $2a_{13} + a_{22} = 0$. The reduced equation is then

(10) $$(x^2)^2 = x^1x^3,$$

which may be referred to as the *pole-polar* form of the equation of a conic.

Note that $x^1:x^2:x^3 = t^2:t:1$ is a useful parametric representation of the conic in (10). To every value of t there is a point on the conic, but no value of t gives the point $(1:0:0)$. This latter point can be arrived at, however, by a limiting process. First divide the coordinates $t^2:t:1$ by t^2, and then let t become infinite to obtain the limit point $(1:0:0)$. This process can be avoided by using the parametric representation $x^1:x^2:x^3 = t^2:tt':t'^2$. To $t = 0$ corresponds the point $(0:0:1)$, and to $t' = 0$ corresponds the point $(1:0:0)$. However, it is simpler to use the single parameter t. Note that as t varies the points $(t^2:t:1)$ are in one-to-one correspondence with the points of the projective line. Hence, the points of the conic are in one-to-one correspondence with the points of a projective line.

The nature of a given problem often indicates the most expeditious form to choose for the equation of a conic. In some instances the general form $a_{ij}x^ix^j = 0$ is best, in some cases the form (9) is to be preferred, while in many exercises the form (10) is advisable. The next three Examples are provided as illustrations of the three cases just mentioned.

EXAMPLE 1

Find the condition under which the pole of the line $l_ix^i = 0$ with respect to the conic $a_{ij}x^ix^j = 0$ is on the line $l'_ix^i = 0$.

Solution: If the point y^i is the pole of $l_ix^i = 0$, then the line $a_{ij}y^ix^j = 0$ is its polar, which is the line $l_ix^i = 0$. Hence, $a_{ij}y^i = \rho l_j$, from which $a_{ij}A^{jk}y^i = \rho l_j A^{jk}$, or $a\delta^k_i y^i = \rho l_j A^{jk}$, or $y^k = hl_j A^{jk}$. Because y^k satisfies $l'_k x^k = 0$, the required condition is $A^{jk}l_j l'_k = 0$.

EXAMPLE 2

Show that the six vertices of two triangles which are self-polar relative to a conic C lie on another conic.

Solution: Take the vertices P_i of one of the triangles as the triangle of reference, with the consequence that the conic C has the form (9); that is, $\alpha(x^1)^2 + \beta(x^2)^2 + \gamma(x^3)^3 = 0$. Let Q_1, Q_2, Q_3 be the vertices of the second triangle with coordinates x^i_1, x^i_2, x^i_3, respectively. The polar of Q_3 with respect to C has the equation

$$\alpha x^1_3 x^1 + \beta x^2_3 x^2 + \gamma x^3_3 x^3 = 0,$$

and the condition that Q_2 lie on this polar is the first of the equations

$$\alpha x^1_2 x^1_3 + \beta x^2_2 x^2_3 + \gamma x^3_2 x^3_3 = 0,$$
$$\alpha x^1_3 x^1_1 + \beta x^2_3 x^2_1 + \gamma x^3_3 x^3_1 = 0,$$
$$\alpha x^1_1 x^1_2 + \beta x^2_1 x^2_2 + \gamma x^3_1 x^3_2 = 0.$$

The second and third equations are obtained in a similar way. The determinant of the coefficients of α, β, γ in this set of equations must vanish. Divide the columns of this determinant respectively by $x^1_i x^2_i x^3_i$, where $i = 1, 2, 3$, to obtain the form

$$\begin{vmatrix} \dfrac{1}{x^1_1} & \dfrac{1}{x^2_1} & \dfrac{1}{x^3_1} \\[2mm] \dfrac{1}{x^1_2} & \dfrac{1}{x^2_2} & \dfrac{1}{x^3_2} \\[2mm] \dfrac{1}{x^1_3} & \dfrac{1}{x^2_3} & \dfrac{1}{x^3_3} \end{vmatrix} = 0,$$

which is a necessary and sufficient condition that there exist constants p, q, r not all zero, such that

$$\frac{p}{x^1} + \frac{q}{x^2} + \frac{r}{x^3} = 0.$$

That is,

$$px^2x^3 + qx^3x^1 + rx^1x^2 = 0,$$

which is a conic satisfied by the three points Q_i. It is evident that this conic contains also the points P_i.

EXAMPLE 3

A variable line of a pencil of lines meets a conic C in the points Q', Q''. The lines determined by Q', Q'' and a fixed point S intersect C again in the points R', R'', respectively. Show that the line through R' and R'' passes through a fixed point. *Solution:* The pole-polar form of equation (10) appears feasible for use in this problem. Assign the coordinates $Q'(\sigma^2:\sigma:1)$ and $Q''(\tau^2:\tau:1)$. The line $Q'Q''$ therefore has coordinates $[1:-\sigma -\tau:\sigma\tau]$. Because $P_2(0:1:0)$ is on $Q'Q''$, it follows that $\sigma + \tau = 0$. Also assign the coordinates $R'(\alpha^2:\alpha:1)$ and $R''(\beta^2:\beta:1)$, and find the coordinates of line $R'R''$ to be $[1:-\alpha -\beta:\alpha\beta]$. The line coordinates of $Q'R'$ are $[1:-\alpha -\sigma:\alpha\sigma]$, and those of $Q''R''$ are $[1:-\beta -\tau:\beta\tau]$. The fixed point $S(y^i)$ is on both $Q'R'$ and $Q''R''$. Hence, with $\tau = -\sigma$,

$$y^1 - (\alpha + \sigma)y^2 + \alpha\sigma y^3 = 0,$$
$$y^1 - (\beta - \sigma)y^2 - \beta\sigma y^3 = 0,$$

from which σ is eliminated to obtain

$$2y^1y^2 - (\alpha + \beta)[(y^2)^2 + y^1y^3] + 2\alpha\beta y^2y^3 = 0.$$

This is the condition that the fixed point

$$x^1:x^2:x^3 = 2y^1y^2:(y^2)^2 + y^1y^3:2y^2y^3$$

satisfy the variable line $R'R''$ with the equation

$$x^1 - (\alpha + \beta)x^2 + \alpha\beta x^3 = 0.$$

(For an extension of this Example see Exercise 17.)

It is to be noted that the analysis in Example 3 would be far more tedious for some other choices of the equation of the conic. Further forms for the equation of a conic, which are useful in certain types of problems, are given in Exercises 7 and 8.

EXERCISES

1. Prove that the conic (1) represents two lines if $|a_{ij}| = 0$, and that equation (2) represents two points if $|A^{ij}| = 0$. *Suggestion:* Change to nonhomogeneous coordinates. If $a_{11} \neq 0$, write the equation as a quadratic in x and demand that the discriminant of the quadratic be a perfect square. If $a_{11} = 0$, $a_{22} \neq 0$, consider a quadratic in y.

2. Find the points of intersection of the conic $(x^1)^2 + (x^2)^2 + (x^3)^2 + 2x^2x^3 + 2x^1x^2 - 2x^1x^3 = 0$ with the line joining the points $(-3:1:2)$ and $(2:-3:1)$.

   Ans. $(0:1:-1)$, $(1:-1:0)$.

3. Find the equation of the tangents from the point $(-1:-1:1)$ to the conic $(x^1)^2 - 2x^1x^3 + (x^2)^2 - (x^3)^2 = 0$.

$$Ans.\ (x^1)^2 - 2(x^2)^2 + 3(x^3)^2 + 4x^1x^2 + 6x^1x^3 = 0.$$

4. Find the values of k for which $(x^1)^2 - 2(x^2)^2 + 2(x^3)^2 + kx^2x^3 + 3x^3x^1 - x^1x^2 = 0$ represents two lines, and find the two lines.

$$Ans.\ [1:1:2],\ [1:-2:1];\ [1:1:1],\ [1:-2:2].$$

5. Find the pole of the line $[1:1:1]$ relative to the conic $(x^2)^2 = x^1x^3$.

$$Ans.\ (2:-1:2).$$

6. Find the pole of the line $l_ix^i = 0$ relative to $a_{ij}x^ix^j = 0$.

7. Show that the equation $a_{ij}x^ix^j = 0$ of a conic takes the form $\alpha x^2x^3 + \beta x^3x^1 + \gamma x^1x^2 = 0$, with $\alpha\beta\gamma \neq 0$, if the vertices of the triangle of reference are on the conic.

8. Show that the equation of the conic has the form $\pm\sqrt{\alpha x^1} \pm \sqrt{\beta x^2} \pm \sqrt{\gamma x^3} = 0$ if the sides of the triangle of reference are tangent to the conic.

9. Show that a conic is determined by five points, no three of which are collinear, and that a singly infinite set of conics pass through four given points. Find the equation of the set of conics which contain the four points $(0:1:1)$, $(1:0:1)$, $(1:2:0)$, $(0:1:2)$.

$$Ans.\ 2\lambda(x^1)^2 - (\lambda + 8)x^1x^2 + 4(x^2)^2 - 2(1 + \lambda)x^1x^3 - 6x^2x^3 + 2(x^3)^2 = 0.$$

10. Take the four vertices of a quadrangle as points on a conic. Let the diagonal triangle of the quadrangle be the triangle of reference, and let one of the vertices of the quadrangle be the unit point. Show that the remaining vertices of the quadrangle have the coordinates $(-1:1:1)$, $(1:-1:1)$, $(1:1:-1)$.

11. Find the equation of the singly infinite set of conics through the vertices of the quadrangle in Exercise 10, and show that the pairs of points in which these conics intersect the line $x^3 = 0$ constitute an involution. (This illustrates a theorem of Desargues. See Section 8-6.)

$$Ans.\ \text{The conics are given by } (x^2)^2 - (x^3)^2 - \lambda[(x^1)^2 - (x^3)^2] = 0.$$

12. Find the line equation of the point conic

$$\alpha(x^1)^2 + \beta(x^2)^2 + \gamma(x^3)^2 = 0, \qquad\qquad \alpha\beta\gamma \neq 0.$$

13. (a) Define a self-polar tetrahedron relative to a quadric surface. (b) Show that a set of ∞^6 self-polar tetrahedrons exist relative to a quadric surface. (c) Generalize to a self-polar *simplex* relative to a hyperquadric in n-space, and show that a set of $\infty^{n(n+1)/2}$ self-polar hyperplanes exist relative to the hyperquadric.

14. Prove that the diagonal triangle of a complete quadrangle inscribed in a conic (vertices on the conic) is self-polar with respect to all of the conics through the four points. *Hint:* Use Exercise 10.

15. In Example 3, let P_1S and P_3S intersect the conic C in F_1 and F_3, respectively. Show that the line F_1F_3 is the polar of the fixed point (call it F_2) found in Example 3. Show further that the triangles $P_1P_2P_3$ and $F_1F_2F_3$ are perspective from S, and that the axis of the perspectivity is the polar of S with respect to C.

16. Two variable chords FP and FQ through a fixed point F of a conic separate two fixed lines through F harmonically. Show that the line PQ passes through a fixed point.

17. Prove that the determinant $|a_{ij}|$ is a projective invariant of the conic (1).

18. Show that the equation (1) of a conic represents a cone in three-space with non-homogeneous cartesian coordinates x^1, x^2, x^3. What is the significance of the vanishing of the invariant $|a_{ij}|$ in this interpretation?

19. Show that the trace $a_{11} + a_{22} + a_{33}$ of the matrix (a_{ij}) in (1) is an invariant under an orthogonal rotation about the origin in three-space.*

8-3. Composite conics

The point conic $a_{ij}x^ix^j = 0$ is a *proper conic* (i.e. noncomposite) in case the matrix (a_{ij}) has rank $r = 3$. A proper point conic is also a proper line conic. There is complete duality between proper point and line conics. To every theorem concerning proper point conics there is a corresponding theorem concerning proper line conics. But if the rank of (a_{ij}) is less than three (that is, the conic is composite), it will be seen that complete duality no longer holds.

The tangent line to the point conic $a_{ij}x^ix^j = 0$ at the point y^i is $a_{ij}y^ix^j = 0$. This line is indeterminate in case $a_{ij}y^i = 0$ for $j = 1, 2, 3$. If $r = 2$, then $|a_{ij}| = 0$, and consequently there exists a unique solution y^i other than the trivial solution $(0:0:0)$. Such a point y^i on a point conic where the tangent line is indeterminate is called a *vertex*. Thus, if $r = 2$, there is just one vertex, and the point conic consists of two lines through the vertex. (See Exercise 1 in Section 8-2.) Now suppose the rank $r = 1$. In this case the three equations $a_{ij}y^i = 0$ reduce to a single equation $\alpha_j y^i = 0$, which means that the point conic consists of a line of vertices with the equation $\alpha_i x^i = 0$. The point conic is then composed of two coincident lines—that is, the line $\alpha_i x^i = 0$ counted twice. If $r = 0$, the point conic is indeterminate.

In order to investigate the composite line conic $A^{ij}u_iu_j = 0$, in which the matrix (A^{ij}) is the adjoint of the matrix (a_{ij}), consider the general

THEOREM:† *If r is the rank of a square matrix of order n, and R is the rank of its adjoint matrix, then*

$$\text{if } r = n, \quad R = n,$$
$$\text{if } r = n - 1, \quad R = 1,$$
$$\text{if } r < n - 1, \quad R = 0.$$

---

* It can be shown that the vanishing of the trace in this interpretation is a necessary and sufficient condition for the cone defined by equation (1) to contain three mutually perpendicular generators. See Robert J. T. Bell, *Coordinate Geometry of Three Dimensions* (Macmillan, New York, 1926), p. 192, and Exercises 9–13 in Section 10-9.

† A proof of this theorem can be found in M. Bôcher, *Introduction to Higher Algebra* (Macmillan, New York, 1907).

In the case of the matrix (a_{ij}) for the point conic in which $n = 3$,

$$\text{if } r = 3, \quad R = 3,$$
$$\text{if } r = 2, \quad R = 1,$$
$$\text{if } r < 2, \quad R = 0.$$

Hence, one concludes that if $r = 3$, the proper point conic is a proper line conic; if $r = 2$, the composite point conic which is two distinct lines is two coincident points regarded as a line conic; and if $r = 1$, the composite point conic, which is two coincident lines, is indeterminate as a line conic.

EXERCISE

Show that the conic $(x^1)^2 - (x^3)^2 + x^1x^2 - x^2x^3 = 0$ is two lines, and that the corresponding line conic is the square of a linear factor which represents the vertex $(1:-2:1)$ counted twice.

Remark: A *proper conic* is also referred to as *noncomposite, nonsingular,* or *irreducible.*

8-4. The conic as defined by Steiner (1796–1863)

Consider two pencils of lines $(a_ix^i) + \lambda(b_ix^i) = 0$ and $(c_ix^i) + \mu(d_ix^i) = 0$, where λ and μ are parameters. If λ and μ are related by the homographic correspondence

(11) $$\mu = \frac{\alpha\lambda + \beta}{\gamma\lambda + \delta}, \qquad \alpha\delta - \beta\gamma \neq 0,$$

then λ and μ can be eliminated from the last three equations to obtain the locus

$$[(\alpha a_i - \beta b_i)d_j + (\gamma a_i - \delta b_i)c_j]x^ix^j = 0,$$

which is an equation of the second degree of the form $a_{ij}x^ix^j = 0$. This proves the

THEOREM OF STEINER: *The locus of the point of intersection of corresponding rays of two projective line pencils (with distinct centers) is a conic.*

A second proof of Steiner's theorem by means of a simpler notation will now be given. Let the centers of the pencils be taken at $P_1(1:0:0)$ and $P_2(0:1:0)$ (Fig. 61). Any line of the first pencil with center at P_1 has an equation of the form $x^2 + \lambda x^3 = 0$, and any line of the second pencil is $x^1 + \mu x^3 = 0$. A projective correspondence between the pencils is of the form of equation (11). Elimination of λ and μ gives the point conic with the equation

(12) $$\alpha x^2x^3 - \beta(x^3)^2 + \gamma x^1x^2 - \delta x^1x^3 = 0.$$

Observe that the coordinates of both P_1 and P_2 satisfy equation (12). The ray P_1P_2 of the pencil with P_1 as center has a corresponding line through P_2, and the ray P_2P_1 of the pencil with P_2 as center has a corresponding line through P_1.

It is readily concluded that the line through P_2 corresponding to P_1P_2 is tangent to the conic at P_2. This is seen analytically as follows. For the line $P_1P_2(x^3 = 0)$ to be given by $x^2 + \lambda x^3 = 0$, λ must become infinite. Equation (11) shows that therefore μ must be α/γ, where $\gamma \neq 0$, so that the corresponding line $x^1 + \mu x^3 = 0$ through P_2 has the equation $\gamma x^1 + \alpha x^3 = 0$. But this is readily shown to be the equation of the tangent at $P_2(0:1:0)$ to the conic (12). Similarly, one shows that the correspondent of line P_2P_1 is the tangent line at $P_1(1:0:0)$ to the conic.

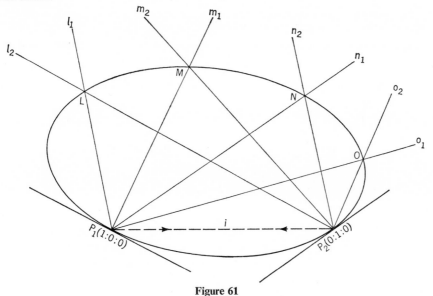

Figure 61

The determinant $|a_{ij}|$ for equation (12) is $\gamma(\beta\gamma - \alpha\delta)$. Because $\beta\gamma - \alpha\delta \neq 0$, the conic is composite in case $\gamma = 0$, which is evident from equation (12). If the conic is composite, with $\gamma = 0$, then one of the two lines in (12) is the line determined by P_1 and P_2. The other line has the equation $\delta x^1 - \alpha x^2 + \beta x^3 = 0$. With $\gamma = 0$, the correspondence (11) takes the form $\mu = (\alpha\lambda + \beta)/\delta$; thus it is seen that as $\lambda \to \infty$, μ also becomes infinite, which means that the line P_1P_2 with equation $x^3 = 0$ considered as a member of the pencil with center at P_1 corresponds to the same line considered as a member of the pencil with center at P_2. Note also that the point of intersection of the corresponding rays $x^2 + \lambda x^3 = 0$ and $x^1 + \mu x^3 = 0$ has coordinates given by

$$\begin{bmatrix} 0 & 1 & \lambda \\ 1 & 0 & \mu \end{bmatrix} \to (\mu:\lambda:-1) = \left(\frac{\alpha\lambda + \beta}{\delta}:\lambda:-1\right) = (\alpha\lambda + \beta:\lambda\delta:-\delta),$$

which satisfy the line $\delta x^1 - \alpha x^2 + \beta x^3 = 0$ for all λ. Two projective pencils with centers at P_1 and P_2 for which the line P_1P_2 is a self-corresponding line are said to be *perspective*. From the foregoing discussion it is seen that the locus of the intersections of corresponding rays of two *perspective* pencils is a line which does not contain the centers of the pencils. (In this case the points *L, M, N, O,* ⋯ in Fig. 61 are collinear.) Note that all points of the self-corresponding line may be considered as part of the locus. In this case, the locus is a composite conic.

Dually, the conic can be defined as the envelope of the lines joining pairs of corresponding points of two projective ranges on coplanar lines. In Fig. 62

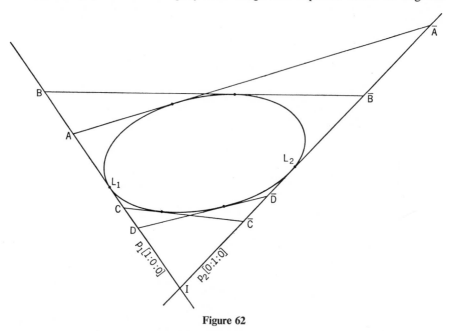

Figure 62

the point range *A, B, C,* ⋯ on line $p_1[1:0:0]$ is projective with the range $\overline{A}, \overline{B}, \overline{C},$ ⋯ on $p_2[0:1:0]$. Any point *P* on p_1 has the line equation $u^2 + \lambda u^3 = 0$, and any point $\overline{P}$ on p_2 is represented by $u^1 + \mu u^3 = 0$, but the projective correspondence $\mu = (\alpha\lambda + \beta)/(\gamma\lambda + \delta)$ relates the points on the two ranges in a one-to-one manner. Elimination of λ and μ gives a second-degree equation in u_i for the line conic which is the envelope of the lines $P\overline{P}$; that is,

(13) $\alpha u_2 u_3 - \beta u_3^2 + \gamma u_1 u_2 - \delta u_1 u_3 = 0.$

The coordinates of both p_1 and p_2 satisfy (13), so the base lines of the ranges are tangents to the line conic. In a manner similar to that used above for the point conic, it can be shown that if $\gamma \neq 0$ the point *I* of intersection of p_1 and p_2 (as a point on p_1) corresponds to the contact point L_2 of p_2, and that *I* (as a point on p_2) corresponds to the contact point L_1 of p_1. As has been seen previously, the composite line conic, with $\gamma = 0$, is merely two points. One is the point $I(u_3 = 0)$, and the other is the point $(\delta:-\alpha:\beta)$. All lines $P\overline{P}$ joining corresponding points of the two ranges are concurrent in the point $(\delta:-\alpha:\beta)$, and *I* is a self-corresponding point. In this case, the point ranges are *perspective*.

Attention is called to the fact that if the four points L, M, N, O in Fig. 61 are held fixed and the center P_1 is allowed to move on the conic, then the cross ratio of the lines P_1L, P_1M, P_1N, P_1O is constant, because any two positions of P_1 determine with L, M, N, O two projective pencils which generate the conic. The cross ratio of four elements of one pencil is the same as the cross ratio of the corresponding elements of the other pencil.

EXAMPLE

In Example 2 of Section 1-2 the projectivity $x\bar{x} - 2\bar{x} = 1$ was considered. The lines joining corresponding points on the two ranges of Fig. 2 appear to be tangent to an ellipse. Show that the curve is an ellipse by finding its equation.

Solution: In Fig. 2 take $\bar{O}$ as the origin and the $\bar{x}$ range along the x-axis. Take $\overline{OO}$ as the y-axis with the x range along the line $y = 1$. Let $(\lambda:0:1)$ be the coordinates of a point on the $\bar{x}$ range. Its corresponding point on the x range is then

$$\left(\frac{2\lambda + 1}{\lambda}:1:1\right),$$

or $(2\lambda + 1:\lambda:\lambda)$. The line joining these points has coordinates u_i given by

$$\begin{pmatrix} 2\lambda + 1 & \lambda & \lambda \\ \lambda & 0 & 1 \end{pmatrix} \rightarrow [\lambda:\lambda^2 - 2\lambda - 1:-\lambda^2].$$

It follows that

$$\frac{u_1}{u_3} = -\frac{1}{\lambda}, \quad \frac{u_2}{u_3} = \frac{\lambda^2 - 2\lambda - 1}{-\lambda^2}.$$

Elimination of λ from the last two equations gives the line conic

$$u_1^2 - 2u_1u_3 - u_2u_3 - u_3^2 = 0,$$

the point equation for which is

$$(x^1)^2 - 4x^1x^2 + 8(x^2)^2 - 4x^2x^3 = 0,$$

or, in nonhomogeneous coordinates,

$$x^2 - 4xy + 8y^2 - 4y = 0,$$

which represents an ellipse. The lines $y = 0$ and $y = 1$ are tangent to the ellipse at the points $(0, 0)$ and $(2, 1)$, respectively.

Another way to find the equation of the envelope curve is the following. The line determined by the points $(\lambda, 0)$ and $((2\lambda + 1)/\lambda, 1)$ has the equation

$$\lambda^2(y - 1) + \lambda(x - 2y) - y = 0,$$

the derivative of which with respect to λ is

$$2\lambda(y - 1) + (x - 2y) = 0.$$

Elimination of λ between the last two equations yields the point conic

$$x^2 - 4xy + 8y^2 - 4y = 0.$$

The Theorem of Chasles (1793–1880)

In Section 8-2 the useful pole-polar form of the equation for a conic was shown to be $(x^2)^2 = x^1x^3$, which is satisfied by the variable point with coordinates

$(\theta^2:\theta:1)$. A line through the fixed point $F_1(\alpha^2:\alpha:1)$ on the conic C meets the conic again in a point $P(\theta^2:\theta:1)$. There is a one-to-one correspondence between the lines of the pencil through F_1 and the points of the conic. If $F_2(\beta^2:\beta:1)$ is a second fixed point on C, there is a one-to-one correspondence between the lines of the two pencils. Corresponding lines of the two pencils meet on the conic, by Steiner's theorem. (Dually, if f_1 and f_2 are any two lines of a line conic, there is a one-to-one correspondence between the range of points on f_1 and the range on f_2, because any tangent line to the conic intersects f_1 and f_2 in two corresponding points.) Because the points of C are in one-to-one correspondence with the values of the parameter θ, one has the cross ratio of four points P_1, P_2, P_3, P_4 on C as the cross ratio of the four corresponding parametric values θ_1, θ_2, θ_3, θ_4. This cross ratio is the same for all parametric representations of points on C. If four lines are drawn to P_1, P_2, P_3, P_4 from a point F on the conic, the cross ratio of the four lines is the same as the cross ratio of the four points P_1, P_2, P_3, P_4. This cross ratio is constant as F moves along the conic (by Steiner's theorem). Hence, one has the

THEOREM OF CHASLES: *The cross ratio of four lines joining a variable point on a conic to four fixed points on the conic is constant and equal to the cross ratio of the four fixed points.*

The converse of Chasles' theorem states that the locus of a point P, which moves so that the cross ratio of the four lines joining P to four fixed points in the plane (no three collinear) is constant, is a conic passing through the four fixed points. (See Exercise 8 in Section 6-3.)

The dual of the theorem of Chasles states that the cross ratio of the intersections of a variable tangent to a conic with four fixed tangents is constant. A consequence of the foregoing discussion is the following: The cross ratio of four given points on a conic is equal to the cross ratio of the four points in which the tangents at the four given points intersect any tangent to the conic.

EXAMPLE

Take four points P_1, P_2, P_3, P_4 on a conic C. A line through P_4 intersects P_2P_3, P_3P_1, P_1P_2 in Q_1, Q_2, Q_3, respectively, and the conic in a second point Q_4. Prove analytically that the sets of points Q_1, Q_2, Q_3, Q_4 and P_1, P_2, P_3, P_4 are projective.

Solution: The cross ratio of the two sets of points will be shown to be equal. Assign the coordinates $P_1(1:0:0)$, $P_2(0:1:0)$, $P_3(1:1:1)$, and take the intersection of the tangents to the conic at P_1 and P_2 as the point $(0:0:1)$ so that the equation of the conic is $(x^3)^2 = x^1x^2$. Consequently, assign the coordinates $P_4(\alpha^2:1:\alpha)$ and $Q_4(\theta^2:1:\theta)$. The cross ratio of P_1, $\cdots$, P_4 is the cross ratio of the four parameters; that is,

$$(P_1P_2P_3P_4) = (\infty, 0, 1, \alpha) = \alpha.$$

The cross ratio of the four points Q_1, $\cdots$, Q_4 is equal to the cross ratio of the four lines P_2P_3, P_2Q_2, P_2P_1, P_2Q_4. The coordinates of these lines are found to be

$$[1:0:-1], \quad [1:0:-\alpha - \theta + \alpha\theta], \quad [0:0:1], \quad [\theta:0:-\theta^2],$$

respectively. Because the second coordinate is zero for all four lines, the cross ratio is given by

$$(-1, -\alpha - \theta + \alpha\theta, \infty, -\theta) = \alpha.$$

Hence, the sets of points P_i and Q_i are projective.

8-5. The theorem of Pascal (1623–1662)

A general conic has five essential coefficients in its equation. Hence, a conic is determined by five points. If six points are on a conic, a condition must be satisfied. This condition is given in the

THEOREM OF PASCAL: *If the six distinct vertices of a hexagon are on a conic, the three points of intersection of pairs of opposite sides are collinear.*

Proof: If the six vertices are designated in some order by $H_1, H_2, \cdots, H_6$, the side H_1H_2 is said to be opposite the side H_4H_5, H_2H_3 is opposite H_5H_6, and H_3H_4 is opposite H_6H_1. (The hexagon need not be a *convex* polygon.) The pairs of opposite sides meet in the points R, S, T, which are to be shown to be collinear. Let the tangents to the conic at H_1 and H_2 intersect in P_3 (Fig. 63), and choose $H_1H_2P_3$ as the triangle of reference. Let the unit point

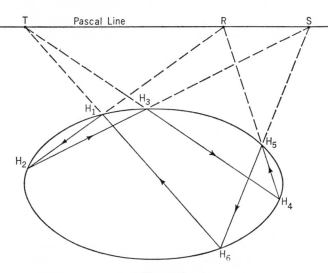

Figure 63

be chosen at H_3. The equation of the conic is then $(x^3)^2 = x^1x^2$. Assign the coordinates $H_4(1:\alpha^2:\alpha)$, $H_5(1:\beta^2:\beta)$, $H_6(1:\gamma^2:\gamma)$ to the remaining vertices of the hexagon. The required points R, S, T are obtained as follows,

H_1H_2: $[0:0:1]$

H_4H_5: $\begin{pmatrix} 1 & \alpha^2 & \alpha \\ 1 & \beta^2 & \beta \end{pmatrix} \rightarrow [\alpha\beta:1:-\alpha-\beta]$

R: $\begin{bmatrix} 0 & 0 & 1 \\ \alpha\beta & 1 & -\alpha-\beta \end{bmatrix} \rightarrow (-1:\alpha\beta:0)$

H_2H_3: $\begin{pmatrix} 0 & 1 & 0 \\ 1 & 1 & 1 \end{pmatrix} \rightarrow [1:0:-1]$

H_5H_6: $\begin{pmatrix} 1 & \beta^2 & \beta \\ 1 & \gamma^2 & \gamma \end{pmatrix} \rightarrow [\beta\gamma:1:-\beta-\gamma]$

S: $\begin{bmatrix} 1 & 0 & -1 \\ -\beta\gamma & 1 & -\beta-\gamma \end{bmatrix} \rightarrow (1:\beta+\gamma-\beta\gamma:1)$

H_3H_4: $\begin{pmatrix} 1 & 1 & 1 \\ 1 & \alpha^2 & \alpha \end{pmatrix} \rightarrow [\alpha:1:-1-\alpha]$

H_6H_1: $\begin{pmatrix} 1 & \gamma^2 & \gamma \\ 1 & 0 & 0 \end{pmatrix} \rightarrow [0:1:-\gamma]$

T: $\begin{bmatrix} \alpha & 1 & -1-\alpha \\ 0 & 1 & -\gamma \end{bmatrix} \rightarrow (\alpha+1-\gamma:\alpha\gamma:\alpha)$

One finds that

$$\begin{vmatrix} -1 & \alpha\beta & 0 \\ 1 & \beta+\gamma-\beta\gamma & 1 \\ \alpha+1-\gamma & \alpha\gamma & \alpha \end{vmatrix} \equiv 0,$$

which means that the points R, S, T are collinear for all choices of the parameters α, β, γ. This completes the proof.

The line RST is called the *Pascal line* of the inscribed hexagon.

The converse of Pascal's theorem can also be shown to hold. Hence, it is true that a conic can contain the six distinct vertices of a given hexagon if and only if the points of intersection of the opposite sides of the hexagon are collinear. This fact can be used to locate (by means of a straight-edge only) as many points as one desires on a conic which is determined by five points. The process is illustrated in Fig. 64. Given the five points $H_1, \cdots, H_5$, it is required to locate a sixth point H_6. Lines H_1H_2 and H_4H_5 determine a point R on the Pascal line. Through H_5 draw an arbitrary line (on which H_6 will be found) to intersect H_2H_3 at S. Draw the Pascal line determined by R and S. Line H_4H_5

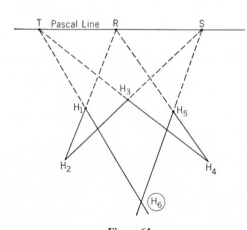

Figure 64

intersects the Pascal line at T. Draw TH_1 to intersect SH_5 in the desired point H_6. By varying the line through H_5, one may locate as many points on the conic as are desired. Note that Fig. 64 illustrates another instance of a linkage. As the line SH_6 turns about the fixed point H_5, the Pascal line rotates about the fixed point R, and H_6 moves along the conic. It should be observed that if two of the five given points come into coincidence, the line joining them becomes a tangent to the conic. Thus, a slight modification of the construction just described can be employed to locate points on a conic determined by four points and a tangent line at one of them. The conic may be determined by three points and the tangents at two of them.

The Theorem of Brianchon (1783–1864)

The dual of Pascal's theorem is that if a conic is tangent to the six sides of a hexagon the three lines joining opposite pairs of vertices of the hexagon are concurrent.

This is due to Brianchon. It is interesting to note the span of time between the result on the Pascal line, published in 1640, and the appearance of the Brianchon point in 1806. A proof of the Brianchon theorem is not needed here because it follows by duality from Pascal's theorem. However, an independent proof is required in Exercise 4. Given five lines in the plane, the Brianchon point can be used to construct a sixth tangent line to the conic which is determined by the five given lines.

It should be observed that if the conic is composed of two lines, the theorem of Pappus (Exercise 10, Section 6-3) appears again. In this special case of Pascal's theorem three vertices of the "inscribed" hexagon are on one of the lines, and the remaining three vertices are on the second line of the composite conic. Observe that the proof given above of Pascal's theorem does not hold for the composite conic. Why?

EXERCISES

1. Find the equation of the point conic which is the envelope of lines joining the points $(\lambda:0:1)$ and $(0:1:\lambda - 2)$ on the orthogonal cartesian x- and y-axes, respectively. (See Example 2, Section 1-2, and the illustrative Example in Section 8-4.)

   Ans. $4xy = (1 + 2y)^2$.

2. Show that a composite conic remains composite under a projectivity.

3. In Fig. 63, if the point H_6 alone is allowed to move on the conic, the Pascal line revolves about the point R. Prove this analytically.

4. Construct an analytic proof of the Brianchon theorem.

5. The tangents to a conic at the vertices of an inscribed hexagon form a circumscribed hexagon. Prove that the Brianchon point of the circumscribed hexagon and the Pascal line of the inscribed hexagon are pole and polar relative to the conic.

6. Prove Pascal's theorem by using the equation of the conic in the form $fx^2x^3 + gx^3x^1 + hx^1x^2 = 0$. *Suggestion:* Use three vertices of the hexagon as vertices of the triangle of reference, and α^i, β^i, γ^i as coordinates of the three remaining vertices of the hexagon.

7. Find the locus of the point $P(y^i)$, the polar lines of which relative to the three conics $(x^1)^2 = x^2 x^3$, $(x^2)^2 = x^3 x^1$, $(x^3)^2 = x^1 x^2$ are concurrent. Find also the locus of the point of intersection of the polar lines.

   Ans. The two loci are the same cubic curve with the equation
   $$(x^1)^3 + (x^2)^3 + (x^3)^3 = 3x^1 x^2 x^3.$$

8. The three sides of a triangle cut a conic. Show that the three pairs of lines through the vertices of the triangle to the points in which the opposite sides meet the conic are tangent to a conic. *Suggestion:* Take the given triangle for the triangle of reference, and $a_{ij}x^i x^j = 0$ as the equation of the given conic. Solve $x^1 = 0$ with $a_{ij}x^i x^j = 0$ to find the equation of the lines from P_1 to the intersection points as $a_{22}(x^2)^2 + 2a_{23}x^2 x^3 + a_{33}(x^3)^2 = 0$. Put $x^1 = 0$ in $u_i x^i = 0$ to see that $x^2/x^3 = -u_3/u_2$, so that the line coordinates of the two lines from P_1 satisfy $a_{22}u_3^2 - 2a_{23}u_2 u_3 + a_{33}u_2^2 = 0$, where $u_1 = 0$. Obtain two more similar pairs of equations and show that all six sets of line coordinates satisfy the line conic

$$a_{22}a_{33}u_1^2 + a_{33}a_{11}u_2^2 + a_{11}a_{22}u_3^2 - 2a_{11}a_{23}u_2 u_3 - 2a_{22}a_{31}u_3 u_1 - 2a_{33}a_{12}u_1 u_2 = 0.$$

8-6. Pencils of conics

The concept of a linear combination of the elements of a set was introduced in Section 3-8. In particular, a pencil of binary forms was considered. In a similar way, a pencil of conics is defined here as follows. If $f \equiv a_{ij}x^i x^j = 0$, and $g \equiv b_{ij}x^i x^j = 0$ are two conics, then $\lambda_1 f + \lambda_2 g$ is a linear combination of the two functions f and g, and $\lambda_1 f + \lambda_2 g = 0$ is a singly infinite set or *pencil* or *family* of conics, all of which contain the intersections of the *base conics* $f = 0$ and $g = 0$. A pencil of conics can be defined as the set of all conics which pass through four points in the plane. Dually, a *range* of conics is the singly infinite set of all conics which are tangent to four lines in the plane. The four points of intersection of two given conics which determine the pencil of conics may be called the *base points*. Evidently there is one conic of the pencil through any point y^i of the plane (other than a base point). This is seen as follows. Substitute the coordinates y^i into $\lambda_1 f + \lambda_2 g = 0$ to determine the ratio $\lambda_1:\lambda_2$ for the unique conic of the pencil through y^i. For some purposes the homogeneous parameter $\lambda_1:\lambda_2$ is desirable, but, in general, the pencil is written as $f + \lambda g = 0$, with $\lambda = \lambda_2/\lambda_1$.

In Exercise 14 of Section 8-2 it was stated that the diagonal triangle of a complete quadrangle with its four points on a conic is self-polar relative to the conic. It follows that this unique triangle is self-polar relative to all conics of the pencil through the four points.

The theorem of Desargues on perspective triangles appeared in Section 6-3. His other famous result (on a pencil of conics) is stated in the

THEOREM OF DESARGUES: *The conics of a pencil intersect any line in the plane (not through a base point) in pairs of points in involution.*

Proof: The line $x^3 = 0$ intersects the conic $(a_{ij} + \lambda b_{ij})x^i x^j = 0$ in two points, the ratios $x^1:x^2$ for which are given by

(14) $(a_{11} + \lambda b_{11})(x^1)^2 + 2(a_{12} + \lambda b_{12})x^1 x^2 + (a_{22} + \lambda b_{22})(x^2)^2 = 0.$

Let x and $\bar{x}$ denote the values of the ratios $x_1:x_2$ which satisfy (14). Then

(15) $$x + \bar{x} = -\frac{2(a_{12} + \lambda b_{12})}{a_{11} + \lambda b_{11}}, \quad x\bar{x} = \frac{a_{22} + \lambda b_{22}}{a_{11} + \lambda b_{11}}.$$

Eliminate λ from equations (15) to obtain

(16) $\quad 2(a_{12}b_{11} - a_{11}b_{12})x\bar{x} + (a_{22}b_{11} - a_{11}b_{22})(x + \bar{x}) + 2(a_{22}b_{12} - a_{12}b_{22}) = 0,$

which is a symmetric bilinear relation in x and $\bar{x}$. Hence, for every λ, the corresponding conic of the pencil cuts the line $x^3 = 0$ in two points which belong to an involution. (Note that any line may be taken as $x^3 = 0$.)

It may be remarked that if the resultant R of $a_{ij}x^ix^j$ and $b_{ij}x^ix^j$ is zero, with $x^3 = 0$, then the line $x^3 = 0$ contains a base point. It is assumed therefore that

(17) $\quad R \equiv (a_{22}b_{11} - a_{11}b_{22})^2 - (a_{12}b_{11} - a_{11}b_{12})(a_{22}b_{12} - a_{12}b_{22}) \neq 0,$

which means that the line $x^3 = 0$ does not contain a base point, and therefore that the involution is a *proper involution*.

COROLLARY 1: *Two distinct conics of the pencil are tangent to any line in the plane.*

Proof: The requirement for the roots of (14) to be equal may be expressed by

(18) $\quad (b_{12}^2 - b_{11}b_{22})\lambda^2 + (2a_{12}b_{12} - a_{22}b_{11} - a_{11}b_{22})\lambda + (a_{12}^2 - a_{11}a_{22}) = 0.$

The roots of (18) are distinct because the discriminant of the quadratic function of λ is the same as the resultant R in (17). Therefore, two distinct conics of the pencil are tangent to every line.

COROLLARY 2: *The fixed points of the involution (16) are the points of contact of the two distinct conics which are tangent to the line containing the involutory points.*

Proof: In order to find the fixed points of the involution on the line $x^3 = 0$, set $x = \bar{x}$ in (16) to obtain the quadratic in x given by

(19) $\quad (a_{12}b_{11} - a_{11}b_{12})x^2 + (a_{22}b_{11} - a_{11}b_{22})x + (a_{22}b_{12} - a_{12}b_{22}) = 0.$

In order to find the contact points, solve (18) for λ and substitute the values into (14). On eliminating λ from equations (14) and (18) one finds equation (19). Hence, the contact points of the conics tangent to the line $x^3 = 0$ are the fixed points of the involution cut on the line by the conics of the pencil.

Classification of Pencils of Conics

If two arcs have a single point in common they are said to have single-point contact, or contact of *zero order*. If the two arcs are tangent to a common line at a point, the arcs have two-point contact, or contact of the *first order*. The arcs may have three (or more) points of contact, or contact of the *second* (or higher) *order*. The contact of two base conics of a pencil may be examined by using the composite conics of the pencil. The conic $a_{ij}x^ix^j = 0$ is composite if

$|a_{ij}| = 0$. (See Exercise 1 on p. 187.) Hence, the values of λ corresponding to composite conics of the pencil $f + \lambda g \equiv (a_{ij} + \lambda b_{ij})x^i x^j = 0$ are solutions of

(20) $$h(\lambda) \equiv |a_{ij} + \lambda b_{ij}| = 0.$$

Because equation (20) is a cubic in λ, there are three composite conics in each pencil. These are the three pairs of opposite sides of the complete quadrangle determined by the four base points. In order to classify the pencils and to examine the contact of the base conics, one may use the multiplicity m of the roots of (20), and the corresponding rank r of the matrix $(a_{ij} + \lambda b_{ij})$ of the coefficients of $f + \lambda g$. Denote the roots of (20) by λ_1, λ_2, λ_3. The following cases arise. (Compare with the classification of collineations in Section 7-3.)

$1°$ $\quad \lambda_1 \begin{pmatrix} m = 1 \\ r = 2 \end{pmatrix} \qquad \lambda_2 \begin{pmatrix} m = 1 \\ r = 2 \end{pmatrix} \qquad \lambda_3 \begin{pmatrix} m = 1 \\ r = 2 \end{pmatrix}$

$2°$ $\quad \lambda_1 \begin{pmatrix} m = 1 \\ r = 2 \end{pmatrix} \qquad \lambda_2 \begin{pmatrix} m = 2 \\ r = 2 \end{pmatrix}$

$3°$ $\quad \lambda_1 \begin{pmatrix} m = 1 \\ r = 2 \end{pmatrix} \qquad \lambda_2 \begin{pmatrix} m = 2 \\ r = 1 \end{pmatrix}$

$4°$ $\quad \lambda_1 \begin{pmatrix} m = 3 \\ r = 2 \end{pmatrix}$

$5°$ $\quad \lambda_1 \begin{pmatrix} m = 3 \\ r = 1 \end{pmatrix}$

Geometrical Interpretation

$1°$. Let the base conics intersect in A, B, C, D (Fig. 65). The three composite conics are the three pairs of lines AB, CD; AD, BC; and AC, BD. Each of the

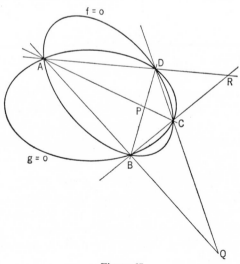

Figure 65

three composite conics is two distinct lines. The diagonal triangle *PQR* is self-polar relative to all conics of the pencil. Note that any line cuts the three pairs of sides of the complete quadrangle *ABCD* in pairs of points in involution. The base conics have one-point contact at the base points.

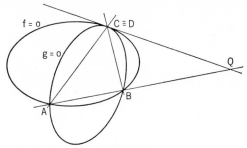

Figure 66

2°. Now let *C* and *D* become coincident (Fig. 66). The conics *f* and *g* now have contact of the first order at *C*. The single composite conic composed of *AB* and the common tangent at *C* remains, but the pair of lines *AC, BC* is counted twice.

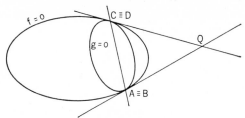

Figure 67

3°. Next allow *A* and *B* to come into coincidence (Fig. 67), so that the base conics have contact of the first order at both *C* and *A*. There are still two distinct composite conics, but one is composed of the two common tangents, and the other is composed of the line *AC* counted twice. But the latter conic is counted twice, which means that line *AC* is counted four times.

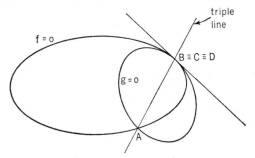

Figure 68

4°. In Fig. 65 let the points *B*, *C*, *D* become coincident to obtain Fig. 68. The conics $f = 0$ and $g = 0$ have three-point or second-order contact at *B*. There is one composite conic composed of two distinct lines—that is, the tangent at *B* and the line *AB*. But this composite conic is counted three times.

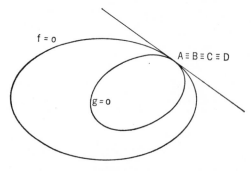

Figure 69

5°. In Fig. 69 all four points *A*, *B*, *C*, *D* are allowed to become coincident, so that the base conics have third-order contact at the point of tangency. There are still three composite conics, but each of them is composed of two coincident lines. Hence, the common tangent line to $f = 0$ and $g = 0$ must be counted six times.

Examples of Pencils of Conics

1°. Consider the family of circles through two distinct fixed points *A* and *B*. Because every circle contains the circular points *I* and *J*, the base points are *I*, *J*, *A*, *B*. For instance, the family of circles given by $x^2 + y^2 + \lambda y - a^2 = 0$, where *a* is a constant and λ a parameter, can be written as $(x^2 + y^2 - a^2 z^2) + \lambda(yz) = 0$ in which the coordinates are made homogeneous. If $f \equiv x^2 + y^2 - a^2 z^2$ and $g \equiv yz$, the family of circles is the pencil $f + \lambda g = 0$, and the three pairs of composite conics of the pencil are the two pairs of minimal lines through *A* and *B* and the x-axis (the radical axis of the family) and the line at infinity with equation $z = 0$.

2°. Consider the composite conic $y(y - 1) = 0$ and the circle $x^2 + y^2 - 1 = 0$, which, in homogeneous coordinates, are

$$x^2 + y^2 - z^2 = 0, \quad y^2 - yz = 0.$$

All conics of the pencil $x^2 + y^2 - z^2 + \lambda(y^2 - yz) = 0$ contain the points $A(1, 0)$, $B(-1, 0)$ and are tangent to the line $y = 1$ at $C(0, 1)$. The lines $x + y - z = 0$ and $x - y + z = 0$ constitute one composite conic. It is to be counted twice. The family of conics through *A*, *B*, *C* may also be written as $(x + y - z)(x - y + z) + \lambda(y^2 - yz) = 0$.

3°. The system of concentric circles $x^2 + y^2 = \lambda$ may be given by $x^2 + y^2 - \lambda z^2 = 0$. Let $f \equiv x^2 + y^2 = 0$ (the minimal lines through the origin) and $g \equiv z^2 = 0$ (the ideal line counted twice) be the base conics. In this instance, the I and J points are counted twice, so this pencil $f + \lambda g = 0$ is of Type 3°.

4°. One may verify that the hyperbola $x^2 + 3xy - 2y^2 + x - 10y = 0$ and the parabola $x^2 = 4y$ have single-point contact at the origin, and triple-point contact at the point $(2, 1)$. The composite conic given by $(x - 2y)(x - y - 1) = 0$ is counted three times.

5°. The conics $y^2 - 4yz = 0$, $y^2 - 4xz + 16 = 0$ are tangent at $(1:0:0)$. The composite conic has the equation $z^2 = 0$.

The Dual

The dual of a pencil is a *range*. The set of all conics tangent to four lines constitute a *range of conics*. With the base conics $F \equiv A^{ij}u_iu_j = 0$, $G \equiv B^{ij}u_iu_j = 0$, one may consider the range $F + \lambda G \equiv (A^{ij} + \lambda B^{ij})u_iu_j = 0$ of conics, and develop again all of the foregoing results of this section. Observe that the lines which satisfy both $F = 0$ and $G = 0$ are the common tangents to the two base conics. Hence, $F + \lambda G = 0$ is a line conic tangent to the common tangents of $F = 0$ and $G = 0$. By proper choice of λ, the conic $F + \lambda G = 0$ is tangent also to an arbitrary line in the plane.

The composite line conics are treated briefly as follows. Let α, β, γ, δ be linear functions of the line coordinates u_i. The vanishing of α, for instance, therefore represents a point. Suppose the conic $G = 0$ is composite—that is, $G \equiv \alpha\beta$, say. Then the conic $F + \lambda\alpha\beta = 0$ is satisfied if $F = 0$ and $\alpha = 0$, which means that this conic is tangent to the tangents to $F = 0$ from the point $\alpha = 0$. Similarly, this conic is tangent to the tangents to $F = 0$ from the point $\beta = 0$. Further degenerate cases appear if $\alpha = 0$ and $\beta = 0$ are on the conic $F = 0$. One case of interest is that for which both $F = 0$ and $G = 0$ are composite. Here, the conic $\alpha\beta + \lambda\gamma\delta = 0$ is tangent to four given lines. The parameter λ can be chosen so that this conic is also tangent to a fifth line. (See Exercise 7.)

Problems involving envelopes of lines or the tangent property of a line to a curve are done preferably by use of line coordinates. This is illustrated in the following examples.

EXAMPLE 1

Find the condition under which the conic $a_{ij}x^ix^j = 0$ is a parabola, where the x^i are homogeneous cartesian coordinates.

Solution: The line equation of the conic is $A^{ij}u_iu_j = 0$. The condition that the line at infinity be tangent to the conic is that the coordinates $[0:0:1]$ satisfy the line equation. This gives $A^{33} = 0$; that is, $a_{11}a_{22} - (a_{12})^2 = 0$. (It is not so easy to express the condition for an ellipse or a hyperbola by use of line coordinates because a tangent property is not used in these cases.)

EXAMPLE 2

Find the envelope of chords of the ellipse $b^2x^2 + a^2y^2 = a^2b^2z^2$, whose midpoints lie on the line $px + qy + rz = 0$.

Solution: Let the variable chord be represented by $ux + vy + wz = 0$. The pole of the line $ux + vy = 0$ relative to the ellipse is the point $(a^2u:b^2v:0)$. The line joining this point to the origin is $b^2vx - a^2uy = 0$. (It is the *conjugate* diameter to $ux + vy = 0$.) The midpoint of the chord $ux + vy + wz = 0$ is the intersection of the lines

$$b^2vx - a^2uy = 0, \quad ux + vy + wz = 0.$$

This intersection is the point $(-a^2uv:-b^2vw:b^2v^2 + a^2u^2)$. The condition that this point be incident with the given line is

$$r(a^2u^2 + b^2v^2) - pa^2uw - qb^2vw = 0.$$

This conic is a parabola because the coefficient of w^2 is zero.

EXAMPLE 3

Find the evolute of the ellipse $b^2x^2 + a^2y^2 = a^2b^2$.

Solution: The line equation of the ellipse is $a^2u^2 + b^2v^2 - w^2 = 0$. Let $[u':v':w']$ be the coordinates of the tangent to this curve at any point P, so that

(21) $$a^2u'^2 + b^2v'^2 - w'^2 = 0.$$

Let $[u:v:w]$ be coordinates of the normal line at P. The perpendicularity of the tangent and normal lines at P is expressed by

(22) $$uu' + vv' = 0.$$

The point of contact of the tangent line at P (see Section 4-4) is $(a^2u':b^2v':-w')$, and the condition for this point to be on the normal is

(23) $$a^2uu' + b^2vv' - ww' = 0.$$

Solve (22) and (23) for

$$u':v':w' = vw:-uw:(a^2 - b^2)uv,$$

and use these values in (21) to obtain the line envelope of the evolute of the ellipse:

$$\frac{a^2}{u^2} + \frac{b^2}{v^2} = \frac{(a^2 - b^2)^2}{w^2}.$$

It can be shown that the point equation of the evolute is

$$(ax)^{2/3} + (by)^{2/3} = (a^2 - b^2)^{2/3}.$$

EXERCISES

1. Show that the polar lines of a point y^i with respect to the conics of the pencil $(a_{ij} + \lambda b_{ij})x^ix^j = 0$ are concurrent.

2. Find the equation of any conic which is tangent to the line $[1:2:3]$.

   Ans. If the conic is also tangent to the sides of the triangle of reference and to the unit line, its line equation is
   $$u_2u_3 - 4u_3u_1 + 3u_1u_2 = 0.$$

3. Find the equations of two parabolas circumscribed about the quadrilateral with sides $x = 0$, $y = 0$, $x - y + 2 = 0$, $3x - y - 6 = 0$. *Suggestion:* Use composite conics.

$$Ans.\ x(3x - y - 6) + (-5 \pm 2\sqrt{6})y(x - y + 2) = 0.$$

4. Use line coordinates to find the evolute of the parabola $avw + bwu + cuv = 0$.

5. Show that the locus of the poles of the line $l_i x^i = 0$ with respect to the conics of the pencil $(a_{ij} + \lambda b_{ij})x^i x^j = 0$ is a conic.

$$Ans.\ (e^{pqr}l_p a_{iq}b_{jr})x^i x^j = 0.$$

6. A variable triangle is circumscribed about a fixed triangle, with two vertices ranging on two fixed lines. Show that the third vertex describes a conic.

7. Find the line equation of the conic which is tangent to the lines $x^1 = 0$, $x^2 = 0$, $x^3 = 0$, $x^1 + x^2 + x^3 = 0$, $x^1 + 2x^2 + 3x^3 = 0$.

$$Ans.\ u_2 u_3 - 4u_3 u_1 + 3u_1 u_2 = 0.$$

8-7. Polar reciprocation

In Section 7-6 it was seen that a *polar* correlation is a correspondence of the type

$$(24) \qquad \rho u_i = a_{ij}x^j,$$

with the inverse

$$(25) \qquad k x^i = A^{ji}u_j,$$

in which the matrix (a_{ij}) is symmetric. To each point of the plane there corresponds a unique line, and conversely. The locus of points which are incident with their corresponding lines is a conic. Thus, one may begin with the correlation (24), as in Section 7-6, and arrive at the point conic $a_{ij}x^i x^j = 0$, or the same conic in line coordinates—that is, $A^{ij}u_i u_j = 0$. On the other hand, one may start with a conic and arrive at the polar correlation. The polar of any point y^i relative to the conic $a_{ij}x^i x^j = 0$ is the line $a_{ij}y^i x^j = 0$. Thus, to every point y^i in the plane there corresponds a line with coordinates $u_j = a_{ij}y^i$. If y^i is on the conic the polar line $u_i x^i = 0$ is the tangent to the conic at y^i. Equations (24) therefore effect a mapping of points into their polar lines, and (25) takes lines into their poles with respect to the conic. Two configurations which correspond to each other by this polar mapping are called *polar reciprocal configurations*. Advantage is taken of polar reciprocation to prove projective theorems (see Example 2). For instance, a complete quadrangle reciprocates relative to a conic into a complete quadrilateral. The projective properties of the quadrangle become automatically projective properties of the quadrilateral. One may say that the polarity ensures the principle of duality.

EXAMPLE 1

Show that any triangle and its polar reciprocal triangle relative to a conic are perspective, and that the center and axis of perspectivity are pole and polar.

Solution: Take the given triangle $P_1P_2P_3$ (Fig. 70) as the triangle of reference, and the conic as $a_{ij}x^ix^j = 0$. The polar lines p_i of P_i are $a_{ij}x^j = 0$, with $i = 1, 2, 3$, which intersect in the points $\overline{P}_1(A^{11}:A^{21}:A^{31})$, $\overline{P}_2(A^{12}:A^{22}:A^{32})$, $\overline{P}_3(A^{13}:A^{23}:A^{33})$. The lines $P_1\overline{P}_1[0:A^{11}:A^{21}]$, $P_2\overline{P}_2[A^{32}:0:-A^{12}]$, $P_3\overline{P}_3[-A^{23}:A^{13}:0]$ intersect in the center S

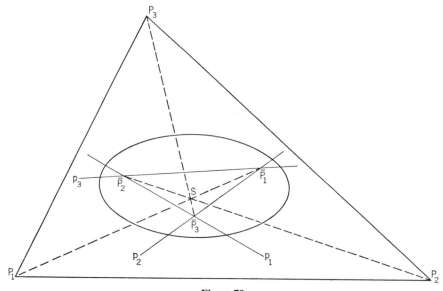

Figure 70

of perspectivity with coordinates $(A^{12}A^{31}:A^{21}A^{32}:A^{31}A^{32})$. The lines $P_2P_3[1:0:0]$ and $\overline{P}_2\overline{P}_3[a_{11}:a_{12}:a_{13}]$ intersect at $(0:-a_{13}:a_{12})$. Similarly, P_3P_1 intersects $\overline{P}_3\overline{P}_1$ at $(a_{23}:0:-a_{21})$, and P_1P_2 intersects $\overline{P}_1\overline{P}_2$ at $(-a_{32}:a_{31}:0)$. The latter three points lie on the axis with coordinates $[a_{13}a_{21}:a_{12}a_{23}:a_{13}a_{23}]$, which can be shown to be the polar of the center S.

The following example indicates the usefulness of polar reciprocation in proving the theorem of Chasles.

EXAMPLE 2

Show, by polar reciprocation relative to a circle, that four given tangents to a parabola are intersected by a variable fifth tangent in four points which have a constant cross ratio.

Solution: Reciprocate the parabola $y^2 = 4px$ with respect to the circle C with equation $(x - p)^2 + y^2 = p^2$. The tangent at any point $(m^2/p, 2m)$ on the parabola has the equation $px - my + m^2 = 0$, the pole of which with respect to C is the point $x = m^2p/(m^2 + p^2)$, $y = mp^2/(m^2 + p^2)$. Eliminate the parameter m to find the polar reciprocal of the parabola with respect to the circle C to be another circle C' with the equation $x^2 + y^2 - px = 0$. The tangents to the parabola map into the points of the circle C'. The angles between the lines from any point T on the circle C' to four points P, Q, R, S on C' are constant as T moves on C'. Hence, by use of the formula for the cross ratio of four lines in a pencil (Section 5-6), the cross ratio of the lines from T to P, Q, R, S is constant. It follows that a variable tangent t to the parabola intersects four fixed tangents in a constant cross ratio (see Exercise 6).

Remark: It is apparent that the success of the method of polar reciprocation illustrated in Example 2 depends upon a judicious choice of the center of the circle of reciprocation.

EXERCISES

1. Take a point P outside a circle with center at O and radius r. Show that if the polar of P with respect to the circle intersects OP in P' then $\overline{OP'}\,\overline{OP} = r^2$.

2. Show that if P in Exercise 1 is inside the circle, the polar of P does not intersect the circle in real points, but that the relation $\overline{OP'}\,\overline{OP} = r^2$ still holds.

3. Show that the polar of the center of a circle with respect to the circle is the line at infinity.

4. Find the polar lines of the points $(1:\pm i:0)$ with respect to the circle $x^2 + y^2 = a^2$.

5. Show that the polar reciprocal of the circle C_1: $(x - h)^2 + (y - k)^2 = r^2$ with respect to the circle C_2: $x^2 + y^2 = a^2$ has the line equation

$$a^4(u^2 + v^2) + 2a^2(hu + kv)w + (h^2 + k^2 - r^2)w^2 = 0,$$

and therefore the point equation

$$(h^2 - r^2)x^2 + 2hkxy + (k^2 - r^2)y^2 - 2a^2hxz - 2a^2kyz + a^4z^2 = 0.$$

This is a hyperbola if $h^2 + k^2 - r^2 > 0$. The center of C_2 is one focus of the polar reciprocal conic of C_1.*

6. Obtain the result of Example 2 for the ellipse $b^2x^2 + a^2y^2 = a^2b^2$. *Suggestion:* Reciprocate with respect to a circle with center at a focus of the ellipse.

7. Show that the polar reciprocal of the conic $a_{ij}x^ix^j = 0$ relative to $\delta_{ij}x^ix^j = 0$ is the conic $A^{ij}x^ix^j = 0$.

8-8. Invariants of pencils of conics

Under the projectivity $kx^i = h^i_j\bar{x}^j$, the pencil of conics $f + \lambda g \equiv (a_{ij} + \lambda b_{ij})x^ix^j = 0$ maps into the pencil $(\bar{a}_{ij} + \lambda\bar{b}_{ij})\bar{x}^i\bar{x}^j = 0$. One has

$$(a_{ij} + \lambda b_{ij})x^ix^j = (a_{ij} + \lambda b_{ij})h^i_k\bar{x}^kh^j_l\bar{x}^l = (a_{ij} + \lambda b_{ij})h^i_kh^j_l\bar{x}^k\bar{x}^l = (\bar{a}_{kl} + \lambda\bar{b}_{kl})\bar{x}^k\bar{x}^l,$$

where

(26) $$\bar{a}_{kl} \equiv a_{ij}h^i_kh^j_l, \quad \bar{b}_{kl} \equiv b_{ij}h^i_kh^j_l.$$

On taking the determinants of the two equations in (26), there results

(27) $$|\bar{a}_{kl}| = |a_{ij}|J^2, \quad |\bar{b}_{kl}| = |b_{ij}|J^2,$$

---

* For further treatment of polar reciprocation with respect to a circle, see W. C. Graustein, *Introduction to Higher Geometry* (Macmillan, New York, 1930), p. 331.

where J is the jacobian of the projectivity. Hence, the determinants of the matrices (a_{ij}) and (b_{ij}) of the base conics are invariants of weight two under a projectivity. It is also true that

(28) $$|\bar{a}_{kl} + \lambda \bar{b}_{kl}| = |a_{ij} + \lambda b_{ij}|J^2.$$

With the assumption that $J \neq 0$, equation (28) shows that noncomposite conics of the pencil map into noncomposite conics. The values of λ which satisfy (20) determine the composite conics of the pencil. The same values of λ satisfy the equation

(29) $$\bar{h}(\lambda) \equiv |\bar{a}_{ij} + \lambda \bar{b}_{ij}| = 0,$$

and these values of λ determine the composite conics of the transformed pencil.

The determinant $h(\lambda) \equiv |a_{ij} + \lambda b_{ij}|$ in (20) will now be expanded. The constant term in the cubic polynomial (obtained by setting $\lambda = 0$) is the determinant $a \equiv |a_{ij}|$. Differentiate $h(\lambda)$ and put $\lambda = 0$ in the derivative $h'(\lambda)$ to see that the coefficient of λ in the polynomial is the double sum $b_{ij}A^{ij}$, where the A^{ij} are the cofactors of the elements in the matrix (a_{ij}). One may differentiate $h'(\lambda)$ and then set $\lambda = 0$ to see that the coefficient of λ^2 is $a_{ij}B^{ij}$, where the B^{ij} are the cofactors of the elements in (b_{ij}). The coefficient of λ^3 is the determinant $b \equiv |b_{ij}|$. Hence, equation (20) takes the form

(30) $$b\lambda^3 - a_{ij}B^{ij}\lambda^2 + A^{ij}b_{ij}\lambda + a = 0.$$

Reference to equations (27) indicates that, because (28) is an identity in λ, the coefficients in

(31) $$\bar{b}\lambda^3 + \bar{a}_{ij}\bar{B}^{ij}\lambda^2 + \bar{A}^{ij}\bar{b}_{ij}\lambda + \bar{a} = 0$$

are invariants of weight two under a projectivity; that is,

(32) $$\bar{b} = bJ^2, \quad \bar{a}_{ij}\bar{B}^{ij} = a_{ij}B^{ij}J^2, \quad \bar{A}^{ij}\bar{b}_{ij} = A^{ij}b_{ij}J^2, \quad \bar{a} = aJ^2.$$

Observe that a and b are invariants of the conics $f = 0$ and $g = 0$, respectively, but that the coefficients of λ^2 and λ in (30) are simultaneous invariants of $f = 0$ and $g = 0$.

One may seek the geometric interpretation of the vanishing of the invariants in (32). For simplicity, write (30) in the form

(33) $$b\lambda^3 + \beta\lambda^2 + \alpha\lambda + a = 0,$$

in which $\beta \equiv a_{ij}B^{ij}$ and $\alpha \equiv A^{ij}b_{ij}$. It has been shown (Exercise 1 on p. 187) that $a = 0$ implies that the conic $f = 0$ is composite. Similarly, if $b = 0$, the conic $g = 0$ is composite.

The interpretation of the vanishing of $\alpha \equiv A^{ij}b_{ij}$ will be considered next. Let C_1 denote the conic $f = 0$, and C_2 the conic $g = 0$. Select a self-polar triangle $P_1P_2P_3$ relative to C_1, and use it as the triangle of reference. The polar of $P_1(1:0:0)$, for instance, relative to C_1: $a_{ij}x^ix^j = 0$ is $a_{1j}x^j = 0$, which is the line $x^1 = 0$. Hence, $a_{12} = a_{13} = 0$. Similarly, $a_{23} = 0$, so the conic C_1 has the equation $a_{11}(x^1)^2 + a_{22}(x^2)^2 + a_{33}(x^3)^2 = 0$. If points P_1 and P_2 are on C_2, then C_2 has the equation

$$b_{23}x^2x^3 + b_{31}x^3x^1 + b_{12}x^1x^2 + b_{33}x^3x^3 = 0.$$

The nonzero elements of the matrix (A^{ij}) are found to be $A^{11} = a_{22}a_{33}$, $A^{22} = a_{33}a_{11}$, $A^{33} = a_{11}a_{22}$. With $b_{11} = b_{22} = 0$ the invariant $\alpha \equiv A^{ij}b_{ij} = A^{33}b_{35} = a_{11}a_{22}b_{33}$. Because, for a proper conic C_1, $a_{11} \neq 0$ and $a_{22} \neq 0$, it follows that $\alpha = 0$ if and only if $b_{33} = 0$; this means that $P_3(0:0:1)$ is on C_2. Hence, the geometrical interpretation of the vanishing of the invariant $\alpha \equiv A^{ij}b_{ij}$ in equation (30) is that *a triangle can be inscribed to C_2 which is self-polar relative to C_1.* It can be seen, moreover, that this property is *poristic;* that is, if there is one such triangle there is a singly infinite set of such triangles. A dual argument shows that there is a triangle circumscribed to C_1 which is self-polar relative to C_2 (and therefore a singly infinite set of them) if and only if $\alpha = 0$. The symmetry of equation (33) indicates that a similar interpretation can be stated for the vanishing of the invariant $\beta \equiv a_{ij}B^{ij}$.

Further Invariants

Each of the coefficients b, β, α, a in equation (33) is seen by equations (32) to be a *relative* invariant of weight two under a projectivity; that is,

$$\bar{b} = bJ^2, \quad \bar{\beta} = \beta J^2, \quad \bar{\alpha} = \alpha J^2, \quad \bar{a} = aJ^2.$$

It follows that

$$\frac{\beta}{b} = \frac{\bar{\beta}}{\bar{b}}, \quad \frac{\alpha}{b} = \frac{\bar{\alpha}}{\bar{b}}, \quad \frac{a}{b} = \frac{\bar{a}}{\bar{b}},$$

which means that the ratio of any two of b, β, α, a is an *absolute* invariant. Any homogeneous function $\phi(a, \alpha, \beta, b)$ is an invariant. This can be seen as follows. If the degree of homogeneity of ϕ is n, then

$$\phi(\bar{a}, \bar{\alpha}, \bar{\beta}, \bar{b}) = \phi(J^2a, J^2\alpha, J^2\beta, J^2b) = J^{2n}\phi(a, \alpha, \beta, b).$$

The vanishing of ϕ implies that some geometric relation obtains relative to the two conics C_1 and C_2.

Two methods of procedure are to be distinguished. On the one hand, given a homogeneous function ϕ of a, α, β, b, it is required to find the geometric meaning of the invariant equation $\phi = 0$ relative to the two conics. This may be styled the *function-theoretic* approach to the geometry of the pair of conics. There is no systematic or straightforward method by which the geometry can be ascertained with this approach. On the other hand, after a geometrical relation between the conics has been discovered, it is possible to establish the corresponding invariantive functional relation $\phi(a, \alpha, \beta, b) = 0$, which is descriptive of the geometrical fact. The latter approach is illustrated in the Example below.

It is shown next that if the homogeneous equation $\phi(a, \alpha, \beta, b) = 0$ is a condition under which a geometric property obtains relative to two conics C_1 and C_2, then the condition for the dual property to hold is given by $\phi(a^2, a\beta, \alpha b, b^2) = 0$.

In Exercise 7 of the last section it is seen that the polar reciprocal of C_1: $a_{ij}x^ix^j = 0$ relative to the conic C given by $\delta_{ij}x^ix^j = 0$ is C_1': $A^{ij}x^ix^j = 0$. Similarly, the conic C_2: $b_{ij}x^ix^j = 0$ reciprocates into C_2': $B^{ij}x^ix^j = 0$ relative to C. Let a, α, β, b be denoted by a', α', β', b' for the polar reciprocal conics. Note that $a' = a^2$, $\alpha' = a\beta$, $\beta' = b\alpha$, $b' = b^2$. The condition $\phi(a', \alpha', \beta', b') = 0$ becomes $\phi(a^2, a\beta, \alpha b, b^2) = 0$. In particular, note that the function $\phi \equiv \alpha$ becomes $a\beta$ for the reciprocal conics. The vanishing of α therefore implies the vanishing of β, if the determinant $a \equiv |a_{ij}| \neq 0$.

EXAMPLE

Find a necessary and sufficient condition that two conics C_1 and C_2 are such that a triangle inscribed in C_1 is circumscribed about C_2.

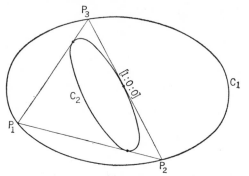

Figure 71

Solution: Let C_1: $a_{ij}x^ix^j = 0$ and C_2: $b_{ij}x^ix^j = 0$ represent the two conics (Fig. 71). Let the triangle of reference be inscribed in C_1, which therefore has the equation reduced to

$$a_{23}x^2x^3 + a_{31}x^3x^1 + a_{12}x^1x^2 = 0.$$

The line equation of C_2 is $B^{ij}u_iu_j = 0$. If the sides of the reference triangle are tangent to C_2, then $B^{11} = B^{22} = B^{33} = 0$, so that C_2 has the line equation

$$B^{23}u_2u_3 + B^{31}u_3u_1 + B^{12}u_1u_2 = 0.$$

Now write the point equation for C_2 and note that under the projectivity $\bar{x}^1 = B^{23}x^1$, $\bar{x}^2 = B^{31}x^2$, $\bar{x}^3 = B^{12}x^3$ the point equations of C_2 and C_1 become respectively

(34)
$$C_2: \quad (\bar{x}^1)^2 + (\bar{x}^2)^2 + (\bar{x}^3)^2 - 2\bar{x}^2\bar{x}^3 - 2\bar{x}^3\bar{x}^1 - 2\bar{x}^1\bar{x}^2 = 0,$$
$$C_1: \quad a_{23}B^{23}\bar{x}^2\bar{x}^3 + a_{31}B^{31}\bar{x}^3\bar{x}^1 + a_{12}B^{12}\bar{x}^1\bar{x}^2 = 0.$$

The second equation in (34) may be divided by any one of its nonzero coefficients. Suppose $a_{23}B^{23} \neq 0$. Conic C_1 may then take the form

(35)
$$C_1: \quad 2\bar{x}^2\bar{x}^3 + 2h\bar{x}^3\bar{x}^1 + 2k\bar{x}^1\bar{x}^2 = 0,$$

for which

(36)
$$a \equiv \begin{vmatrix} 0 & k & h \\ k & 0 & 1 \\ h & 1 & 0 \end{vmatrix} = 2hk.$$

Also, relative to conic C_2,

(37)
$$b \equiv \begin{vmatrix} 1 & -1 & -1 \\ -1 & 1 & -1 \\ -1 & -1 & 1 \end{vmatrix} = -4$$

and, relative to equations (35) and (34),

(38) $\qquad \alpha \equiv A^{ij}b_{ij} = -(h + k + 1)^2, \quad \beta \equiv a_{ij}B^{ij} = 4(h + k + 1).$

From equations (36), (37), and (38), it is seen that $\beta^2 - 4\alpha b = 0$. Because $\beta^2 - 4\alpha b$ is an invariant under a projectivity, it vanishes for the original forms of C_1 and C_2. Thus, a necessary condition for a triangle to be inscribed in C_1 and circumscribed to C_2 is that the invariant $\beta^2 - 4\alpha b$ vanish.

The sufficiency of the condition $\beta^2 - 4\alpha b = 0$ can be shown as follows. Take $P_1(1:0:0)$ and $P_2(0:1:0)$ on C_1 with the line P_1P_2 tangent to C_2, and draw the other two tangents to C_2 through P_1 and P_2 to intersect in $P_3(0:0:1)$. The equations of the conics may then be taken in the form

$$C_1: \qquad a_{33}(x^3)^2 + 2a_{23}x^2x^3 + 2a_{31}x^3x^1 + 2a_{12}x^1x^2 = 0,$$

$$C_2: \qquad (x^1)^2 + (x^2)^2 + (x^3)^2 - 2x^2x^3 - 2x^3x^1 - 2x^1x^2 = 0,$$

for which

$$\alpha \equiv 2a_{12}a_{33} - (a_{12} + a_{13} + a_{23})^2,$$

$$\beta \equiv 4(a_{12} + a_{13} + a_{23}),$$

$$b = -4.$$

The condition $\beta^2 - 4\alpha b = 0$ requires that $32a_{12}a_{33} = 0$, so that either $a_{12} = 0$ or $a_{33} = 0$. But if $a_{12} = 0$, the conic C_1 is composite. Therefore, take $a_{12} \neq 0$ and $a_{33} = 0$, which means that the point $P_3(0:0:1)$ is on C_1. Hence, under the condition $\beta^2 - 4\alpha b = 0$, a triangle exists which is inscribed to C_1 and circumscribed to C_2.

It can be shown that the property just described is poristic; that is, if one triangle exists which is inscribed to C_1 and circumscribed to C_2, then a singly infinite set of such triangles exist. (See Exercises 1 and 2.)

EXERCISES

1. Show that the six vertices of two triangles which are circumscribed to a conic lie on a conic. (See Example 2 in Section 8-2.)

2. By use of Exercise 1, show that if one triangle exists which is inscribed to conic C_1 and circumscribed to C_2, then a singly infinite set of such triangles exist. *Hint:* A conic is determined by five points.

3. Show that two conics have contact of the first order if and only if the invariant
$$\alpha^2\beta^2 + 18ab\alpha\beta - 27a^2b^2 - 4a\beta^3 - 4b\alpha^3$$
vanishes. (See Sections 8-6 and 3-10.) The invariant may be expressed in the alternative form
$$(\alpha\beta - 9ab)^2 - 4(\alpha^2 - 3a\beta)(\beta^2 - 3\alpha b).$$

4. Show that two conics have three-point contact if and only if the three invariants
$$3\alpha b - \beta^2, \quad 9ab - \alpha\beta, \quad 3a\beta - \alpha^2$$
vanish.

5. Compute the invariants α and β for the conics C_1: $a_{ij}x^ix^j = 0$ and C_2: $x^2x^3 = 0$, where C_1 is noncomposite. Show that $\alpha = 0$ if and only if the lines of C_2 are conjugate relative to C_1, and that $\beta = 0$ if and only if the intersection of the lines of C_2 is on C_1. (Two lines through a point A are conjugate relative to a conic C if they separate the tangents from A to C harmonically.)

6. Show that triangles can be inscribed in the ellipse $p^2x^2 + q^2y^2 = 1$ and circumscribed to the ellipse $r^2x^2 + s^2y^2 = 1$ only if

$$(ps \pm qr)^2 = r^2s^2.$$

7. It was seen in Section 8-2 that if a self-polar triangle of the conic $a_{ij}x^ix^j = 0$ is taken as the triangle of reference, then $a_{23} = a_{31} = a_{12} = 0$. Show that if the common self-polar triangle of the conics $a(\bar{x}^1)^2 + b(\bar{x}^2)^2 + c(\bar{x}^3)^2 = 0$ and $a'(\bar{x}^1)^2 + b'(\bar{x}^2)^2 + c'(\bar{x}^3)^2 = 0$ is taken as the triangle of reference, then the transformation $x^1 = \sqrt{a'}\,\bar{x}^1$, $x^2 = \sqrt{b'}\,\bar{x}^2$, $x^3 = \sqrt{c'}\,\bar{x}^3$ allows the two equations of the conics to be written as C_1: $x^2 + y^2 + z^2 = 0$ and C_2: $px^2 + qy^2 + rz^2 = 0$, where $pqr \neq 0$.

8. Show that the common points of C_1 and C_2 in Exercise 7 are given by $A(l:m:n)$, $B(l:-m:n)$, $C(-l:m:n)$, $D(-l:-m:n)$, where $l^2:m^2:n^2 = q - r:r - p:p - q$.

9. Take any point $H(x:y:z)$, for which $x^2:y^2:z^2 = -(1 + \lambda^2):\lambda^2:1$, on the conic C_1 in Exercise 8, and show that the set of four lines HA, HB, HC, HD is harmonic for all positions of H on C_1 if and only if $p + r = 2q$.

10. Show that the invariants a, α, β, b for the conics C_1 and C_2 are given by

$$a \equiv |a_{ij}| = 1, \quad \alpha \equiv A^{ij}b_{ij} = p + q + r, \quad \beta \equiv a_{ij}B^{ij} = qr + rp + pq, \quad b \equiv |b_{ij}| \equiv pqr.$$

Use the result of Exercise 9 to eliminate p, q, r homogeneously from the last four equations to obtain the invariant equation

$$2\alpha^3 - 9a\alpha\beta + 27a^2b = 0.$$

This is a necessary and sufficient condition that the four lines joining any point on the conic C_1 with the four points of intersection of C_1 with a conic C_2 form a harmonic set.

11. By use of the result in Exercise 10, verify that if any point on the conic C_1: $x^2 + y^2 + 3z^2 + 2yz + 2xz = 0$ is joined to the points where C_1 intersects the conic C_2: $x^2 + y^2 + 3z^2 + 6yz + 2xz = 0$, then the set of four joins is harmonic.

8-9. The tensor concept

The inverse of the transformation $x^i = h^i_j\bar{x}^j$ is obtained by multiplying both members by H^k_i, which is the cofactor of h^i_k in the determinant $h \equiv |h^i_j|$. Thus

$$H^k_ix^i = H^k_ih^i_j\bar{x}^j = h\delta^k_j\bar{x}^j = h\bar{x}^k,$$

so that

$$\bar{x}^k = \frac{H^k_i}{h}x^i.$$

In order to simplify the notation write $h_i^{\prime k}$ for H_i^k/h, so that the transformation reads as $\bar{x}^k = h_i^{\prime k}x^i$, with the consequence that $h_i^{\prime k}h_j^i = \delta_j^k$. Thus, the transformation and its inverse are

(39) $$x^i = h_j^i\bar{x}^j, \quad \bar{x}^i = h_j^{\prime i}x^j.$$

Now consider the form u_ix^i. Its vanishing is the incidence condition for the point x^i and the line u_i. The form u_ix^i transforms under (39) as

$$u_ix^i = u_ih_j^i\bar{x}^j.$$

The incidence relation after the projectivity (or change of coordinates) is written as $\bar{u}_j\bar{x}^j = 0$. This means that

(40) $$\bar{u}_j = h_j^iu_i, \quad u_i = h_i^{\prime k}\bar{u}_k.$$

Hence, the projectivity $x^i = h_j^i\bar{x}^j$ induces a transformation of the u_i coordinates if the form u_ix^i is to remain invariant, which means that $u_ix^i = \bar{u}_j\bar{x}^j$. The form u_ix^i is called an *algebraic tensor*. The u_i are said to transform in a *covariant* manner by (40), and the x^i in a *contravariant* manner by (39). One has

$$u_ix^i = (h_i^{\prime k}\bar{u}_k)(h_j^i\bar{x}^j) = h_j^ih_i^{\prime k}\bar{u}_k\bar{x}^j = \delta_j^k\bar{u}_k\bar{x}^j = \bar{u}_j\bar{x}^j,$$

which exhibits the invariance of the form u_ix^i, the vanishing of which describes the geometric condition that the line u_i is incident with the point x^i and that the line $\bar{u}_i$ is incident with the point $\bar{x}^i$.

Consider next the transformation of the quadratic form $a_{ij}x^ix^j$ under (39). One has

$$a_{ij}x^ix^j = a_{ij}h_k^i\bar{x}^kh_l^j\bar{x}^l = a_{ij}h_k^ih_l^j\bar{x}^k\bar{x}^l \equiv \bar{a}_{kl}\bar{x}^k\bar{x}^l.$$

If $a_{ij}x^ix^j$ is to be invariant, the coefficients $\bar{a}_{kl}$ of the transformed form must be related to the coefficients of the original form by the equations

(41) $$\bar{a}_{kl} = a_{ij}h_k^ih_l^j.$$

The invariant form $a_{ij}x^ix^j$ is a tensor. The quantities a_{ij} are the *components* of the tensor in the x^i coordinates, and the $\bar{a}_{kl}$ are its components in the $\bar{x}^i$ coordinates. The two sets of covariant components are related by (41).

It is to be shown next that the a_{ij} can be expressed in terms of the $\bar{a}_{ij}$ by equations similar to (41). First, multiply both members of (41) by $h_p^{\prime k}$ and sum on k to obtain

$$\bar{a}_{kl}h_p^{\prime k} = a_{ij}h_k^ih_p^{\prime k}h_l^j = a_{ij}\delta_p^ih_l^j = a_{pj}h_l^j.$$

Now multiply on both sides by $h_q^{\prime l}$ to have

$$\bar{a}_{kl}h_p^{\prime k}h_q^{\prime l} = a_{pj}h_l^jh_q^{\prime l} = a_{pj}\delta_q^j = a_{pq}.$$

Hence,

(42) $$a_{pq} = \bar{a}_{kl}h_p^{\prime k}h_q^{\prime l}$$

gives the desired result. Compare (42) with (41) to see that the h's become primed when the bar is shifted from one side of the equation to the other. The so-called "inverse" of (42) is readily found to be given by (41). The a_{ij} and the $\bar{a}_{ij}$ may be styled the components of a covariant tensor of the second order in their respective coordinate systems.

The vanishing of an invariant always has some geometrical significance. The equation $a_{ij}x^ix^j = 0$ represents a conic, which is determined by the ratios of the ordered set of six numbers a_{ij}. These six numbers may be interpreted as the coordinates of a point in a projective space of five dimensions. There is a one-to-one correspondence between the conics of the projective plane and the points of a five-dimensional projective space. The coefficients a_{ij} may be called the coordinates of a conic. If equations (39) are viewed as a transformation of coordinates, the conic is unchanged under (39) but assumes the equation $\bar{a}_{ij}\bar{x}^i\bar{x}^j = 0$ in the $\bar{x}^i$ coordinates. The conic coordinates transform by (42), which is induced by (39). If (39) is viewed as a projective mapping, the conic $a_{ij}x^ix^j = 0$ is projected into the conic $\bar{a}_{ij}\bar{x}^i\bar{x}^j = 0$. It has been observed previously that $|\bar{a}_{kl}| = |a_{ij}|J^2$; that is, $|a_{ij}|$ is an invariant of weight two. If $|a_{ij}| = 0$, the original conic is composite, and therefore, after projection, the conic remains composite.

Consider next the form $a^{ij}u_iu_j$ and its transformed form under (40). One has

$$a^{ij}u_iu_j = a^{ij}h_i'^k\bar{u}_kh_j'^l\bar{u}_l = a^{ij}h_i'^kh_j'^l\bar{u}_k\bar{u}_l \equiv \bar{a}^{kl}\bar{u}_k\bar{u}_l,$$

from which the relation between the a^{ij} and $\bar{a}^{kl}$ is given by

$$(43) \qquad \bar{a}^{kl} = a^{ij}h_i'^kh_j'^l.$$

The quantities a^{ij} and $\bar{a}^{kl}$ in their respective coordinate systems are called components of a *contravariant* tensor of the second order. The expressions for a^{ij} in terms of $\bar{a}^{kl}$ can be obtained by multiplying both members of (43) by $h_k^p h_l^q$ and summing on k and l to obtain

$$\bar{a}^{kl}h_k^p h_l^q = a^{ij}h_i'^k h_k^p h_j'^l h_l^q = a^{ij}\delta_i^p\delta_j^q = a^{pj}\delta_j^q = a^{pq},$$

or, with a change of umbral indices,

$$(44) \qquad a^{ij} = \bar{a}^{kl}h_k^i h_l^j.$$

The vanishing of the invariant function $a^{ij}u_iu_j$ may be interpreted as the line equation of a conic. If the conic in point coordinates is written as $a_{ij}x^ix^j = 0$, the corresponding equation in line coordinates is $A^{ij}u_iu_j = 0$. Here the $a^{ij} \equiv A^{ij}$ are the cofactors of the elements a_{ij} in $|a_{ij}|$. It follows from (44) that $|\bar{a}^{kl}| = |a^{ij}|J^{-2}$, and, from this, that a composite line conic ($|a^{ij}| = 0$) projects into a composite line conic.

The point coordinates x^i are contravariant variables and the line coordinates u_i are covariant variables. In a tensor there are no free indices. All of the indices sum to give a single term—that is, an invariant expression. The covariant components of a tensor always appear with lower indices, as in a_{ij} of the tensor $a_{ij}x^ix^j$. The contravariant components of a tensor always appear with upper indices as in the A^{ij} of the tensor (or invariant) $A^{ij}u_iu_j$.

One more instance of a tensor will now be adduced to indicate that the components of a tensor may be *mixed;* that is, they may have indices of covariance and also indices of contravariance. Consider the form $a_{ij}{}^{kl}x^ix^ju_ku_l$ of the fourth order, which is quadratic in the point variables and also quadratic in the line variables. The form transforms under (39) and (40) as follows

$$a_{ij}{}^{kl}x^ix^ju_ku_l = a_{ij}{}^{kl}h^t_p\bar{x}^ph^j_q\bar{x}^qh''_k\bar{u}_rh'^s_l\bar{u}_s$$

$$= a_{ij}{}^{kl}h^t_ph^j_qh''_kh'^s_l\bar{x}^p\bar{x}^q\bar{u}_r\bar{u}_s \equiv \bar{a}_{pq}{}^{rs}\bar{x}^p\bar{x}^q\bar{u}_r\bar{u}_s,$$

where

(45) $$\bar{a}_{pq}{}^{rs} = a_{ij}{}^{kl}h^t_ph^j_qh''_kh'^s_l$$

gives the law of transformation of the components $a_{ij}{}^{kl}$ of the mixed tensor of the fourth order. This tensor is covariant of order two and contravariant of order two. The extended pattern for the law of transformation for the components of tensors of order higher than four should be clear from equation (45). In (45) the indices p, q, r, s are free, each taking on the range 1, 2, 3, while i, j, k, l are umbral (or dummy) indices which indicate sums. Equation (45) represents eighty-one equations because each of p, q, r, s takes on the values 1, 2, 3 independently. Various instances of tensors appear in the following sections.

The tensor concept as introduced here is capable of several types of generalization. For instance, the range of the indices in (39) may be 1, 2, $\cdots$, $n + 1$ for a projectivity (or for a change of coordinates) in a projective space of n dimensions. Further, the linear homogeneous substitution in (39) may be replaced by a much more general transformation given by $x^i = x^i(\bar{x}^1, \bar{x}^2, \bar{x}^3)$ where the x^i functions of the new coordinates are such that the inverse $\bar{x}^i = \bar{x}^i(x^1, x^2, x^3)$ exists in the region under consideration. Moreover, the components of a tensor such as those in (45) may be functions of the space coordinates. Observe that, from (39), $\partial x^i/\partial \bar{x}^j = h^i_j$ are constants. In the more extended tensor analysis the quantities $\partial x^i/\partial \bar{x}^j$ (calculated from the transformation equations $x^i = x^i(\bar{x}^1, \bar{x}^2, \bar{x}^3)$) are functions of $\bar{x}^i$, and therefore of x^i.

Concomitants

A tensor has been defined as an invariant form involving point coordinates, or line coordinates, or both. And the law of transformation of the components of the tensor is induced by the invariance of the form under the transformations (39) and (40). For instance, $f \equiv a_{ij}x^ix^j = \bar{a}_{kl}\bar{x}^k\bar{x}^l \equiv \bar{f}$ under (39), so the a_{ij} are components of a covariant tensor.

A *covariant* of a form f was defined in Section 3-7. Note that from this definition and the fact that $\bar{a}_{kl}\bar{x}^k\bar{x}^l = (a_{ij}x^ix^j)|h^p_q|^0$, the form f itself is a covariant of weight zero, where $f \equiv a_{ij}x^ix^j$. The form f is also a tensor with covariant components a_{ij}. In a similar way, if $F \equiv a^{ij}u_iu_j = \bar{a}^{kl}\bar{u}_k\bar{u}_l \equiv \bar{F}$ under (40), then F is called a *contravariant* of weight zero. If $\bar{b}^{ij}\bar{u}_i\bar{u}_l = (b^{ij}u_iu_j)|h^p_q|^w$ under (40), then the form $b^{ij}u_iu_j$ is a contravariant of weight w, and the coefficients of the form may be styled the components of a contravariant tensor of the second order and of weight w. In this case

$$\bar{b}^{kl} = b^{pq}h'^k_ph''_qJ^w,$$

where $J = |h^i_j|$. Similarly, one may define a covariant of weight w, and a covariant tensor of weight w.

Finally, the invariant function may contain both point and line coordinates. For instance, consider

$$\bar{\phi} \equiv \bar{c}^{pq}_{rs}\bar{u}_p\bar{u}_q\bar{x}^r\bar{x}^s = c^{ij}_{kl}u_iu_jx^kx^lJ^w \equiv \phi J^w.$$

The coefficients c^{ij}_{kl} are then components of a mixed tensor of the fourth order of weight w. Also, the function ϕ is called a *concomitant* of weight w, because it contains both point and line coordinates. Evidently, then, a concomitant is a mixed tensor.

Invariants of a Set of Forms

A simultaneous concomitant of a set of forms $f_1, \cdots, f_k$ is considered next. A simultaneous invariant of two linear forms appeared in Section 3-2, and a simultaneous invariant (the harmonic invariant) of two quadratic forms was introduced in Section 3-5. Here, the forms $f_1, \cdots, f_k$ may be of arbitrary degree in any number of variables (x^i, u_i). Under the transformation (39) or (40) the forms go into $\bar{f}_1, \cdots, \bar{f}_k$. A concomitant ϕ of the set of forms $f_1, \cdots, f_k$ is a function of the coefficients of $f_1, \cdots, f_k$ and of the x^i and u_i coordinates with the property that if the same function of the corresponding coefficients and variables in $\bar{f}_1, \cdots, \bar{f}_k$ is formed, the latter function differs from ϕ only by a factor which is a power of the jacobian of the point transformation of the type of (39). If the u_i are absent in ϕ, then ϕ is a covariant of the set of forms. If the x^i are not involved in ϕ, then ϕ is a contravariant of the set of forms. Finally, if both the x^i and the u_i are absent in ϕ, then ϕ is called an invariant of the set of forms. The instances to appear in the following section involve a set of no more than three ternary quadratic forms—that is, three conics.

It was seen in Equation (32) of Section 8-8 that the quantities a, α, β, b are invariants of two conics $f_1 \equiv a_{ij}x^ix^j = 0$ and $f_2 \equiv b_{ij}x^ix^j = 0$, and that any homogeneous function of a, α, β, b is an invariant of the set f_1, f_2. It can be shown that the invariants a, α, β, b constitute a *basis* for the invariants of f_1, f_2, which means that any invariant of the set is a polynomial function of a, α, β, b. More generally, for any set of arbitrary forms $f_1, \cdots, f_k$, there exists a finite set of invariants $I_1, \cdots, I_n$ such that any further invariant can be expressed as a polynomial in $I_1, \cdots, I_n$. This is Gordan's theorem.*

8-10. Conics and tensors

The conics

(46) C_1: $a_{ij}x^ix^j = 0,$ C_2: $b_{ij}x^ix^j = 0$

---

* A more extended treatment of the classical theory of invariants can be found in the book by J. H. Grace and A. Young, *Algebra of Invariants* (Cambridge, 1903), or in R. Weitzenböck, *Invariantentheorie* (Groningen, 1923).

have the respective line equations

(47) $\qquad\qquad$ Γ_1: $\qquad$ $A^{ij}u_iu_j = 0,$ $\qquad\qquad$ Γ_2: $\qquad$ $B^{ij}u_iu_j = 0.$

The pencil $(a_{ij} + \lambda b_{ij})x^ix^j = 0$ has the line equation $M^{ij}u_iu_j = 0$, where the M^{ij} are the cofactors of the elements $a_{ij} + \lambda b_{ij}$ in the matrix $(a_{ij} + \lambda b_{ij})$. For instance, note that

$$M^{11} \equiv \begin{vmatrix} a_{22} + \lambda b_{22} & a_{23} + \lambda b_{23} \\ a_{32} + \lambda b_{32} & a_{33} + \lambda b_{33} \end{vmatrix} = A^{11} + \lambda \begin{vmatrix} a_{22} & a_{23} \\ b_{32} & a_{33} \end{vmatrix} + \lambda \begin{vmatrix} a_{22} & b_{23} \\ a_{32} & b_{33} \end{vmatrix} + \lambda^2 B^{11}.$$

The coefficient of λ in M^{11} is seen to be the polarized form of

$$2 \begin{vmatrix} a_{22} & a_{23} \\ a_{32} & a_{33} \end{vmatrix} \equiv 2A^{11}$$

with respect to the b's. For the general term, one has

$$M^{ij} \equiv A^{ij} + 2\lambda S^{ij} + \lambda^2 B^{ij},$$

where $2S^{ij}$ denotes the polarized form of $2A^{ij}$, as a form in the a_{ij}, with respect to the b_{ij}. Hence, the line equation of the point pencil is

(48) $\qquad\qquad$ $A^{ij}u_iu_j + 2\lambda S^{ij}u_iu_j + \lambda^2 B^{ij}u_iu_j = 0.$

If a fixed line given by $u_ix^i = 0$ is selected in the plane, the u_i are constants for which the quadratic (48) in λ has, in general, two distinct roots. Thus, there are, in general, two conics through the four points of intersection of C_1 and C_2 which are tangent to the line $u_ix^i = 0$. The envelope of lines for which the roots λ_1 and λ_2 of equation (48) are equal is represented by

$$(S^{ij}u_iu_j)^2 - (A^{ij}u_iu_j)(B^{kl}u_ku_l) = 0,$$

or, equivalently, by

(49) $\qquad\qquad$ $(S^{ij}S^{kl} - A^{ij}B^{kl})u_iu_ju_ku_l = 0.$

But observe that if only one conic through four points is tangent to a line, then that line must pass through one of the four points. Hence, equation (49) represents the four points of intersection of the conics (46). Equation (49) must therefore factorize into four linear factors, each of which represents one of the four intersection points of C_1 and C_2.

It should be observed that if the transformation (40) is carried out on equation (48) the result is equation (48) in the quantities with bars. The geometric situation is unchanged, and the roots of (48) are the same as those of the same equation in the barred quantities. Further, because $A^{ij}u_iu_j$ and $B^{ij}u_iu_j$ are tensors (A^{ij} and B^{ij} being the respective contravariant components), the form $S^{ij}u_iu_j$ is a tensor. Hence, the quantities S^{ij} are components of a contravariant tensor. Because $S^{ij}u_iu_j$ is an invariant, the equation

(50) $\qquad\qquad\qquad$ $S^{ij}u_iu_j = 0$

must have some geometric significance of a projective nature. Of course, equation (50) represents a line conic, but how is it related to the original conics C_1 and C_2? The answer to this question is supplied by the

THEOREM: *Every line which satisfies equation* (50) *intersects the conics* C_1 *and* C_2 *in a set of harmonic points.*

Proof: A change of coordinates from u_i to $\bar{u}_i$ can be effected, under which any particular line with coordinates u_i has the new coordinates $[1:0:0]$ in the $\bar{u}_i$ system. The induced coordinate change on the point coordinates from x^i to $\bar{x}^i$ changes the equations of the conics C_1 and C_2 to the forms $\bar{a}_{ij}\bar{x}^i\bar{x}^j = 0$ and $\bar{b}_{ij}\bar{x}^i\bar{x}^j = 0$. The line $[1:0:0]$, with the equation $\bar{x}^1 = 0$, intersects the conics in the pairs of points given by

(51)
$$\bar{x}^1 = 0, \quad \bar{a}_{22}(\bar{x}^2)^2 + 2\bar{a}_{23}\bar{x}^2\bar{x}^3 + \bar{a}_{33}(\bar{x}^3)^2 = 0,$$
$$\bar{x}^1 = 0, \quad \bar{b}_{22}(\bar{x}^2)^2 + 2\bar{b}_{23}\bar{x}^2\bar{x}^3 + \bar{b}_{33}(\bar{x}^3)^2 = 0.$$

These four points are harmonic if and only if the harmonic invariant $\bar{a}_{22}\bar{b}_{33} - 2\bar{a}_{23}\bar{b}_{23} + \bar{a}_{33}\bar{b}_{22}$ is zero. Now equation (50) becomes $\bar{S}^{ij}\bar{u}_i\bar{u}_j = 0$ in the new coordinates, and this equation is satisfied by the line $[1:0:0]$. Hence, $\bar{S}^{11} \equiv \bar{a}_{22}\bar{b}_{33} - 2\bar{a}_{23}\bar{b}_{23} + \bar{a}_{33}\bar{b}_{22}$ must vanish. Because of the invariance of the form $S^{ij}u_iu_j$, this form must vanish for the line u_i in the original coordinates. This completes the proof of the theorem.*

The Dual

The line conics (47) determine the pencil of line conics given by

(52)
$$A^{ij}u_iu_j + \lambda B^{ij}u_iu_j = 0.$$

For any assigned value of λ, equation (52) represents a line conic which is tangent to the four common tangents to the two base conics C_1 and C_2. The pencil (52) has the point equation $m_{ij}x^ix^j = 0$, where the m_{ij} are proportional to the cofactors of the elements $A^{ij} + \lambda B^{ij}$ in the matrix $(A^{ij} + \lambda B^{ij})$. (For instance, recall that $\begin{vmatrix} A^{22} & A^{23} \\ A^{32} & A^{33} \end{vmatrix} = aa_{11}$, and that $|A_{ij}| = a^2$.) The expression for m_{11} is given by

$$m_{11} \equiv \begin{vmatrix} A^{22} & A^{23} \\ A^{32} & A^{33} \end{vmatrix} + \lambda \begin{vmatrix} A^{22} & B^{23} \\ A^{32} & B^{33} \end{vmatrix} + \lambda \begin{vmatrix} B^{22} & A^{23} \\ B^{32} & A^{33} \end{vmatrix} + \lambda^2 \begin{vmatrix} B^{22} & B^{23} \\ B^{32} & B^{33} \end{vmatrix}.$$

The general coefficient m_{ij} is given by

$$m_{ij} \equiv aa_{ij} + 2\lambda s_{ij} + \lambda^2 bb_{ij},$$

where $2s_{ij}$ is the polarized form of $2aa_{ij}$, as a form in the A^{ij}, with respect to the B^{ij}. Hence, the point equation of the line pencil is

(53)
$$aa_{ij}x^ix^j + 2\lambda s_{ij}x^ix^j + \lambda^2 bb_{ij}x^ix^j = 0.$$

If a fixed point given by $u_ix^i = 0$ is selected in the plane, the x^i are constants for which the quadratic (50) in λ has, in general, two distinct roots. Thus, there

---

* For an extension to quadric surfaces in three-space of the foregoing projective theory of conics, see J. A. Todd, *Projective and Analytical Geometry* (Pitman, London, 1947), Chapter 7.

are, in general, two conics tangent to the four common tangents to C_1 and C_2 which contain the selected point. The locus of points for which the roots of (53) are equal is given by

(54) $$(s_{ij}s_{kl} - aba_{ij}b_{kl})x^ix^jx^kx^l = 0.$$

If only one conic tangent to four lines passes through a given point, then that point must be on one of the four tangents. Hence, equation (54) factorizes into four linear factors, each of which corresponds to one of the four tangent lines to C_1 and C_2. Equation (54) represents the four tangent lines common to two conics. The tensor character of equation (53) indicates that the invariant conic given by $s_{ij}x^ix^j = 0$ must have some projective significance. This is stated in the

THEOREM: *The covariant tensor with components s_{ij} determines a point conic $s_{ij}x^ix^j = 0$, which is the locus of points from which the four tangent lines to the base conics of the pencil form a harmonic set.*

The proof is similar to that of the preceding theorem.

EXERCISES

1. Obtain equation (41) from (42).

2. The conics C_1 and C_2 can be represented by C_1: $ax^2 + by^2 + cz^2 = 0$ and C_2: $x^2 + y^2 + z^2 = 0$ by using the common self-polar triangle as the triangle of reference. Calculate the matrices (a_{ij}), (b_{ij}), (A^{ij}), (B^{ij}), and the matrix (s_{ij}) for the covariant conic $s_{ij}x^ix^j = 0$. One finds from

$$s_{11} \equiv \begin{vmatrix} ac & 0 \\ 0 & 1 \end{vmatrix} + \begin{vmatrix} 1 & 0 \\ 0 & ab \end{vmatrix} = a(b + c), \quad s_{12} \equiv \begin{vmatrix} 0 & 0 \\ ab & 0 \end{vmatrix} + \begin{vmatrix} 0 & 0 \\ 1 & 0 \end{vmatrix} = 0, \text{ etc.,}$$

that the covariant conic has the equation

$$a(b + c)x^2 + b(c + a)y^2 + c(a + b)z^2 = 0.$$

Deduce, therefore, that a triangle self-polar relative to C_1 and C_2 is also self-polar relative to the covariant conic $s_{ij}x^ix^j = 0$.

3. Show that if Γ: $A^{ij}u_iu_j = 0$ is a proper line conic, and P_1: $\alpha^iu_i = 0$ and P_2: $\beta^iu_i = 0$ are two points, then $A^{ij}u_iu_j + \lambda(\alpha^iu_i)(\beta^ju_j) = 0$ is the line equation of a family of conics tangent to the lines from the points P_1, P_2 to Γ.

4. Show that $(\alpha^iu_i)(\beta^ju_j) + \lambda(\gamma^iu_i)(\delta^ju_j) = 0$ is a family of conics tangent to the two lines joining the point $\alpha^iu_i = 0$ to $\gamma^iu_i = 0$ and $\delta^iu_i = 0$, and to the two lines joining $\beta^iu_i = 0$ to $\gamma^iu_i = 0$ and $\delta^iu_i = 0$.

5. In the form $2A^{ij}u_iu_j$, write $a_{11} = X$, $a_{22} = Y$, $a_{33} = Z$, $a_{23} = U$, $a_{31} = V$, $a_{12} = W$, and polarize with respect to the "point" $(\overline{X}, \overline{Y}, \overline{Z}, \overline{U}, \overline{V}, \overline{W}) \equiv (b_{11}, b_{22}, b_{33}, b_{23}, b_{31}, b_{12})$ to obtain the contravariant form $2S^{ij}u_iu_j$.

6. Show that a given point conic C: $a_{ij}x^ix^j = 0$ is a covariant of itself, and that the polar reciprocal (see Exercise 7 on p. 207) of C relative to $\delta_{ij}x^ix^j \equiv (x^1)^2 + (x^2)^2 + (x^3)^2 = 0$ is a contravariant of C.

7. Write the equation of the polar line of the point $P(y^i)$ with respect to each of the three conics C_1: $a_{ij}x^ix^j = 0$, C_2: $b_{ij}x^ix^j = 0$, C_3: $c_{ij}x^ix^j = 0$, and show that the locus of the points P for which their polars relative to C_1, C_2, C_3 are concurrent is the cubic covariant curve given by

$$\begin{vmatrix} a_{1j}y^j & a_{2j}y^i & a_{3j}y^i \\ b_{1k}y^k & b_{2k}y^k & b_{3k}y^k \\ c_{1l}y^l & c_{2l}y^l & c_{3l}y^l \end{vmatrix} \equiv e^{pqr}a_{pj}b_{qk}c_{rl}y^iy^ky^l = 0.$$

This is the jacobian cubic curve, which is a projective invariant of the three conics.

8. Show that if the three conics in Exercise 7 have two points in common, then the line determined by these points is part of the jacobian curve, so that the residual part is a conic. Deduce that this always happens if the three given conics are circles, in which case the line of the locus is the line at infinity, and the residual conic is a circle orthogonal to the three given circles.

8-11. The absolute conic

The circular points at infinity, and the isotropic lines through a point were introduced in Section 6-5. It was seen that two lines are perpendicular if and only if they separate harmonically the isotropic lines through their common point. It is of interest to treat the circular points by use of their line equation. The points $I(1:i:0)$, $J(1:-i:0)$ have the respective line equations $u_1 + iu_2 = 0$, $u_1 - iu_2 = 0$. These may be combined into the single equation $u_1^2 + u_2^2 = 0$, which is the line equation of the line at infinity ($x^3 = 0$) counted twice. This composite conic is referred to as the *absolute conic*.* In the projective plane there are no such special lines. Any line may be given the equation $x^3 = 0$. One may replace the improper absolute conic (which is useful in affine and euclidean interpretations of projective geometry) by a proper conic in the projective plane and treat it as the absolute conic. Two lines which have their intersection on this absolute conic are called parallel, and two lines which are conjugate relative to this conic are said to be perpendicular. These notions produce a noneuclidean geometry which will be treated in the following chapter.

The equation of the absolute as the double line at infinity will be denoted for simplicity by $\Omega = 0$. It is necessary in metric and affine applications to develop the form of $\Omega = 0$ for the particular coordinate system employed. The form of $\Omega = 0$ for areal coordinates will now be found.

In Exercises 2 and 6 of Section 5-8 it was observed that the equation of the line at infinity is $x^1 + x^2 + x^3 = 0$, and that a circle has an equation of the form

(55) $$(p_1)^2x^2x^3 + (p_2)^2x^3x^1 + (p_3)^2x^1x^2 = 0$$

in areal coordinates x^i, where p_i, for $i = 1, 2, 3$, are the lengths of the sides of the reference triangle. It is proposed to find a condition under which the line

---

* A. Cayley (1821–1895) introduced the notion of the absolute conic in his Sixth Memoir upon Quantics, 1859 (*Collected Papers*, vol. 2, No. 158).

$u_i x^i = 0$ contains a point of intersection of the line at infinity and the circle (55)—that is, the circumcircle of the triangle of reference. The lines with coordinates $[u_1:u_2:u_3]$ and $[1:1:1]$ intersect in the point $(u_2 - u_3:u_3 - u_1:u_1 - u_2)$, which lies on the circle (55) if

(56)
$$\frac{p_1^2}{u_2 - u_3} + \frac{p_2^2}{u_3 - u_1} + \frac{p_3^2}{u_1 - u_2} = 0.$$

This is the line equation of the circular points. It can be rearranged (using the law of cosines for the triangle of reference) to obtain the form

$$\Omega \equiv \sum_{i=1}^{3} p_i^2 u_i^2 - 2(p_2 p_3 \cos \alpha_1) u_2 u_3 - 2(p_3 p_1 \cos \alpha_2) u_3 u_1 - 2(p_1 p_2 \cos \alpha_3) u_1 u_2 = 0,$$

or, more briefly,

(57)
$$\Omega(u_1, u_2, u_3) \equiv \sum [p_i^2 u_i^2 - 2(p_2 p_3 \cos \alpha_1) u_2 u_3] = 0.$$

Because $\Omega = 0$ represents a composite line conic, Ω must be the product of two linear factors. It can be shown that

$$\Omega = (p_1 u_1 - e^{i \alpha_3} u_2 i^{\alpha_3} - e^{-i \alpha_2} p_3 u_3)(p_1 u_1 - e^{-i \alpha_3} p_2 u_2 - e^{i \alpha_2} p_3 u_3),$$

from which the areal point coordinates of the circular points are

$$(p_1 : -e^{i \alpha_3} p_2 : e^{-i \alpha_2} p_3), \quad (p_1 : -e^{-i \alpha_3} p_2 : -e^{i \alpha_2} p_3).$$

These are awkward to use. Only Ω itself will be employed here.

The condition for perpendicularity in areal coordinates can now be obtained. Let u_i and u_i' be the respective coordinates of two lines. Any line $u_i + \lambda u_i'$ through their intersection contains a circular point at infinity if, from (57),

$$\Omega(u_1 + \lambda u_1', u_2 + \lambda u_2', u_3 + \lambda u_3') = 0,$$

that is,

$$\Omega(u_1, u_2, u_3) + 2\lambda \Omega(u_1, u_2, u_3; u_1', u_2', u_3') + \lambda^2 \Omega(u_1', u_2', u_3') = 0,$$

or

(58)
$$\Omega(u) + 2\lambda \Omega(u, u') + \lambda^2 \Omega(u') = 0,$$

in which $\Omega(u, u')$ is used to denote the polarized form of $\Omega(u)$ relative to u_i'. Equation (58) gives two roots λ_1, λ_2 for the isotropic lines through the intersection of the two given lines. The condition for the lines u_i, u_i' and the isotropic lines to form a harmonic set is $\lambda_1 + \lambda_2 = 0$, which means that

(59)
$$2\Omega(u, u') \equiv u_i \frac{\partial \Omega}{\partial u_i'} \equiv u_i' \frac{\partial \Omega}{\partial u_i} = 0,$$

in which a summation takes place on the index i. Actually, equation (59) gives the condition for perpendicularity of two lines u_i and u_i' in any coordinate system, if the proper form of Ω is used for that system. For areal coordinates, Ω is defined in (57). It can be shown that

$$\Omega(u) \equiv \sum u_i^2 - 2 \sum u_2 u_3 \cos \alpha_1$$

for trilinear coordinates (see Section 5-7). In orthogonal cartesian coordinates,

$$\Omega(u) \equiv u_1^2 + u_2^2.$$

Hence, the condition for perpendicularity of u_i and u_i' in this system is $u_1 u_1' + u_2 u_2' = 0$.

Evolute of a Conic

The absolute can be used to find the equation of the evolute of a conic—that is, the envelope of the normals to the conic. Let the conic Γ have the line equation $A^{ij}u_i u_j = 0$, and write the absolute as $\Omega \equiv \alpha^{ij}u_i u_j = 0$. Let u_i' be any tangent to Γ, and u_i the corresponding normal line. Because the tangent and normal are perpendicular, one has $\alpha^{ij}u_i'u_j = 0$. The contact point of the tangent line to Γ is $A^{ij}u_i'$, and this is on the normal. Hence, $A^{ij}u_i'u_j = 0$. Solve the last two equations for the ratios of the u_i' to obtain

$$(60) \qquad\qquad \rho u_i' = e_{ijk}\alpha^{jl}A^{km}u_l u_m.$$

The u_i' satisfy the line equation of Γ; that is, $A^{ij}u_i'u_j' = 0$. On substituting from (60) into this last equation, one finds the line equation of the evolute of Γ in the form

$$(61) \qquad e_{pqi}\alpha^{pl}u_l A^{qm}u_m A^{ij}e_{jrs}\alpha^{rk}u_k A^{st}u_t = 0.$$

This equation expresses the vanishing of a quartic contravariant of Γ. In the notation of jacobians, equation (61) can be written as

$$(62) \qquad e_{ipq}\frac{\partial(\Omega,\ \Gamma)}{\partial(u_p,\ u_q)}A^{ij}e_{jrs}\frac{\partial(\Omega,\ \Gamma)}{\partial(u_r,\ u_s)} = 0.$$

EXAMPLE

Find the equation of the evolute of the ellipse $b^2x^2 + a^2y^2 = a^2b^2$.

Solution: The line equation may be taken as $\Gamma \equiv a^2u_1^2 + b^2u_2^2 - u_3^2 = 0$. For rectangular cartesian coordinates, $\Omega \equiv u_1^2 + u_2^2$. Hence,

$$\frac{\partial(\Omega,\ \Gamma)}{\partial(u_2,\ u_3)} = \begin{vmatrix} 2b^2u_2 & -2u_3 \\ 2u_2 & 0 \end{vmatrix} = -4u_2 u_3,$$

$$\frac{\partial(\Omega,\ \Gamma)}{\partial(u_3,\ u_1)} = 4u_3 u_1,$$

$$\frac{\partial(\Omega,\ \Gamma)}{\partial(u_1,\ u_2)} = -4(a^2 - b^2)u_1 u_2.$$

Use of these jacobian expressions in (62) yields

$$\frac{a^2}{u_1^2} + \frac{b^2}{u_2^2} = \frac{(a^2 - b^2)^2}{u_3^2}$$

for the line equation of the evolute of the given ellipse. It can be verified that the line coordinates of the normals to the ellipse satisfy this line equation of the evolute. (See Example 3 on p. 204.)

Foci of a Conic

Another metric application of the line equation ($\Omega = 0$) of the absolute relates to the foci of a curve, defined in Section 6-5 as the intersection of the tangents to the curve from the circular points. A curve of class n has n^2 foci. A conic has four foci, two of which are real if the conic is real.

If a conic has the line equation $\Gamma \equiv A^{ij}u_iu_j = 0$, then $\Gamma + \lambda\Omega = 0$ is a family of conics each of which is tangent to the lines from I and J tangent to Γ. Hence, the family is a set of conics confocal with $\Gamma = 0$. In order to find the set of conics confocal with C: $a_{ij}x^ix^j = 0$, first write the line equation of C, and use $\Omega \equiv u_1^2 + u_2^2$ to obtain

$$(63) \qquad \Gamma + \lambda\Omega \equiv A^{ij}u_iu_j + \lambda(u_1^2 + u_2^2) = 0$$

as the line equation of the set of confocal conics. The point equation of the family may then be written by use of (63).

If the value of λ is such that $\Gamma + \lambda\Omega$ factorizes, then (63) represents two points which must be on the lines joining these points to I and J. Hence, the two points are foci of the conic. Thus, a straightforward method for finding the foci of a conic is at hand. This is illustrated in the following example.

EXAMPLE

Find the foci of the conic $7x^2 - 6xy + 15y^2 - 10x + 18y + 31 = 0$.

Solution: The line equation is $8u^2 + 4v^2 + 2w^2 + 2uv + 2uw - 2vw = 0$. Hence, equation (63) is

$$(8 + \lambda)u^2 + (4 + \lambda)v^2 + 2w^2 - 2vw + 2wu + 2uv = 0.$$

The condition for two linear factors is

$$\begin{vmatrix} 8 + \lambda & 1 & 1 \\ 1 & 4 + \lambda & -1 \\ 1 & -1 & 2 \end{vmatrix} = 0,$$

from which $\lambda_1 = -8$ and $\lambda_2 = -3$. Corresponding to $\lambda_1 = -8$, the factors are $v + w$ and $u - 2v + w$. Therefore, the real foci are $(0, 1)$ and $(1, -2)$.

For $\lambda_2 = -3$, the line equation of the foci may be written as $(u + v - w)^2 + (2u + w)^2 = 0$, or, in factored form,

$$[(1 + 2i)u + v + (-1 + i)w][(1 - 2i)u + v + (-1 - i)w] = 0.$$

Hence, the foci have the point coordinates

$$(1 + 2i:1:-1 + i), \quad (1 - 2i:1:-1 - i),$$

which are equivalent to

$$\left(\frac{1 - 3i}{2}, \frac{-1 - i}{2}\right), \quad \left(\frac{1 + 3i}{2}, \frac{-1 - i}{2}\right)$$

in cartesian form.

EXERCISES

1. Use the method of this section to find the foci of the parabola $y^2 = 4x$.

2. Find the foci of the parabola $(x + y)^2 + 8x - 4y = 6$.

   Ans. $(-\frac{2}{3}, -\frac{1}{3})$ and the point at infinity on the line $y = x$.

3. Find the point equation corresponding to equation (57).

   Ans. $(x^1 + x^2 + x^3)^2 = 0$.

CHAPTER 9

Noneuclidean Geometries

A brief introduction to a projective interpretation of two noneuclidean geometries (elliptic and hyperbolic) is set forth in this chapter in order to establish the relation between these geometries and euclidean geometry. It will be seen that euclidean (that is, parabolic) geometry appears as a particular limiting case of both elliptic and hyperbolic geometry. For this reason euclidean geometry may be said to occupy a transitional position between the elliptic and hyperbolic geometries.

9-1. Measure of a one-dimensional extent

It was seen in Section 2-4 that, according to the choice of values for the real coefficients a, b, c, d in the projectivity on a line given by

(1)
$$\bar{x} = \frac{ax + b}{cx + d},$$

the fixed points of the projectivity are real and distinct (hyperbolic case), real and coincident (parabolic case), or complex (elliptic case). For the particular case in which $c = 0$ and $d = a$, the mapping (1) is a translation $\bar{x} = x + p$ (parabolic case) for which the fixed points may be described as coinciding at the "point at infinity." It is readily seen that the euclidean measure of the distance between two points on a line is invariant under a translation.

If $c \neq 0$, the condition for coincident fixed points in (1) is $(d - a)^2 + 4bc = 0$, and the abscissa of the double fixed point is $(a - d)/2c$. If d is set equal to a (without loss of generality) it follows that $b = 0$, so that (1) takes the form

$$\frac{1}{\bar{x}} = \frac{1}{x} + \frac{c}{a},$$

a translation relating the points with abscissas $1/x$ and $1/\bar{x}$.

The euclidean measure of distance (euclidean metric) is said to be parabolic. The coincident points at infinity are referred to as the *absolute* of the metric on the line. A definition is now given for the projective measure of distance on a line between two points A, A' relative to two arbitrarily selected base points M, M' which are called the absolute of the metric on the line.

DEFINITION: *The projective distance δ between two points A, A' on a line with respect to two points M, M' on the line is given by*

(2) $\delta(AA') \equiv k \log(AA'MM')$,

where k is an arbitrary real or complex constant.

Because the cross ratio $(AA'MM')$ is invariant under the mapping (1), the distance δ is invariant under a projectivity. The measure defined by (2) is hyperbolic, parabolic, or elliptic according as the points M, M' of the absolute are real and distinct, real and coincident, or complex points on the line determined by A, A'. The points A, A' are taken as real.

It is to be observed that the following usual requirements for a metric are satisfied by the metric in (2).

$1°$ $\delta(AA') + \delta(A'A'') = \delta(AA'')$,

$2°$ $\delta(AA) = 0$,

$3°$ $\delta(AA') + \delta(A'A) = 0$.

For the proof of $1°$, note that

$$\delta(AA') + \delta(A'A'') = k[\log(AA'MM') + \log(A'A''MM')]$$
$$= k \log(AA'MM')(A'A''MM') = k \log(AA''MM') = \delta(AA'').$$

If A and A' coincide, equation (2) gives $\delta(AA) = k \log 1 = 0$, which verifies $2°$. The third attribute is seen to hold by replacing A'' in $1°$ by A.

It should be noted that if M' coincides with M (parabolic case), the formula (2) for the distance between distinct points A, A' gives

$$\delta(AA') = k \log 1 = 0$$

for all finite values of k. It will be seen in the analysis below that if k is allowed to become infinite as M' approaches M, the distance for the parabolic case is obtained from (2) by a limiting process.

The foregoing relates to a one-dimensional extent of points on a line l. It has been seen previously that if only real points are considered on the line, there are two fixed points under the projectivity (1) in the hyperbolic case, one (double) fixed point in the parabolic case, and *no* fixed point in the elliptic case. However, if the complex numbers are added to the line, then there are two fixed points in the elliptic case, and they are imaginary. The complex projective line is equivalent to a real *two-dimensional* extent of points, because each complex number is determined by a pair of real numbers.

Angle in a Pencil

Projective measure of an angle can be defined in a dual manner in which use is made of the one-dimensional extent of lines in a pencil of lines through a point L.

DEFINITION: *The projective measure α of the angle between two lines a, a' through a point L, with respect to two arbitrarily chosen lines m, m' through L, is given by*

(3)
$$\alpha(aa') \equiv k \log{(aa'mm')},$$

where k is an arbitrary constant.

Again, as in the case of formula (2), the measure given by (3) is said to be hyperbolic, parabolic, or elliptic according as the lines m, m' of the pencil are real and distinct, real and coincident, or complex. The lines a, a' are taken as real.

Three geometries arise from the three types of measure applied in the one-dimensional point range (and in the line pencil), and these geometries also carry the names hyperbolic, parabolic, and elliptic according to the respective measures employed. Euclidean geometry on the line is a parabolic type of geometry. Euclidean measure of angle from a single fixed line is also seen to be of the parabolic type. Note that the duals of 1°, 2°, 3° for linear measure follow, by use of (3), if the distance $\delta(AA')$ is replaced by the angle $\alpha(aa')$. For instance, $\alpha(aa') + \alpha(a'a'') = \alpha(aa'')$. (See Section 6-5.) It should be observed that with three choices for distance and three choices for angle measure nine geometries are to be considered. However, by tradition the elliptic measure of angle is employed, and this will be used below.

9-2. Analytical view

Let the fixed points M, M' on line l be represented by the quadratic form

(4)
$$f(x) \equiv a_{ij}x^ix^j = 0, \qquad a_{ij} = a_{ji}, i, j = 1, 2.$$

If the points A and A' have coordinates ξ^i and $\xi^{i'}$, then any point on l has coordinates of the form $\xi^i + \lambda\xi^{i'}$, and the values λ_1, λ_2 of λ corresponding to the points M, M' are roots of the quadratic equation

$$a_{ij}(\xi^i + \lambda\xi^{i'})(\xi^j + \lambda\xi^{j'}) = 0,$$

or

(5)
$$\lambda^2 a_{ij}\xi^{i'}\xi^{j'} + 2\lambda a_{ij}\xi^i\xi^{j'} + a_{ij}\xi^i\xi^j = 0.$$

Note from (4) that the coefficient of λ^2 in (5) may be expressed by $f(\xi')$, that the coefficient of λ is the polarized form of $f(\xi)$ relative to ξ'—denoted by $f(\xi, \xi')$—and that the remaining coefficient is $f(\xi)$. Hence, equation (5) may be written in the form

(6)
$$\lambda^2 f(\xi') + 2\lambda f(\xi, \xi') + f(\xi) = 0.$$

Because the points A, A', M, M' are represented by $\xi^i + \lambda\xi^{i'}$ for the respective values 0, ∞, λ_1, λ_2 of λ, the cross ratio $(AA'MM') = (0, \infty, \lambda_1, \lambda_2) = \lambda_1/\lambda_2$. On replacing λ_1, λ_2 by their expressions as roots of (6) into the formula (2), the distance $\delta(AA')$ takes the form

(7)
$$\delta(AA') = k \log\frac{f(\xi, \xi') - \sqrt{f^2(\xi, \xi') - f(\xi)f(\xi')}}{f(\xi, \xi') + \sqrt{f^2(\xi, \xi') - f(\xi)f(\xi')}},$$

which was given by F. Klein (1849–1925).*

Elliptic Metric

In case the metric in (7) is elliptic, the expression under the radical sign is negative. A real angle ϕ can be defined by

(8)
$$\cos\phi = \frac{f(\xi, \xi')}{\sqrt{f(\xi)f(\xi')}}, \quad \sin\phi = \frac{\sqrt{f(\xi)f(\xi') - f^2(\xi, \xi')}}{\sqrt{f(\xi)f(\xi')}},$$

by means of which (7) becomes

(9)
$$\delta(AA') = k \log\frac{\cos\phi - i\sin\phi}{\cos\phi + i\sin\phi} = k \log\frac{e^{-i\phi}}{e^{i\phi}} = -2ki\phi.$$

The arbitrary constant k may be taken as $ic/2$, so that the elliptic measure in (9) is given by $\delta(AA') = c\phi$, which is real.

Because the fixed points M, M' are complex, they may be represented by $\alpha + i\beta, \alpha - i\beta$. Equation (4) therefore becomes

(10) $f(x) \equiv [x - (\alpha + i\beta)][x - (\alpha - i\beta)] = x^2 - 2\alpha x + \alpha^2 + \beta^2 = 0,$

and $f(x)$ may be given the homogeneous form

(11)
$$f(x) \equiv (x^1)^2 - 2\alpha x^1 x^2 + (\alpha^2 + \beta^2)(x^2)^2.$$

If the expression for $\cos\phi$ in (8) is written by use of (11) and if $\xi^{1\prime}/\xi^{2\prime}$ is allowed to approach the ratio ξ^1/ξ^2, it is seen that $\cos\phi$ approaches unity, and therefore ϕ approaches zero; thus when A and A' coincide, the distance $\delta(AA) = (c)(0) = 0$. On the other hand, with $\xi^{1\prime}$ positive and ξ^1 negative, let ξ^2 and $\xi^{2\prime}$ approach zero. The value of $\cos\phi$ is seen to approach -1, which means that ϕ approaches π. Thus, the elliptic measure of the entire line is finite and equal to $c\pi$. For any choice of c ($\neq 0$), the entire length of a line provides a unit of length in elliptic geometry. This is in contrast with euclidean geometry, in which the unit of length is arbitrary.

It is of interest to plot the points A, A', M, M' in the complex plane (Fig. 72). (*Caution:* The complex plane used here is geometrically equivalent to the euclidean plane, and is not to be confused with the complex affine plane or the complex projective plane.) Let the real points A, A' have abscissas $x \equiv \xi^1/\xi^2$, $x' \equiv \xi^{1\prime}/\xi^{2\prime}$. The angle ϕ between AM and $A'M$ can be obtained from the cross ratio of the slopes of the lines AM, $A'M$, and the minimal lines through M. Let the inclinations of AM and $A'M$ be taken as α and β. The slopes of the minimal lines are $\pm i$. The cross ratio of the four slopes is

$$(\tan\alpha, \tan\beta, i, -i) = \frac{(\sin\alpha - i\cos\alpha)(\sin\beta + i\cos\beta)}{(\sin\alpha + i\cos\alpha)(\sin\beta - i\cos\beta)} = \frac{e^{-i\alpha}e^{i\beta}}{e^{i\alpha}e^{-i\beta}}$$

$$= e^{-2i(\alpha-\beta)} = e^{-2i\phi}.$$

---

* "Über die sogenannte Nicht-Euklidische Geometrie," *Math. Ann.*, Bd. IV, 1871.

Hence,

$$\phi = -\frac{1}{2i} \log (\tan \alpha, \tan \beta, i, -i).$$

It follows that the euclidean measure of the angle ϕ is the elliptic measure of the line segment AA'. But it must also be demonstrated that the inclinations of AM and $A'M$ are α and β. This will be done by showing that the angle ϕ in Fig. 72 is the same as the angle ϕ determined by the formulas in (8). Write out

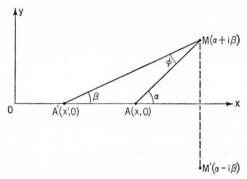

Figure 72

the expression for $\cos \phi$, using $f(x)$ from (11), and then use the nonhomogeneous coordinates $x \equiv \xi^1/\xi^2$ and $x' \equiv \xi^{1\prime}/\xi^{2\prime}$ to obtain

$$\cos \phi = \frac{(\alpha - x)(\alpha - x') + \beta^2}{\sqrt{(x - \alpha)^2 + \beta^2} \sqrt{(x' - \alpha)^2 + \beta^2}}$$

$$= \cos \alpha \cos \beta + \sin \alpha \sin \beta = \cos (\alpha - \beta),$$

where α and β represent the point M and also the angles indicated in Fig. 72. Then it follows that $\phi = \alpha - \beta$.

Hyperbolic Metric

Assume next that the fixed points under the projectivity (1) on the line l are real and distinct. In this case the expression under the radical sign in (7) is positive, and the angle ϕ in (8) is pure imaginary. Hyperbolic functions are therefore employed. Recall the definitions

$$\cosh \theta = \frac{e^\theta + e^{-\theta}}{2}, \quad \sinh \theta = \frac{e^\theta - e^{-\theta}}{2},$$

from which

$$\cosh i\theta = \frac{e^{i\theta} + e^{-i\theta}}{2} = \cos \theta, \quad \sinh i\theta = \frac{e^{i\theta} - e^{-i\theta}}{2} = i \sin \theta.$$

The identity $\cosh^2 \theta - \sinh^2 \theta = 1$ holds.

Formulas similar to (8) can be written as

$$(12) \qquad \cosh \phi = \frac{f(\xi, \xi')}{\sqrt{f(\xi)f(\xi')}}, \quad \sinh \phi = \frac{\sqrt{f^2(\xi, \xi') - f(\xi)f(\xi')}}{\sqrt{f(\xi)f(\xi')}},$$

by means of which (7) becomes

$$(13) \qquad \delta(AA') = k \log \frac{\cosh \phi - \sinh \phi}{\cosh \phi + \sinh \phi} = k \log e^{-2\phi} = -2k\phi.$$

The arbitrary constant k may be taken as $-c/2$, so that the hyperbolic measure in (13) is given by $\delta(AA') = c\phi$, where ϕ is the unique angle defined by (12).

It is to be observed that if the points A, A' separate the points M, M', the cross ratio $(AA'MM')$ is negative, which makes $\delta(AA')$ complex. Therefore, take A, A' as not separating M, M'. Let the point A' coincide with M' to obtain the distance from A to M'. One finds

$$\delta(AM') = k \log (AM'MM') = -\infty,$$

and, similarly,

$$\delta(AMMM') = \infty.$$

The points M, M' are therefore referred to as *ideal points* in the hyperbolic geometry on a line.

Parabolic Metric

It was mentioned in the preceding section that if M and M' coincide, the distance between every pair of points A, A' is zero unless the constant k is allowed to become infinite as M' approaches M. This is evident from equation (7) if the roots of (6) are equal. First verify that

$$(14) \qquad f(\xi)f(\xi') - f(\xi, \xi') \equiv D(\xi^1 \xi^{2'} - \xi^{1'} \xi^2)^2,$$

where $D \equiv a_{11}a_{22} - a_{12}^2$. From the Maclaurin expansion

$$\text{arc sin } x = x + \frac{1}{2} \frac{x^3}{3} + \cdots,$$

one finds from the second formula in (8), and by use of (14), that

$$(15) \qquad \phi = \text{arc sin } \frac{\sqrt{D}(\xi^1 \xi^{2'} - \xi^{1'} \xi^2)}{\sqrt{f(\xi)f(\xi')}} = \frac{\sqrt{D}(\xi^1 \xi^{2'} - \xi^{1'} \xi^2)}{\sqrt{f(\xi)f(\xi')}} + \cdots.$$

Write $k = k'/\sqrt{D}$ in (9), and use (15) to obtain

$$(16) \qquad \lim_{M' \to M} \delta(AA') = \lim_{D \to 0} \left(-\frac{2k'}{\sqrt{D}} i\phi \right) = -2k'i \frac{\xi^1 \xi^{2'} - \xi^{1'} \xi^2}{\sqrt{f(\xi)f(\xi')}}$$

for the parabolic metric in the limiting case in which M' coincides with M. The last member of (16) can be reduced by use of the fact that $D = 0$, which means that $f(x)$ is the square of a linear factor, say $(px^1 + qx)^2$. Equation (16) becomes

(17)
$$\delta(AA') = -2k'i\frac{\xi^1\xi^{'} - \xi^{1'}\xi^2}{(p\xi^1 + q\xi)(p\xi^{1'} + q\xi^{\cdot'})}.$$

Now suppose that M and M' coincide at the ideal point on the line l, so that $f(x) \equiv (x^\cdot)^2$, for which $p = 0, q = 1$. Thus, (17) gives

(18) $$\delta(AA') = -2k'i\frac{\xi^1\xi^{2'} - \xi^{1'}\xi^2}{\xi^2\xi^{2'}} = -2k'i\left(\frac{\xi^1}{\xi^2} - \frac{\xi^{1'}}{\xi^{2'}}\right) = -2k'i(x - x').$$

If k' is taken as $-c/2i$, the parabolic metric takes the form $\delta(AA') = c(x - x')$, which shows that the euclidean metric on a line is a *parabolic* metric. The euclidean measure of an angle was seen to be equivalent to the *elliptic* metric on a line. Hence, these statements preclude a principle of duality relating to lines and angles in euclidean geometry.

A Canonical Form

If the form $f(x)$ in (4) is taken as $(x^1)^2 - a(x^2)^2$, where a is positive, the abscissas of M, M' are $\sqrt{a}, -\sqrt{a}$ in the hyperbolic measure. From (12)

$$\delta = c\phi = c \text{ arc tanh } \frac{\sqrt{f^2(\xi, \xi') - f(\xi)f(\xi')}}{f(\xi, \xi')} = c \text{ arc tanh } \frac{\sqrt{a}(\xi^1\xi^{2'} - \xi^{1'}\xi^2)}{\xi^1\xi^{1'} - a\xi^2\xi^{2'}}.$$

Take the abscissa of A as $x = \xi^1/\xi^2$ and that of A' as zero ($\xi^{1'} = 0$) to have

(19)
$$\delta = c \text{ arc tanh}\left(-\frac{x}{\sqrt{a}}\right) = -c\left[\frac{x}{\sqrt{a}} + \frac{1}{3}\left(\frac{x}{\sqrt{a}}\right)^3 + \cdots\right].$$

However, if $f(x)$ is taken as $(x^1)^2 + a(x^2)^2$, where a is positive, the abscissas of M, M' are $\sqrt{-a}, -\sqrt{-a}$ in the elliptic measure. From (8), one finds

(20)
$$\delta = c \text{ arc tanh}\left(\frac{x}{\sqrt{a}}\right) = c\left[\frac{x}{\sqrt{a}} - \frac{1}{3}\left(\frac{x}{\sqrt{a}}\right)^3 + \cdots\right].$$

Comparison of (19) and (20) shows that the parabolic metric (18)—that is, $\delta = c'x$, with $x' = 0$—coincides with the elliptic and hyperbolic metrics in the neighborhood of the origin to terms of order less than three.

Remark: The metric of the theory of relativity is elliptic. Because the metric of euclidean geometry is parabolic, it can be seen that some difficulty is encountered in comparing measurements in relativity theory with measurements in the more classical theory.

9-3. Measure in the plane

The composite line conic composed of the two points M, M' of the absolute on the line are now generalized to a proper conic in the plane; that is, equation (4) is generalized to

(21) $$f(x) \equiv a_{ij}x^ix^j = 0, \qquad a_{ij} = a_{ji}, i, j = 1, 2, 3,$$

with $a \equiv |a_{ij}| \neq 0$. If the points A, A' have coordinates ξ^i, $\xi^{i'}$, the coordinates of M, M' (Fig. 73) are $\xi^i + \lambda_1 \xi^{i'}$, $\xi^i + \lambda_2 \xi^{i'}$, where λ_1, λ_2 are roots of

(22) $$\lambda^2 f(\xi') + 2\lambda f(\xi, \xi') + f(\xi) = 0,$$

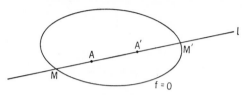

Figure 73

as in (6). The measure $\delta(AA')$ is given by formula (7) except that f is now given by (21). Again, the respective hyperbolic, parabolic, and elliptic cases appear, according as $f \cdot (\xi, \xi') - f(\xi)f(\xi')$ is positive, zero, or negative.

Fixed Conic Under Projectivity

It should be observed that whereas the absolute composite line conic composed of the points M, M' was invariant under the projectivity (1) in Section 9-1, in the present case the proper absolute conic given by (21) is invariant under a projectivity in the plane. The problem of finding the most general projectivity which leaves a conic invariant will now be solved by use of a particular choice of coordinates, in which the conic is represented by the standard form of Section 8-2; that is, $(x^2)^2 - x^1 x^3 = 0$, which has the parametric equations given by $x^1 : x^2 : x^3 = (t)^2 : t : 1$. Because the points of the conic are in one-to-one correspondence with the points of the projective line, there are two points of the conic which map into themselves. Let these points (which are taken as distinct) be denoted by P_1, P_3. The line joining P_1 and P_3 is also fixed, as are the tangents to the conic at P_1 and P_3. Hence, the point of intersection of these tangents is a third fixed point under the desired collineation. If these three fixed points are used as the vertices of the reference triangle, the most general collineation leaving these points fixed is given by (Section 7-3)

(23) $$k\bar{x}^1 = \alpha x^1, \quad k\bar{x}^2 = \beta x^2, \quad k\bar{x}^3 = \gamma x^3,$$

and the equation of the conic is $(x^2)^2 = x^1 x^3$. Since $(\bar{x}^2)^2 = \bar{x}^1\bar{x}^3$, also, it follows from (23) that $\beta^2 = \alpha\gamma$, by use of which the collineation (23) may be written as

(24) $$\bar{x}^1 : \bar{x}^2 : \bar{x}^3 = \sigma^2 x^1 : \sigma x^2 : x^3,$$

where $\sigma^2 (= \alpha/\gamma)$ is a parameter.* (See Exercises 1 and 2.)

In Section 7-5 it was seen that the subgroup of projectivities under which a line in the projective plane remains fixed is the group of affine mappings. It was

---

* A. Clebsch (1833–1872) in *Vorlesungen über Geometrie* (Teubner, 1906), p. 559, considered the determination of the collineation which leaves a conic fixed without special choice of the triangle of reference. For an approach different from that of Clebsch, see Exercise 10 on p. 250.

also seen that the euclidean mappings form a subgroup of the affine mappings if it is further required that two points (the circular points) of the fixed line be fixed. The additional feature of the present treatment is that the invariant absolute composite conic consisting of the two fixed points is generalized here to an invariant *proper* conic.

Angle Measurement

The point conic (21) has the line equation

(25) $$F(u) \equiv A^{ij}u_iu_j = 0.$$

The angle α between any two lines a, a' through a point L is defined as in (3) by

(26) $$\alpha(aa') = k \log (aa'mm'),$$

where k is an arbitrary constant and m, m' are the tangents to the conic through L. The analytical development for the logarithmic expression in (26) in terms of the form $F(u)$ in (25) follows precisely the steps in Section 9-2. Thus, if v_i and v'_i are the line coordinates of a and a', then the coordinates of any line of the pencil on L are of the form $v_i + \lambda v'_i$. The values λ_1, λ_2 of λ corresponding to the tangents m, m' are roots of the quadratic equation

$$\lambda^2 A^{ij}v'_iv'_j + 2\lambda A^{ij}v_iv'_j + A^{ij}v_iv_j = 0,$$

or

(27) $$\lambda^2 F(v') + 2\lambda F(v, v') + F(v) = 0.$$

The cross ratio $(aa'mm') = (0, \infty, \lambda_1, \lambda_2) = \lambda_1/\lambda_2$. On using the roots λ_1, λ_2 from (27) in (26), the dual formula to (7) becomes

(28) $$\alpha(aa') = k \log \frac{F(v, v') - \sqrt{F^2(v, v') - F(v)F(v')}}{F(v, v') + \sqrt{F^2(v, v') - F(v)F(v')}},$$

which is the projective measure of the angle α in Fig. 74.

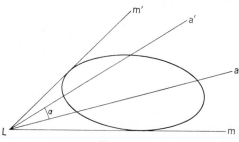

Figure 74

Three cases arise according as $F(v, v') - F(v)F(v')$ is negative, zero, or positive—that is, whether the angle measurement is elliptic, parabolic, or hyperbolic. If the choice of the roots of (27) is such that λ_1 and λ_2 are interchanged, the magnitude of the angle α is unchanged but its direction is reversed. It is to be observed that the definitions of distance in (7) and of angle in (28) are invariant under projectivities which leave the absolute conic fixed.

9-4. The elliptic canonical form

Let the absolute conic (21) be referred to a self-polar reference triangle. It was seen in Section 8-2 that the equation of the conic can then be expressed as $\alpha^2(\bar{x}^1)^2 + \beta^2(\bar{x}^2)^2 + \gamma^2(\bar{x}^3)^2 = 0$. By the further change of coordinates given by $x^1 = \alpha\bar{x}^1$, $x^2 = \beta\bar{x}^2$, $x^3 = \gamma\bar{x}^3$, the point conic takes the form

$$(29) \qquad\qquad f(x) \equiv (x^1)^2 + (x^2)^2 + (x^3)^2 = 0,$$

and its line equation is

$$(30) \qquad\qquad F(u) \equiv u_1^2 + u_2^2 + u_3^2 = 0.$$

Because the point coordinates ξ^i, $\xi^{i'}$ of A, A' in Fig. 73 and the line coordinates v_i, v_i' of a, a' in Fig. 74 are taken as real, it is found that the radical expressions in both (7) and (28) relative to (29) and (30) are negative. Hence, both the measure of distance and of angle are elliptic for the absolute conic as represented by (29).

As in (8) and (9), a real angle ϕ is determined, and if k in (7) is taken again as $ic/2$, the distance formula (7) gives $\delta(AA') = c\phi$, so that, from (8),

$$(31) \qquad\qquad \cos\phi = \cos\frac{\delta}{c} = \frac{f(\xi,\xi')}{\sqrt{f(\xi)f(\xi')}}.$$

Similarly, for the dual, a real angle θ is defined for which

$$(32) \qquad\qquad \cos\theta = \cos\frac{\alpha}{k} = \frac{F(v,v')}{\sqrt{F(v)F(v')}},$$

where k (and c) are arbitrary.

It is seen from (29) that no real points ξ^i, $\xi^{i'}$ exist for which the denominator in (31) vanishes, which means that every pair of points is at a finite distance apart. Hence, there are no parallel lines in elliptic geometry. Note also that if the pair of points ξ^i and $\xi^{i'}$ is such that $f(\xi,\xi') = 0$, then $\cos(\delta/c) = 0$, and consequently $\delta/c = \pi/2$. But $f(\xi,\xi') \equiv \xi^1\xi^{1'} + \xi^2\xi^{2'} + \xi^3\xi^{3'}$ is the polarized form of f. Hence, $f(\xi,\xi') = 0$ means that $\xi^{i'}$ is any point on the polar line of ξ^i with respect to the absolute conic. Hence, the distance from ξ^i to any point $\xi^{i'}$ on the polar of ξ^i is constant and is given by $\delta/c = \pi/2$, where c is any nonzero real constant. One may start from a point ξ^i and proceed along a straight line toward a point $\xi^{i'}$ on the polar of ξ^i. If the opposite direction from ξ^i on the line is followed, the distance to $\xi^{i'}$ is again the constant $\delta/c = \pi/2$. Hence, the length of any line in the elliptic plane is $c\pi$. The three sides of a self-polar triangle of the absolute are equal in length. Dually, from formula (30) it is seen that $F(v)$ and $F(v')$ cannot vanish for real lines v_i and v_i', and that $F(v,v')$ is zero. Consequently $\delta/k = \pi/2$ for two lines v_i and v_i' which separate harmonically the tangents from their intersection L to the absolute. (The latter are the isotropic lines, or minimal lines, through L.) One may conclude therefore that each angle of a self-polar triangle has the measure given by $\alpha/k = \pi/2$.

Equation of a Circle

In equation (31) let δ be a constant r and let $\xi^{i'}$ be the coordinates c^i of a fixed point C in the elliptic plane. With $f \equiv (x^1)^2 + (x^2)^2 + (x^3)^2$, one obtains

$$(33) \quad (c^1\xi^1 + c^2\xi^2 + c^3\xi^3)^2 = [(\xi^1)^2 + (\xi^2)^2 + (\xi^3)^2][(c^1)^2 + (c^2)^2 + (c^3)^2] \cos^2 \frac{r}{c}$$

as the equation of the locus of a variable point ξ^i which is always a fixed distance r from the fixed point c^i. From the form of equation (33), any circle in the elliptic plane is seen to be a conic which is tangent to the absolute at the points where the line $c^i\xi^i = 0$ intersects the absolute. The line $c^i\xi^i = 0$ is the polar of the center c^i with respect to the absolute, and also with respect to the circle itself.

9-5. Elliptic and spherical geometry

There is an interesting correspondence between the geometry of the elliptic plane and the geometry of the surface of a sphere. Let x^1, x^2, x^3 be interpreted as nonhomogeneous orthogonal cartesian coordinates of a point in three-space. The sphere with center at the origin and radius R has the equation

$$(34) \qquad\qquad (x^1)^2 + (x^2)^2 + (x^3)^2 = R^2.$$

The coordinates may be made homogeneous by inserting $(x^4)^2$ to have $(x^1)^2 + (x^2)^2 + (x^3)^2 - R^2(x^4)^2 = 0$. For euclidean geometry the coordinate x^4 is always taken as 1, but for projective interpretations in three-space the plane at infinity given by $x^4 = 0$ is considered. The plane $x^4 = 0$ intersects the sphere (34) in the absolute conic $(x^1)^2 + (x^2)^2 + (x^3)^2 = 0$ at infinity. The latter equation may be interpreted also as the *isotropic cone* with real vertex at the origin and containing the absolute conic at infinity.

In Section 7-7 it was observed that the points of the projective plane are in one-to-one correspondence with the lines through a point in three-space. The point with coordinates x^i in the elliptic plane corresponds to the line through the origin with direction numbers x^i. To the points A, A' in the projective plane with elliptic metric correspond the lines a, a' of the bundle of lines through the origin, and to the complex points M, M' in which the line AA' intersects the absolute, correspond the minimal (isotropic) lines m, m' through O in the plane of a, a' (Fig. 75). By formula (3) the angle α between the lines a, a' is $k \log (aa'mm')$. But by (2) this is also the distance δ between the points A, A' in the elliptic plane. Hence, elliptic measure in the plane is the same as euclidean measure in the bundle. The plane of the lines a, a' in Fig. 75 intersects the sphere (34) in a great circle, along which the euclidean measure is equivalent to elliptic measure in the projective plane. Consider the plane π, which is tangent to the sphere at the point $H(0, 0, R)$. A line a through the origin intersects the sphere

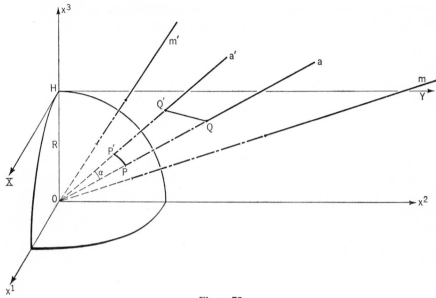

Figure 75

at point P and intersects the tangent plane π in the point Q. The great circle PP' on the sphere corresponds to the straight line QQ' in π. The euclidean measure of the arc PP' is the noneuclidean (elliptic) measure of the straight line segment QQ'. Observe that to each point P of the sphere there corresponds a unique point Q of the plane π, but that to each point Q of π there correspond two antipodal points P and P^* on the sphere. A unique one-to-one correspondence is obtained between the hemisphere for which $x^3 \geq 0$ and the (projective) plane π by means of the half rays through the origin. The equatorial circle in the x^1x^2-plane is the image of the line which closes the projective plane π. However, diametrically opposite points on the equator must be considered as identified, so that the equator is the image of the "line at infinity" in the elliptic plane taken twice. With this correspondence, the geometry of the elliptic plane is the geometry on the closed hemisphere.

The topological distinction between the elliptic plane and the sphere can be seen as follows. To every half ray through O there corresponds a unique point of the sphere. It is not possible to pass continuously from a half ray above the equatorial plane to a half ray below this plane without passing through a half-ray position in the equatorial plane. To every line (entire line) through O there corresponds a unique point of the projective plane π. It is possible to pass continuously from any line through O to any other line through O without encountering a line in the equatorial plane. This means that a line (great circle) of the sphere separates the sphere into two parts, while a line of the elliptic plane does not separate π into two parts. It is then possible to join any two points of the elliptic plane by a line which does not meet the image of the great circle in the equatorial plane. The geometry of the elliptic plane is *locally* the geometry of the sphere in the sense that only a closed hemisphere can be employed for the image of the projective plane. (See Section 6-6.)

On the sphere there are no parallel great circles. Therefore, if a line *l* and a point *Q* (not on *l*) are given in the elliptic plane, there is no line through *Q* which is parallel to *l*. Every pair of lines in the elliptic plane intersect in a unique point. This shows that although some of the axioms of euclidean geometry hold in the geometry of the sphere (and therefore in the elliptic geometry), the fifth (parallel) postulate of Euclid does not hold in elliptic and spherical geometry. As a consequence, the theorems of euclidean geometry which depend upon the parallel postulate are not valid in elliptic geometry.

Note that on the sphere it is possible to find two points (antipodal points) such that a single infinity of lines (great circles) pass through the two points. However, in the elliptic plane this is not possible. Given one point on the sphere, it is possible to have a single infinity of great circles which are perpendicular to the polar great circle of the point. In the elliptic plane this means that through a point *Q* there is a single infinity of lines perpendicular to the polar line of the point *Q* relative to the absolute $(x^1)^2 + (x^2)^2 + (x^3)^2 = 0$. This can be seen as follows.

Let x^i, $x^{i'}$ be the coordinates of two points *Q*, *Q'* in the plane π (Fig. 75). The direction cosines of the lines *OQ*, *OQ'* are then

$$\frac{x^i}{R}, \quad \frac{x^{i'}}{R}.$$

The angle α between *OQ* and *OQ'* is measured by δ/R, where δ is the euclidean measure of the arc *PP'* on the sphere. One has

(35) $$\cos \alpha \equiv \cos \frac{\delta}{R} = \frac{x^i x^{i'}}{R^2},$$

where δ is the noneuclidean (elliptic) distance between *Q* and *Q'* in π. It follows that $\delta/R = \pi/2$ if and only if $x^i x^{i'} = 0$, which means that *Q* and *Q'* are at a quadrant's distance apart if and only if *Q'* is on the polar line of *Q* relative to the absolute conic in the elliptic plane, or *Q* is on the polar of *Q'*. Relative to the sphere the equation $x^i x^{i'} = 0$ is that of the plane through *O* parallel to the tangent plane to the sphere at the point $x^{i'}$, so that the points x^i and $x^{i'}$ are at a quadrant's distance apart.

Note that if $\phi = \pi/2$ in formula (9) and $k = ic/2$, then $\delta/c = \pi/2$. On comparing this with $\delta/R = \pi/2$, one may define $1/c$ as the "curvature" of the elliptic plane. It will be seen next that if the curvature of the elliptic plane approaches zero, the measure in the elliptic plane approaches euclidean measure.

Differential of Arc

Consider a system of orthogonal cartesian coordinates *X*, *Y* in the plane π, as indicated in Fig. 75. The *euclidean* element of arc $d\sigma$ in π is given by

$d\sigma^2 = dX^2 + dY^2$. It is desired to find the *elliptic* measure ds of the differential of arc in π. The sphere with center at O and radius R has the parametric equations

(36) $$x = R \sin u \cos v, \quad y = R \sin u \sin v, \quad z = R \cos u,$$

where x, y, z are used instead of x^i. Consider the arc PP' as of length ds, with x, y, z as the coordinates of P. Calculate, by use of (36),

$$ds^2 = dx^2 + dy^2 + dz^2 = R^2 du^2 + R^2 \sin^2 u \, dv^2.$$

Any point on the line OP has coordinates (xt, yt, zt). If this point is in the plane π, then $zt = R$ and the parameter $t = R/z$. Hence, the point $Q(X, Y)$ in π has the coordinates $(xR/z, yR/z)$, which, from (36), take the form

(37) $$X = R \tan u \cos v, \quad Y = R \tan u \sin v,$$

which can be solved to obtain

(38) $$R \tan u = \sqrt{X^2 + Y^2}, \quad \tan v = \frac{Y}{X}.$$

Observe that (37) are the equations of the mapping from the sphere to the XY-plane.

A *geodesic curve* joining two points on a surface may be defined as the curve of shortest distance between the two points. It is known that the geodesics on a sphere are arcs of great circles. Any great circle of the sphere (36) is the circle lying in a plane given by $Ax + By + Cz = 0$; therefore any geodesic of the sphere has an equation of the form

$$A \sin u \cos v + B \sin u \sin v + C \cos u = 0.$$

By (37), the latter equation, on being divided by $\cos u$, gives

$$AX + BY + C = 0$$

as the straight lines in the XY-plane into which the geodesics of the sphere map by the equations (37).

Use of (38) in (36) yields

$$\frac{ds^2}{R^2} = du^2 + \sin^2 u \, dv^2$$

$$= \frac{R^2(X \, dX + Y \, dY)^2 + (R^2 + X^2 + Y^2)(X \, dY - Y \, dX)^2}{(X^2 + Y^2)(R^2 + X^2 + Y^2)^2},$$

which can be written as

(39) $$\frac{ds^2}{R^2} = \frac{R^2(dX^2 + dY^2) + (X \, dY - Y \, dX)^2}{(R^2 + X^2 + Y^2)^2}.$$

Let $1/R^2$ be replaced by k^2 to write (39) in the form

(40) $$ds^2 = \frac{dX^2 + dY^2 + k^2(X \, dY - Y \, dX)^2}{[1 + k^2(X^2 + Y^2)]^2},$$

which exhibits the elliptic measure of the differential of arc in the elliptic plane of constant curvature k.

Two important observations should be made about equation (40). The first is that as $k \to 0$ the elliptic measure approaches the euclidean measure given by $d\sigma^2 = dX^2 + dY^2$. The second is that in a neighborhood of the origin H (Fig. 75), where X and Y are sufficiently small, the expression for ds^2 in (40) is approximated by the euclidean measure $d\sigma^2 = dX^2 + dY^2$. This should be compared with the situation involving the parabolic metric on a line (discussed in Section 9-2). As on the line, it will be seen to be true in the plane that the euclidean (parabolic) metric is in a transitional position between the elliptic metric and the hyperbolic metric (introduced in Section 9-7).

9-6. The hyperbolic canonical form

The proper absolute conic which is left invariant under projectivity in the plane is now taken to be a real conic with the canonical form

(41) $$f(x) \equiv (x^1)^2 + (x^2)^2 - (x^3)^2 = 0.$$

The *inside* of this conic can be defined as the set of points for which the corresponding polar lines relative to the conic do not intersect the conic in real points. The polar line of any point *outside* the conic intersects it in two real points. The line determined by any two points A, A' inside the conic (Fig. 76) intersects the conic in two real points M, M'. The hyperbolic distance δ from A to A' is defined by

(42) $$\delta(AA') = k \log (AA'MM'),$$

where, as in (2), k is an arbitrary constant. Note that if A, A' separate M, M', then, for k real, the distance δ is complex. Hence, only points inside the conic will be considered to determine the fundamental region under study. Observe that if the point A in Fig. 76 goes to the point M, then $\delta(MA') =$

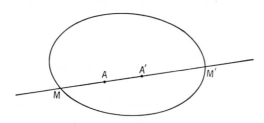

Figure 76

$k \log (MA'MM') \to -\infty$. Also, if A is an interior point and A' goes to M', then $\delta(AM') = k \log (AM'MM') \to \infty$. Hence, the distance from any interior point to the boundary of the region is infinite, and there are two points at infinity on any line AA'. The points on the conic will be called points at infinity, and the exterior points may be styled *ideal* points in the plane.

Now consider any interior point P not on the line AA' (Fig. 77). Two lines join P to the points M, M' at infinity on the line AA'. Hence, in the geometry

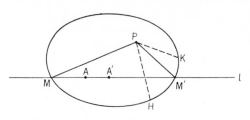

Figure 77

of the fundamental region (which will be called the hyperbolic plane) there are two parallel lines through a point P to a line AA' not containing P. These are the parallels of Lobachevsky (1793–1856). Actually, the lines PM and PM' parallel to the line l through A, A' divide the lines of the pencil with center at P into two categories—those lines (such as PH) which intersect l in the region, and those lines (such as PK) which do not intersect l in the region.

The line equation of the conic (41) is $F(u) \equiv u_1^2 + u_2^2 - u_3^2 = 0$, which is the same as the form of the point equation. The distance between two points A, A' with coordinates ξ^i, $\xi^{i'}$ is given by (13); that is, $\delta(AA') = -2k\phi$, where ϕ is defined by (12) with f given by (41). The angle $\alpha(aa')$ between two lines a, a' (Fig. 78) which intersect in a point P of the region is given by

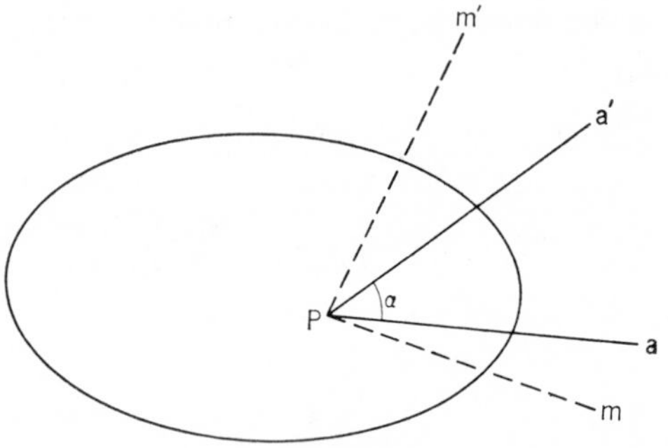

$$\alpha(aa') = k \log (aa'mm'),$$

Figure 78

where m, m' are the (complex) tangents to the absolute from P. If u_i, u_i' are the coordinates of a, a', formulas (12) and (13) give

$$\alpha(aa') = -2k\phi,$$

where

$$\cosh \phi = \cos i\phi = \frac{F(u, u')}{\sqrt{F(u)F(u')}},$$

with $F(u, u') \equiv u_1 u_1' + u_2 u_2' - u_3 u_3'$. Thus, two lines are orthogonal in hyperbolic geometry if and only if each line contains the pole of the other with respect to the absolute conic.

9-7. Hyperbolic geometry

Consider the locus of a point $P(x^i)$ for which the hyperbolic distance from a fixed point $C(c^i)$ is a constant r. With $\delta(PC) = -2k\phi = r$, one finds from (12)

$$\frac{f^2(c, x)}{f(c)f(x)} = \cosh^2 \left(-\frac{r}{2k} \right) \equiv h^2.$$

Hence, the required locus, which is called a *pseudocircle* (or *cycle*), has the equation

(43) $$f^2(c, x) - h^2 f(c) f(x) = 0.$$

The function h of r is a constant. If $h = 0$, the equation of the pseudocircle reduces to $f^2(c, x) = 0$; that is, $(c^1 x^1 + c^2 x^2 - c^3 x^3)^2 = 0$, which is the polar line (counted twice) of the point c^i relative to the absolute. Hence, if h is now regarded as a parameter, all pseudocircles are seen to be conics of the pencil of conics determined by $f^2(c, x) = 0$ and $f(x) = 0$. The form of the equation of the pseudocircle shows that it is tangent to the absolute at the points where the polar line $f(c, x) = 0$ of C relative to the absolute intersects the absolute $f(x) = 0$. Three cases appear.

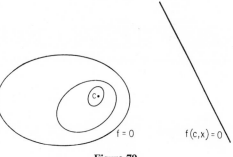

Figure 79

First, the center C lies inside the absolute (Fig. 79), and therefore its polar line relative to the absolute does not intersect the absolute in real points. The pseudocircles are closed curves which lie inside the absolute and intersect it in complex points.

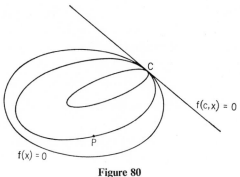

Figure 80

Next, let the center C lie on the absolute (Fig. 80). Its polar line is therefore tangent to the absolute at C. The distance from C to any other point P of a pseudocircle is infinite. The pseudocircles are all tangent to the polar line of C at C. The pseudocircles in Fig. 80 constitute the limiting positions of the pseudocircles in Fig. 79 as the point C moves toward the absolute, thus causing the radii to become infinite. These pseudocircles are called *limit circles* or *horicycles* in hyperbolic geometry.

In the third case, with the point C outside the absolute (Fig. 81), the pseudocircles are called *hypercycles*. The polar line of C intersects the absolute, and is one of the hypercycles. The distances from C to points of the polar line $f(c, x) = 0$ are all equal but complex. Any hypercycle is the locus of points equidistant from the polar line of C. In order to see this, consider any line through C intersecting its polar line in M and a hypercycle in the points L and N. The lengths CM and CL are each constant as the line CM turns about C; hence, LM is constant. Thus, the locus of points equidistant from a straight line is not a straight line but a hypercycle with an ideal point as center and a complex radius.

It should be observed that the pole S of any line CM (Fig. 81) is on the polar

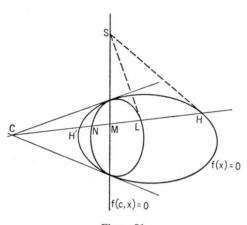

Figure 81

$f(c, x) = 0$ of C relative to the absolute (or to a hypercycle). Hence, all lines CM are perpendicular to the polar of C. The polar of C is the orthogonal trajectory (in a noneuclidean sense) of all lines through C. In differential geometry it is shown that if equal distances are laid off along the geodesics which are normal to a fixed geodesic curve on a surface, then the locus of the end points of the equal segments is a curve orthogonal to all of the geodesics normal to the given geodesic. In the hyperbolic plane the geodesics are straight lines. In Fig. 81 the locus of the points L and N, which are equidistant from the geodesic $f(c, x) = 0$, is the hypercycle with center C. Similar interpretations can be given the loci which are the cycles and horicycles in Fig. 79 and Fig. 80, respectively.

Angle of Parallelism

Lobachevsky's angle of parallelism will be investigated next. The perpendicular from any point $P(a^i)$ inside the absolute (Fig. 82) to a given line l is obtained by joining P to the pole of l relative to the absolute. The point H is then the foot of the perpendicular from P on l. Let θ denote the angle HPM'. This is the *angle of parallelism*. It will be shown to be a function of the distance $p \equiv PH$. Let $x^1 = 0$ be the equation of line l. Its pole relative to the absolute with equation $f(x) \equiv (x^1)^2 + (x^2)^2 - (x^3)^2 = 0$ is the point $L(1:0:0)$.

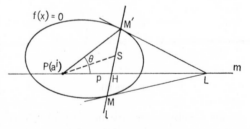

Figure 82

The coordinates of line PL are $[0: -a^3: a^2]$. Therefore, the intersection H of PL and $l[1:0:0]$ has coordinates $(0: a^2: a^3)$. If the length $p \equiv PH$ is used in (12) and (13) with $k = -c/2$, there results

$$\cosh \frac{p}{c} = \frac{f(\xi, \xi')}{\sqrt{f(\xi)f(\xi')}} = \frac{a^1 0 + a^2 a^2 - a^3 a^3}{\sqrt{f(a)}\sqrt{(a^2)^2 - (a^3)^2}} = \frac{\sqrt{(a^3)^2 - (a^2)^2}}{\sqrt{(a^3)^2 - (a^1)^2 - (a^2)^2}},$$

$$\sinh \frac{p}{c} = \frac{a^1}{\sqrt{(a^3)^2 - (a^1)^2 - (a^2)^2}},$$

so that

$$\tanh \frac{p}{c} = \frac{a^1}{\sqrt{(a^3)^2 - (a^2)^2}} \cdot$$

The line l intersects the absolute at $M'(0:1:1)$. Hence, the coordinates of line PM' are $[a^3 - a^2 : a^1 : -a^1]$. Now use

$$\cos \frac{\theta}{k} = \frac{F(v, v')}{\sqrt{F(v)F(v')}}$$

to find the measure of the angle θ between PH and PM'. With v^i as the coordinates of PL (that is, $v^1 = 0$, $v^2 = -a^3$, $v^3 = a^2$) and with $v^{i'}$ as the coordinates of PM' (that is, $v^{1'} = a^3 - a^2$, $v^{2'} = a^1$, $v^{3'} = -a^1$), one finds

$$\cos \frac{\theta}{k} = -\frac{a^1}{\sqrt{(a^3)^2 - (a^2)^2}} \cdot$$

It follows that

(44) $$\cos \frac{\theta}{k} = -\tanh \frac{p}{c},$$

so θ is a function of the distance p. This geometric result is independent of the particular choice of equation for the absolute. It is invariant under the group of projectivities which leave the absolute invariant. Equation (44) can be cast in the form

(45) $$\tan \frac{\theta}{2k} = e^{p/c}$$

in which both c and k are arbitrary. If k is taken as 1 and $c \to \infty$, then $\tan \theta/2 \to 1$ and $\theta \to \pi/2$, which is the euclidean measure of θ if PM' and HM' are parallel. With $k = 1$, the parameter c may be fixed by choosing a certain length as the unit distance. This shows that similitude of figures does not exist in hyperbolic geometry because the unit of length is fixed.

The analytic expressions for distance and angle may be used further to develop the geometry of the hyperbolic plane. Theorems of euclidean geometry that do not involve the fifth (parallel) postulate of Euclid carry over to hyperbolic geometry. The geometry of the interior of a real conic is completely equivalent to the geometry of Lobachevsky in the plane.

In hyperbolic geometry the sum of the angles of any triangle is less than π. This can be seen from Fig. 82. If S is any point between M' and H, the angle HSP varies continuously from zero at M' to $\pi/2$ at H. The sum of the angles of any triangle is therefore less than π.

Gaussian Curvature

In Section 9-5 a mapping was exhibited under which the geodesics (straight lines) of the elliptic plane of constant curvature k correspond to the geodesics (great circles) of a sphere of radius R. It is natural to ask if there exists a surface S

in three-space and a mapping from the hyperbolic plane to the surface such that the geodesics (straight lines) on the hyperbolic plane map into the geodesics (curves of shortest distance) on S. Because the sphere employed in the elliptic case is a surface of constant positive total curvature, it is well to give next the meaning of the *total curvature* of a general surface at any point on it.

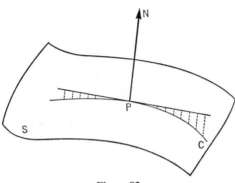

Any plane π through the normal PN to a surface S at a point P intersects S in a plane curve C (Fig. 83). Let ρ denote the radius of plane curvature of C at P. As the normal plane π revolves about the normal line PN, the curve C of normal section varies, and so does its radius of curvature. The two directions through P on S for which the radii of normal curvature are maximum and minimum are called the *principal directions* on S at P. Let ρ_1 and ρ_2 denote these extreme values for the radii of normal curvature of S at P. Gauss defined the product $1/\rho_1\rho_2$ as a measure of the *total curvature* of S at P. If the total (Gaussian) curvature of a surface is the same at every point, the surface is said to have constant total curvature. It is evident that a sphere of radius R has *positive* constant total curvature equal to $1/R^2$. After the discussion to follow on the differential of arc in the hyperbolic plane it will be seen that one needs to consider a surface of *negative* constant total curvature whose geodesics map (at least locally) into the straight lines of the hyperbolic plane.

Figure 83

Differential of Arc

If the curvature k^2 of the elliptic plane in the expression (40) for the element of arc is replaced by $-k^2$, one obtains the formula for the element of arc in a space of constant negative curvature. However, this may also be established in the following manner.

Introduce a set of "normalized" coordinates such that the conic $(x^1)^2 + (x^2)^2 - (x^3)^2 = 0$ takes the form $X^2 + Y^2 - R^2 = 0$. This may be interpreted as using the circle $X^2 + Y^2 = R^2$ as the fundamental region's boundary for hyperbolic geometry. Formulas (12) and (13) of Section 9-2 are used to calculate the element of arc $ds \equiv \delta(AA')$ joining the neighboring points $A(X, Y)$ and $A'(X + dX, Y + dY)$. Note that

$$f(\xi) = X^2 + Y^2 - R^2,$$
(46)
$$f(\xi') \equiv (X + dX)^2 + (Y + dY)^2 - R^2,$$
$$f(\xi, \xi') \equiv X(X + dX) + Y(Y + dY) - R^2.$$

Let the constant k of (13) be taken as $-R/2$, and use the fact that $\sinh \phi = i \sin (-i\phi)$, to obtain

$$-\sin^{-1}\left(-\frac{i\delta}{R}\right) = \frac{\begin{aligned}[X(X + dX) + Y(Y + dY) - R^2]^2 \\ - [X^2 + Y^2 - R^2][(X + dX)^2 + (Y + dY)^2 - R^2]\end{aligned}}{[X^2 + Y^2 - R^2][(X + dX)^2 + (Y + dY)^2 - R^2]}.$$

Because δ is small, replace the sine of the angle by the angle, and neglect infinitesimals of order higher than the second to find that the last equation reduces to

(47)
$$\delta^2 \equiv ds^2 = \frac{dX^2 + dY^2 - \frac{1}{R^2}(X\,dY - Y\,dX)^2}{\left[1 - \frac{1}{R^2}(X^2 + Y^2)\right]^2},$$

which exhibits the differential of arc in the hyperbolic plane of curvature $-1/R^2$. Observe that formula (40) gives (47) if $k^2 = -1/R^2$.

The reader may verify that equation (47) becomes

(48)
$$\frac{ds^2}{R^2} = \left(\frac{R}{R^2 - \rho^2}\right)^2 d\rho^2 + \frac{\rho^2}{R^2 - \rho^2}\,d\psi^2$$

under the transformation

(49)
$$X = \rho \cos \psi, \quad Y = \rho \sin \psi,$$

and that (48) transforms, in turn, into

(50)
$$ds^2 = R^2\left(d\bar{\rho}^2 + \sinh^2\frac{\bar{\rho}}{R}\,d\bar{\psi}^2\right)$$

under the change of coordinates given by

(51)
$$\rho = R \tanh \frac{\bar{\rho}}{R}, \quad \psi = \bar{\psi}.$$

Hence, by the product of the transformations (49) and (51), that is, by the transformation

(52)
$$X = R \tanh \frac{\bar{\rho}}{R} \cos \bar{\psi}, \quad Y = R \tanh \frac{\bar{\rho}}{R} \sin \bar{\psi},$$

the linear element in (47) takes the form (50), which is the typical form of the linear element for a class of pseudospherical surfaces.

By integration of the differential equations of geodesics on a surface (found in books on differential geometry), it can be shown that the geodesics on a surface with the linear element (50) are represented by

(53)
$$A \tanh \frac{\bar{\rho}}{R} \cos \bar{\psi} + B \tanh \frac{\bar{\rho}}{R} \sin \bar{\psi} + C = 0,$$

with A, B, C arbitrary constants. Hence, by use of (52), it is seen that the geodesics on the surface with the linear element (50) correspond to the lines $AX + BY + CR = 0$ in the XY-plane. The constant CR may be replaced by C'.

Compare the linear element for the sphere with that of surfaces for which (50) holds. Essentially, one changes from the hyperbolic to the elliptic plane by changing $\tanh \bar{p}/R$ to $\tan u$ in (52) to obtain (37).*

It should be emphasized that whereas the hemisphere (with antipodal points of the boundary identified) served as a model for the whole elliptic plane, with geodesics on the model and geodesics (straight lines) on the plane in correspondence, the situation is quite in contrast in the pseudospherical model for the hyperbolic plane. Geodesics on any pseudospherical surface meet singular curves on the surface, so that the lines of infinite length in the hyperbolic plane are not represented by entire geodesic lines on a smooth surface. The geodesic correspondence is therefore local. There is no smooth surface† with complete geodesic correspondence between it and the hyperbolic plane.

The surface model for the hyperbolic plane differs in another respect from the surface model for the elliptic plane. The principal radii of normal curvature ρ_1 and ρ_2 are not themselves constants at points of the pseudosphere, as they are for the sphere. It is the *product* $1/\rho_1\rho_2$, which is a negative constant over the pseudosphere.

9-8. Significance of noneuclidean geometries

The postulates of euclidean geometry (stated by Euclid about 300 B.C.) were regarded as inviolate and as "self-evident" truths until the early part of the nineteenth century. In all of this period only one geometry was thought to be possible. However, many followers of Euclid attempted to prove the fifth (parallel) postulate as a consequence of the other postulates, but without success. Saccheri (1667–1733), an Italian Jesuit priest, did not doubt the necessity of the fifth (parallel) postulate. He obtained some properties of elliptic and hyperbolic geometry by denying the parallel axiom of Euclid, but then tried to prove the falsity of his assumption; thus, in vindicating Euclid, Saccheri stopped short of becoming the founder of noneuclidean geometry. His work was important, however, in opening the way for further investigation.

It was Gauss (1777–1855) who first saw that a consistent geometry results if the fifth (parallel) postulate is replaced by a contradictory one. But Gauss declined to publish—perhaps to avoid controversy—his discoveries in this connection. Thus, it was left to J. Bolyai (1802–1860) of Hungary and to N. I. Lobachevsky (1793–1856) of Russia to share the honor of being the first to publish their independent results in hyperbolic geometry. Because of the more thorough nature of his work, the name of Lobachevsky is now attached to hyperbolic geometry.

---

* For a more extended account of spherical and pseudospherical surfaces the reader is referred to L. P. Eisenhart, *Differential Geometry*, Princeton University Press, 1947 (rev. ed.).

† G. Lütkemeyer. *Über den analytischen Charakter der Integrale von partiellen Differentialgleichungen*, Göttingen, 1902 (dissertation).

F. Klein* (1849–1925) was the first to realize elliptic geometry in which no parallel lines exist. Klein also extended the notions of Cayley (1821–1895) on the absolute, and introduced the logarithmic measures of angle and of distance. Geometers tended to view the new noneuclidean geometry with misgivings as to its consistency until the advent of Klein's paper in 1871. The evidence of the model for hyperbolic geometry showed the impossibility of a proof by which the fifth (parallel) postulate of Euclid could be deduced from the remaining euclidean postulates. In the model all five of the euclidean axioms hold, with one exception—that of the parallel axiom. If the parallel axiom could be deduced from the others in euclidean geometry, then this would have to be true in hyperbolic geometry, but this has been shown not to be the case.

Significant differences between elliptic, euclidean, and hyperbolic geometries were seen in this chapter in relation to the nature of the absolute conic left invariant by projectivity. The euclidean geometry appeared as a particular kind of projective geometry—the transitional state between the elliptic and hyperbolic geometries.

In Erlangen, Germany, in 1872 Klein read a paper in which he defined a geometry as the study of invariants of configurations under a group of transformations. The number of invariants obtainable under the group of the euclidean transformations involving translation and rotation decreases as the transformations become more general. As one proceeds through the progressively more general affine, projective, and topological groups of transformations, the number of invariants decreases, but there are still interesting invariants to study in the topological group. Although geometry has passed beyond the confines set for it by Klein in the Erlangen Programme of 1872, his classification and definition of geometries are still very significant.

The geometry of a curved space is another instance of noneuclidean geometry. If the measure of distance in the space is expressed by a quadratic form—that is, $ds^2 = g_{\alpha\beta} \, du^\alpha \, du^\beta$, where α and β are summed from 1 to n—the geometry is called Riemannian after G. F. B. Riemann (1826–1866), who published a paper of far-reaching importance in 1854.†

9-9. Postulational geometry of planes

As stated in the Preface, the reader should become acquainted with some of the concepts and results of projective geometry before attempting to read an axiomatic (postulational) development of the subject. The serious student of geometry should now have the experience of realizing how projective geometry can be developed as an abstract mathematical system—that is, as a set of theorems arranged in a sequence of logical deduction. In such a system each theorem

---

* Klein, "Über die sogenannten Nicht-Euklidische Geometrie," *Math. Ann.*, Vol. 4, 1871.

† Riemann, *Über die Hypothesen welche der Geometrie zu Grunde liegen*, Göttingen, 1854 (dissertation).

must be a logical consequence of one or more theorems which precede it in the set. The first theorem of the set (with no preceding theorem) must necessarily be deduced from a set of statements which are assumed to be true without proof. The statements of this latter set are called the postulates (or axioms) of the mathematical system.

In a similar way, the definitions of various entities and relations arising in the system must be expressed in terms of other entities and relations, so it is necessary to select certain fundamental entities and relations (which remain undefined) in terms of which further entities may be defined. There is some degree of arbitrariness in the selection of the undefined notions. As was indicated in Section 4-4, point, line, and incidence are a useful set of undefined notions. To these may be added the notion of separation of a pair of points (or lines) by another pair of points (or lines). With these undefined terms and relations a set of axioms concerning incidence, order, and continuity can be formulated to obtain a basis from which projective geometry can be deduced.*

Although a full account of the postulational development is not presented here, it is of interest to state the following axioms of incidence.

A. Any pair of points is incident with a unique line.
B. Any pair of lines is incident with at least one point.
C. Every line is incident with at least three points.
D. A point and a line exist which are not incident.

It can be shown that the theorem of Desargues on perspective triangles in the plane (Section 6-3) cannot be deduced from these four stated axioms of incidence. Indeed, there exist non-Desarguesian planes which satisfy *A, B, C, D*. Therefore, a fifth axiom of incidence is added. The theorem of Desargues may be used for this. However, it can be shown that the theorem of Pappus (see Exercises 10 and 12, pp. 136-137) implies the theorem of Desargues. As a consequence, the theorem of Pappus may be used for the fifth incidence axiom.†
It is an interesting fact that although the theorem of Desargues in the plane cannot be deduced from the four incidence relations in the plane, it is quite simple to prove the theorem in three-space by use of incidence relations. Hilbert first revealed the full significance of the theorems of Pappus and Desargues.‡

EXERCISES

1. Show that the matrix equation

$$\begin{pmatrix} \bar{x}^1 & \bar{x}^2 \\ \bar{x}^2 & \bar{x}^3 \end{pmatrix} = \begin{pmatrix} a & b \\ c & d \end{pmatrix}\begin{pmatrix} x^1 & x^2 \\ x^2 & x^3 \end{pmatrix}\begin{pmatrix} a & c \\ b & d \end{pmatrix}$$

---

* For an excellent treatment of the postulational approach the reader is referred to L. M. Blumenthal, *A Modern View of Geometry* (Freeman, San Francisco, 1961) and also to A. Seidenberg, *Lectures in Projective Geometry* (Van Nostrand, New York, 1962).
† See G. de B. Robinson, *The Foundations of Geometry* (University of Toronto, 1940).
‡ See Hilbert, *Foundations of Geometry* (Open Court, Chicago, 1938).

determines the collineation

$$k\bar{x}^1 = (a)^2x^1 + 2abx^2 + (b)^2x^3,$$
$$k\bar{x}^2 = acx^1 + (ad + bc)x^2 + bdx^3,$$
$$k\bar{x}^3 = (c)^2x^1 + 2cdx^2 + (d)^2x^3,$$

which is nonsingular if and only if the homography

$$\bar{t} = \frac{at + b}{ct + d}$$

is nonsingular.

2. Show that the conic $(x^2)^2 = x^1x^3$ maps into itself under the nonsingular collineation in Exercise 1. *Suggestion:* Take the determinant of both sides of the matrix equation.

3. Verify that any point $(t^2:t:1)$ of the conic $(x^2)^2 = x^1x^3$ maps by the homography $\bar{t} = (at + b)/(ct + d)$ into a point which is the same as that given by the collineation in Exercise 1.

4. Show that the particular case of the mapping (24), for which $\sigma = -1$, is an involution on the conic and a harmonic homology (see Section 7-3) for which the point P_2 is the center and the line P_1P_3 is the axis.

5. Show that if the homography on the conic is given by $\bar{t} = t + \sigma$ the two fixed points on the conic coincide and the collineation of Exercise 1 becomes

$$k\bar{x}^1 = x^1 + 2\sigma x^2 + \sigma^2 x^3,$$
$$k\bar{x}^2 = \qquad\quad x^2 + \sigma x^3,$$
$$k\bar{x}^3 = \qquad\qquad\qquad x^3.$$

6. Carry out the details to verify equation (14).

7. Use equation (8) to verify the expansion in (20).

8. Verify that equation (19) becomes equation (20) if a in (19) is changed to $-a$.

9. Consider the parametric representation of a conic

$$kx^i = a_i\lambda^2 + b_i\lambda + c_i, \qquad\qquad i = 1, 2, 3,$$

where λ is the parameter. Eliminate λ to obtain

$$(B_ix^i)^2 = (A_ix^i)(C_jx^j)$$

for the equation of the conic, in which A_i, for instance, is the cofactor of a_i in the determinant

$$D \equiv \begin{vmatrix} a_1 & b_1 & c_1 \\ a_2 & b_2 & c_2 \\ a_3 & b_3 & c_3 \end{vmatrix}.$$

Show that under the projectivity

$$\lambda = \frac{\alpha\bar{\lambda} + \beta}{\gamma\bar{\lambda} + \delta}$$

on the conic, one obtains the new parametric form

$$k'\bar{x}^i = \bar{a}_i\bar{\lambda}^2 + \bar{b}_i\bar{\lambda} + \bar{c}_i,$$

for which

$$\bar{D} = D(\alpha\delta - \beta\gamma)^3.$$

10. In Exercise 9 the equation of the conic in barred coordinates is

$$(\overline{B}_i\overline{x}^i)^2 = (\overline{A}_i\overline{x}^i)(\overline{C}_j\overline{x}^j).$$

Deduce that the collineation which leaves the conic invariant is

$$\rho x^\sigma = (a_\sigma\overline{A}_i + b_\sigma\overline{B}_i + c_\sigma\overline{C}_i)\overline{x}^i, \qquad\qquad \sigma = 1, 2, 3,$$

where

$$\overline{A}_i = (\alpha\delta - \beta\gamma)[\delta^2 A_i - 2\beta\delta B_i + \beta^2 C_i],$$
$$\overline{B}_i = -(\alpha\delta - \beta\gamma)[\gamma\delta A_i - (\alpha\delta + \beta\gamma)B_i + \alpha\beta C_i],$$
$$\overline{C}_i = (\alpha\delta - \beta\gamma)[\gamma^2 A_i - 2\gamma\alpha B_i + \alpha^2 C_i].$$

11. If the equation of the absolute conic is $(x^1)^2 + (x^2)^2 - (x^3)^2 = 0$, show that the distance δ between the points $A(0:0:1)$ and $A'(0:x:1)$, with $|x| < 1$, is given by

$$\delta(AA') = k \log \frac{1 - x}{1 + x}.$$

12. Show that if the absolute has the equation $(x^1)^2 + (x^2)^2 - c^2(x^3)^2 = 0$, the lines $l_ix^i = 0$, $l_i'x^i = 0$ are perpendicular under the condition

$$c^2(l_1l_1' + l_2l_2') - l_3l_3' = 0.$$

13. In elliptic geometry show that the sum of the angles of any self-polar triangle with respect to the absolute is $3\pi/2$.

14. Develop the equation (45) by use of the form $(x^2)^2 - x^1x^3 = 0$ for the equation of the absolute conic.

15. In elliptic geometry show that a self-polar triangle relative to the absolute has maximum area.

16. In hyperbolic geometry prove the theorem that the base angles of an isosceles triangle are equal. *Note:* This euclidean theorem holds in hyperbolic geometry because it does not involve the parallel axiom.

17. Deduce from formula (32), by use of the euclidean absolute conic $u_1^2 + u_2^2 = 0$, that the cosine of the angle between the lines with direction cosines $(\lambda_1, \mu_1, 0)$ and $(\lambda_2, \mu_2, 0)$ is $\lambda_1\lambda_2 + \mu_1\mu_2$.

18. If the absolute in hyperbolic geometry has the equation $x^{2^2} - x^1x^3 = 0$, show that the sum of the angles of the triangle with sides $[0:1:-1]$, $[-2:3:0]$, $[4:-11:4]$ is less than π.

19. Find the equation of the curve in the xy-plane with the property that the length of the tangent from the curve to the y-axis is everywhere the constant c. This curve is called a *tractrix*.

Ans. The differential equation of the curve takes the form

$$dy = \pm\frac{\sqrt{c^2 - x^2}}{x} dx,$$

which has the solution

$$x = c \sin \theta,$$

$$y + k = \pm c \left(\log \tan \frac{\theta}{2} + \cos \theta\right),$$

where k is a constant.

20. Show that if the tractrix of Exercise 19 is revolved about the y-axis the surface of revolution obtained has the parametric equations

$$x = c \sin u \cos v, \quad y = c \left(\log \tan \frac{u}{2} + \cos u \right), \quad z = c \sin u \sin v,$$

where $u = \theta$ and v is the angle through which the tractrix is revolved. This surface of revolution is called a *tractroid*.

21. Show that the element of arc ds on the tractroid of Exercise 20 is given by

$$ds^2 = c^2(\cot^2 u \, du^2 + \sin^2 u \, dv^2),$$

and that this becomes

$$ds^2 = c^2(d\bar{u}^2 + e^{2\bar{u}} \, d\bar{v}^2)$$

under the mapping $\sin u = e^{\bar{u}}$, $v = \bar{v}$. (It is shown in differential geometry that a surface with the latter form of linear element is a surface of constant negative total curvature. Such a surface is one of three types of pseudospherical surfaces of revolution. Surfaces with the linear element (50) belong to another of the three types.)

CHAPTER 10

Higher-dimensional Geometry

The foregoing geometry of the projective plane can be extended to projective spaces of three and higher dimensions. The notation to be employed for n-dimensional space will be found convenient for three dimensions ($n = 3$). In general, results will be obtained for projective three-space, but the generalization to higher-dimensional projective spaces will often be suggested by virtue of the notation employed. Many of the generalizations from two- to three-space will be found in the Exercises. The novel features of three and higher-dimensional spaces which have no specializations in the plane will be emphasized in this chapter.

10-1. Linear spaces

A point in real projective n-space is defined as an ordered set of $n + 1$ real numbers denoted by x^i, with $i = 1, 2, \cdots, n + 1$. The point with coordinates kx^i, where $k \neq 0$, is the same as the point with coordinates x^i. The totality of ordered sets of $n + 1$ real numbers constitutes real projective n-space. For some interpretations it is convenient to allow the coordinates to be complex numbers. Actually, the coordinates x^i may be elements from a more general field than that of the complex numbers, but such an extension is left to more advanced treatments.

A line is determined by two points x_1^i, x_2^i. Any point on the line has coordinates $\lambda^1 x_1^i + \lambda^2 x_2^i \equiv \lambda^\sigma x_\sigma^i$. The line is the totality of points $\lambda^\sigma x_\sigma^i$ obtained by allowing the two parameters λ^σ to take on all real (or complex) values (not both zero). Note that the Greek subscript on x_σ^i denotes the point, and the Latin superscript the coordinates of the point. This will be the convention in what follows.

One should verify that any two distinct points on the line determine it. To see this, let $\mu^\sigma x_\sigma^i$ and $\nu^\sigma x_\sigma^i$ be two points other than the points x_1^i, x_2^i on the line, and write the linear combination

$$\alpha^1(\mu^\sigma x_\sigma^i) + \alpha^2(\nu^\sigma x_\sigma^i) \equiv (\alpha^1 \mu^\sigma + \alpha^2 \nu^\sigma)x_\sigma^i,$$

which is again a linear combination of the form $\lambda^\sigma x_\sigma^i$ of the points x_1^i and x_2^i.

The index σ will now be allowed to range over 1, 2, 3. Just as the line is the totality of linear combinations of two points, the plane is defined as the point set obtained by taking the totality of linear combinations of three independent (noncollinear) points. Thus, given three independent points x_σ^i, with $\sigma = 1, 2, 3$, the point $\lambda^\sigma x_\sigma^i$ is a point in the plane determined by x_σ^i for all choices of λ^σ (not all zero). Observe that the $3 \times (n + 1)$ matrix

$$(x_\sigma^i) \equiv \begin{pmatrix} x_1^1 & x_1^2 & \cdots & x_1^{n+1} \\ x_2^1 & x_2^2 & \cdots & x_2^{n+1} \\ x_3^1 & x_3^2 & \cdots & x_3^{n+1} \end{pmatrix}$$

is assumed to be of rank three, which means that at least one nonvanishing third-order determinant can be selected from the matrix. Otherwise, the three points x^i would not be independent; that is, they would lie on a line, and therefore they could not determine a plane.

Extension to higher-dimensional linear point sets is immediate. A linear three-space immersed in the n-space is determined by four points x_σ^i, with $\sigma = 1, \cdots, 4$, for which the $4 \times (n + 1)$ matrix (x_σ^i) is of rank four. In general, a linear k-space is the totality of points $\lambda^\sigma x_\sigma^i$, with $\sigma = 1, \cdots, k + 1$, for which the $(k + 1) \times (n + 1)$ matrix (x_σ^i) has rank $k + 1$. In the case $k = n - 1$, the linear $(n - 1)$-dimensional subspace of n-dimensional space is called a *hyperplane*. Observe that if $n = 3$ and $k = 2$, the hyperplane is the ordinary plane in three-space.

EXAMPLE 1

Find the equation of the plane determined by the three points x_1^i, x_2^i, x_3^i in three-space, and extend the result to a hyperplane in n-dimensional space.

Solution: The coordinates x^i of any point in the plane are expressible as $x^i = \lambda^\sigma x_\sigma^i$, with $\sigma = 1, 2, 3$:

$$x^1 = \lambda^1 x_1^1 + \lambda^2 x_2^1 + \lambda^3 x_3^1,$$
$$x^2 = \lambda^1 x_1^2 + \lambda^2 x_2^2 + \lambda^3 x_3^2,$$
$$x^3 = \lambda^1 x_1^3 + \lambda^2 x_2^3 + \lambda^3 x_3^3,$$
$$x^4 = \lambda^1 x_1^4 + \lambda^2 x_2^4 + \lambda^3 x_3^4.$$

Eliminate λ^1, λ^2, λ^3 from the set of four equations to obtain

$$\begin{vmatrix} x^1 & x^2 & x^3 & x^4 \\ x_1^1 & x_1^2 & x_1^3 & x_1^4 \\ x_2^1 & x_2^2 & x_2^3 & x_2^4 \\ x_3^1 & x_3^2 & x_3^3 & x_3^4 \end{vmatrix} = 0,$$

which, on expanding, is a linear equation of the form $u_i x^i = 0$. For a fourth point x_4^i to be on the plane, the determinant $|x_\sigma^i| = 0$, or $u_i x_4^i = 0$. It follows that the coefficients u_i are proportional to the cofactors of x_4^i in the determinant $|x_\sigma^i|$. Let the cofactor of x_σ^i in the matrix (x_σ^i) be denoted by X_i^σ. Hence, the plane coordinates u_i may be taken as X_i^4, so that the plane determined by three points in three-space has the equation

$$X_i^4 x^i = 0, \qquad\qquad i = 1, 2, 3, 4.$$

The extension to the case of a hyperplane in n-space is immediate. For this let i range from 1 to $n + 1$, and let σ range from 1 to n. The equation of the hyperplane determined by n points x_σ^i in n-space, with $\sigma = 1, \cdots, n$, is $u_i x^i = 0$, with $i = 1, \cdots, n + 1$, where the hyperplane coordinates u_i may be taken as the $n + 1$ cofactors X_i^{n+1} of the last row in the matrix (x_σ^i), with $i, \sigma = 1, \cdots, n + 1$.

EXAMPLE 2

Show that k hyperplanes in n-space intersect in a linear space of dimensionality $n - k$.

Solution: Let $a_i^\sigma x^i = 0$, with $i = 1, \cdots, n + 1$ and $\sigma = 1, \cdots, k$, represent the k hyperplanes, where it is assumed that the matrix (a_i^σ) is of rank σ. It is possible therefore to select k of the given equations which can be solved for k of the variables x^i as linear functions of the remaining $n - k + 1$ variables, which determine a space of $n - k$ dimensions.

It is convenient to denote a linear space of k dimensions by S_k. If $k = 0$, the space S_0 consists of one point. If $k = 1$, then S_1 denotes a line, S_2 is a plane, S_3 a three-space, etc. The symbol S_{-1} may be used for a space which is vacuous. For instance, two lines S_1 and S_1' in S_3 have, in general, no intersection. Hence, the intersection space of S_1 and S_1' in S_3 is a space S_{-1}. It is further convenient to employ the notation of set theory. The symbolism $S_k \subset S_n$ means that the points of the space S_k belong to (or lie in) the space S_n. It may be said that the space S_k is "immersed" in the space S_n, and that S_n is the ambient space in which spaces of lower dimensionality are immersed (or embedded).

It is readily verified that if two points of a line are in a plane, then all points of the line belong to the plane (Exercise 1). In a similar way, it is shown next that if $k + 1$ points which determine S_k belong to S_n, then every point of S_k belongs to S_n. Let $\lambda_\tau^\sigma x_\sigma^i$, with $i = 1, \cdots, n + 1$ and $\sigma, \tau = 1, \cdots, k + 1$, denote $k + 1$ points in S_n. The linear combination $\alpha^\tau(\lambda_\tau^\sigma x_\sigma^i) \equiv (\alpha^\tau \lambda_\tau^\sigma) x_\sigma^i \equiv \mu^\sigma x_\sigma^i$ is a point of S_k, but, being a linear combination of x_σ^i, it is also in S_n.

In the projective plane S_2 it was seen that the coordinates of any point could be written as a linear combination of the base points $P_1(1:0:0)$, $P_2(0:1:0)$, $P_3(0:0:1)$, the vertices of the triangle of reference. In S_3 the base points $P_1(1:0:0:0)$, $P_2(0:1:0:0)$, $P_3(0:0:1:0)$, $P_4(0:0:0:1)$ are used as the vertices of a *tetrahedron* of reference. Note that the coordinates of any vertex P_σ are expressed by the Kronecker delta δ_σ^i, which is one if $i = \sigma$ and zero otherwise. The coordinates of any point $P(x^i)$ may be expressed by the linear combination $x^i = x^\sigma \delta_\sigma^i$ of the four base points. The four base points are linearly independent because the determinant $|\delta_\sigma^i| = 1 \neq 0$.

In the extension to S_n, the $n + 1$ base points $P_1(1:0:\cdots:0)$, $P_2(0:1:\cdots:0)$, $\cdots$, $P_{n+1}(0:0:\cdots:1)$ constitute an independent set of points, so that any point x^i in S_n is given by the combination $x^i = x^\sigma \delta_\sigma^i$. The configuration of the $n + 1$ base points $P_1, P_2, \cdots, P_{n+1}$ is called the *simplex* of reference in S_n.

Join and Intersection

Consider two lines S_1 and S_1' which lie in a plane S_2. The lines have an intersection S_0. The ambient space S_2 can be determined by noting that $1 + 1$ points are required to determine S_1, and $1 + 1$ points for S_1', but that the four points are not all necessary to determine S_2 because the intersection S_0 of S_1 and S_1' is a linear combination of two points of S_1 and also of two points of S_1'. The ambient space of least dimensionality which contains two or more subspaces is called the *join* of those spaces. The join of S_1 and S_1', denoted by $S_1 \cup S_1'$ is therefore S_2 if S_1 and S_1' intersect. In case S_1 and S_1' do not intersect, they determine a space S_3. In the latter case, $S_1 \cup S_1' = S_3$. Let the space of intersection of two spaces S_h and S_k be denoted by $S_h \cap S_k$. If S_h and S_k have no points in common, they are called *disjoint*. In this case, $S_h \cap S_k = S_{-1}$.

It is desired to write formulas for the dimensionality of the join and intersection of two spaces S_h and S_k. For the join, note that S_h is determined by $h + 1$ points, and S_k by $k + 1$ points. If the spaces are disjoint, the total of $(h + k + 1) + 1$ points determine a space of $h + k + 1$ dimensions. Hence, the join of S_h and S_k is given by

$$(1) \qquad S_h \cup S_k = S_{h+k+1},$$

if S_h and S_k are disjoint. On the other hand, if the spaces S_h and S_k have a space S_l in common, the $l + 1$ points which determine S_l must be subtracted from the sum $h + 1 + k + 1$ to obtain $h + k - l + 1$ as the number of points which determine the join of S_h and S_k. One has now

$$(2) \qquad S_h \cup S_k = S_{h+k-l}, \quad S_h \cap S_k = S_l.$$

As an example, note that for a point (S_0) and a line (S_1) not through the point, the join is $S_0 \cup S_1 = S_{0+1-(-1)} = S_2$.

Enumeration of Parameters

A point in S_2 depends upon two parameters, and a line $u_i x^i = 0$ in S_2 also depends upon two parameters. Because two points determine a line, it might appear that a line in a plane depends upon four parameters. But this is erroneous; cognizance of the fact that a point on a line depends upon one parameter reduces the number from four to $2 + 2 - 2 = 2$. For a line in S_3 each of the two points determining it depends upon three parameters. Hence, a line $S_1 \subset S_3$ depends upon $3 + 3 - 2 = 4$ parameters.

The question arises: Upon how many parameters does a space S_k in S_n depend? A point $S_0 \subset S_n$ depends upon n parameters. A line $S_1 \subset S_n$ depends upon $n + n - 2 = 2n - 2$ parameters. (Each point is on a line, so the number of parameters for two points on a line must be decreased by 2.) More generally, an S_k is determined by $k + 1$ points, and each of these points depends upon

n parameters in S_n. Hence, the total is $n(k + 1)$, but each point in S_k depends upon k parameters, so $k(k + 1)$ must be subtracted from $n(k + 1)$ to obtain $(n - k)(k + 1)$ parameters for $S_k \subset S_n$. Note that if $k = 1$, the number of parameters is $2n - 2$ for $S_1 \subset S_n$, as found previously.

Next, consider the number of parameters for a space $S_k \subset S_n$, where $S_l \subset S_k$. In order to find a method of attack for this, consider first the number of parameters for a line S_1 to contain a point S_0 in S_3. Intersect the lines of the bundle of lines through S_0 by a plane not containing S_0. There are as many lines through S_0 as there are points in this plane. Hence, the number of parameters is found to be two. In order to find the number of parameters for $S_l \subset S_k \subset S_n$, intersect S_k by a space S_r which has no point in common with S_l. The dimensionality r must be $n - l - 1$, because $r + 1 = (n + 1) - (l + 1)$ shows that S_r and S_l are disjoint. Now, if S_t is the intersection of S_k and S_r (S_n being the join), one has

$$n + 1 = (r + 1) + (k + 1) - (t + 1),$$

from which, with $r + 1 = n - l$, one finds

$$t = k - l - 1.$$

This means that $S_k \cap S_{n-l-1} = S_{k-l-1}$. Thus, instead of counting the parameters for a space S_k containing a space S_l in S_n, one may count the parameters for S_{k-l-1} in S_{n-l-1}. For this, use the formula $(n - k)(k + 1)$ for $S_k \subset S_n$ (derived above) with n now replaced by $n - l - 1$ and k by $k - l - 1$, to obtain

(3) $[(n - l - 1) - (k - l - 1)](k - l - 1 + 1) \equiv (n - k)(k - l).$

This is the number of parameters upon which a space $(S_k \supset S_l) \subset S_n$ depends. Observe that if $l = -1$ in (3) the formula for $S_k \subset S_n$, or $(n - k)(k + 1)$, is regained.

EXAMPLE 1

Find the number of planes through a point in S_4.

Solution: In this case $n = 4$, $k = 2$, $l = 0$. Formula (3) yields $(n - k)(k - l) = (4 - 2)(2 - 0) = 4$. Hence, ∞^4 planes pass through a point in S_4.

EXAMPLE 2

Upon how many parameters does a space S_4 containing a space S_2 in S_5 depend?

Solution: Here $n = 5$, $k = 4$, $l = 2$. Hence, $(n - k)(k - l) = (5 - 4)(4 - 2) = 2$ so that ∞^2 spaces S_4 contain a plane in S_5.

A final formula is desired for the number of conditions to be satisfied for two spaces S_h and S_k to intersect in S_l and lie in S_n. First consider the instance of two lines S_1 and S_1' in S_3. It has been seen that each line depends upon four parameters. Only one condition is required to be satisfied for S_1 and S_1' to meet in a point S_0.

The number of parameters for $S_k \subset S_n$ was found to be $(n - k)(k + 1)$, and the number of parameters for S_k to contain S_i in S_n is $(n - k)(k - l)$ by (3). Now use $(n - k)(k + 1)$ to find the number of parameters for S_l in S_h, with $n = h$ and $k = l$, to obtain $(h - l)(l + 1)$. The total number of conditions is now $(n - k)(k - l) + (h - l)(l + 1)$. Hence, the number of conditions to be satisfied for a space S_k to intersect a space S_h in a space S_l, all in S_n, is given by

$$(n - k)(k + 1) - [(n - k)(k - l) + (h - l)(l + 1)],$$

which reduces to

$$(4) \qquad\qquad (n - h - k + l)(l + 1).$$

For the case of the two lines intersecting in S_3, one has $n = 3$, $h = 1$, $k = 1$, $l = 0$, with which (4) yields $(3 - 1 - 1 + 0)(0 + 1) = 1$.

EXAMPLE 3

How many conditions are to be satisfied for the spaces S_2 and S_3 to intersect in a line (S_1) in S_5?

Solution: With $n = 5$, $h = 2$, $k = 3$, $l = 1$, formula (4) gives 2 as the required number of conditions.

EXERCISES

1. Show that if two points of a line lie in a plane, then all points of the line lie in the plane.

2. What is the dimensionality of the join of (a) a line and a plane in S_3? (b) two planes in S_4? (c) two planes in S_5?

3. What is the intersection of two planes in S_4?

4. How many conditions are to be satisfied in S_4 for two hyperplanes to intersect in a plane?
   Ans. None.

5. How many conditions are to be satisfied for two planes to intersect in a line in S_5?
   Ans. Four.

6. Point and hyperplane are dual elements in S_n. State and solve the dual problem of Example 1.

10-2. Projectively related spaces

Let point coordinates in S_k be denoted by x^i, with $i = 1, \cdots, k + 1$, and in $\bar{S}_k$ by $\bar{x}^i$ with $i = 1, \cdots, k + 1$. A projectivity between S_k and $\bar{S}_k$ is defined by

$$(5) \qquad\qquad \rho\bar{x}^i = a^i_j x^j, \qquad\qquad i, j = 1, \cdots, k + 1,$$

where the determinant $|a^i_j| \neq 0$. (See Exercise 2.)

Let it be shown first that the points of any subspace $S_h \subset S_k$ map under (5) into a space $\bar{S}_h \subset \bar{S}_k$. Let the $h + 1$ points P_σ with coordinates y^i_σ, and

$i = 1, \cdots, k + 1$, determine the space S_h. Any point y^i in S_h is given by $y^i = \lambda^\sigma y_\sigma^i$. The image point $\bar{y}^i$ in $\bar{S}_k$ is given by (5) as

$$\rho \bar{y}^i = a_j^i(y^j) = a_j^i \lambda^\sigma y_\sigma^j = \lambda^\sigma (a_j^i y_\sigma^j) = \lambda^\sigma \bar{y}_\sigma^i,$$

which shows that the image point $\bar{y}^i$ belongs to the $\bar{S}_k$ space of the image points of S_k. As in Section 7-1, equations (5) above are said to determine a collineation from S_k to $\bar{S}_k$.

Observe that there are $(k + 1)^2$ elements in the matrix (a_j^i) in (5). The arbitrariness of the proportionality factor ρ allows one nonzero element in (a_j^i) to be divided out of each of equations (5). Hence, there are $(k + 1)^2 - 1$ or $k(k + 2)$ essential parameters in (5). One may say that there is a group of $\infty^{k(k+2)}$ projectivities (5) between S_k and $\bar{S}_k$. For $k = 1$, one obtains the case of ∞^3 projectivities between two lines, which was discussed in Chapter 1. Recall that a projectivity between two lines is determined by three pairs of corresponding points. For $k = 2$, one has the case of ∞^8 projectivities between two planes, which was studied in Chapter 6. It was seen there that one of these projectivities is determined by four pairs of corresponding points. For $k = 3$, one has the fifteen-parameter group of projectivities between two three-dimensional spaces, and any such projectivity is determined by five pairs of corresponding points. For the general case, a projectivity from S_k to $\bar{S}_k$ is determined by $k + 2$ pairs of corresponding points.

Two projective spaces S_k and $\bar{S}_k$ in S_n are said to be perspective if there exists a third space S_p in the join of S_k and $\bar{S}_k$ such that the projection of a point of S_k from a point of S_p onto $\bar{S}_k$ is accomplished by lines of the projectivity. That is, the space $\bar{S}_k$ is a section of the projection of S_k from points of S_p.

Recall from Chapter 2 the case with $n = 2$, $k = 1$, $p = 0$, which is that of two lines S_1 and $\bar{S}_1$ in S_2. The joins of corresponding points on S_1 and $\bar{S}_1$ meet in the point S_0. In this case the intersection of S_1 and $\bar{S}_1$ is self-corresponding under the perspectivity. One might hazard the conjecture here that two projective spaces S_k and $\bar{S}_k$ with a nonempty intersection S_p are perspective if and only if the points of S_p are self-corresponding under the projectivity. Although this is actually the case, the statement will be verified next for the case of two projective planes which have just one point in common. The ambient space (join) of the two planes must therefore be S_4.

Consider two projective planes S_2 and $\bar{S}_2$ with one point S_0 of intersection (Fig. 84). Let S_0 correspond to itself under the projectivity. Take two lines S_1, S_1' in S_2 and their corresponding lines $\bar{S}_1$, $\bar{S}_1'$ in $\bar{S}_2$, the latter two lines containing S_0. The projectivity induced on S_1 and $\bar{S}_1$ is a perspectivity because S_0 is self-corresponding. Likewise, S_1' and $\bar{S}_1'$ are perspective. Let C and C' be the respective centers of the perspectivities between S_1, $\bar{S}_1$ and S_1', $\bar{S}_1'$. Any point P in S_2 can be projected into its correspondent $\bar{P}$ in $\bar{S}_2$ from some point on the join of C and C'. In order to see this, take any line through P in S_2 intersecting S_1 in A and S_1' in A'. Project A from C into $\bar{A}$ on $\bar{S}_1$, and project A' from C' into $\bar{A}'$ on $\bar{S}_1'$ to obtain the line $\bar{A}\bar{A}'$ in $\bar{S}_2$ as the projection of the line AA' in

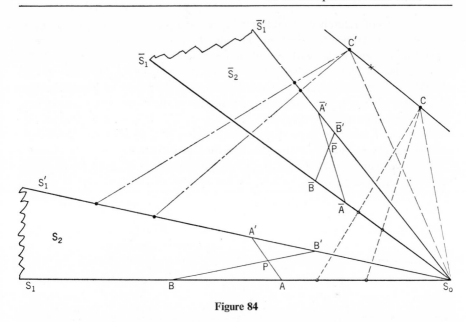

Figure 84

S_2. Now perform a similar construction for a second line BB' through P in S_2 to obtain its image $\overline{B}\overline{B}'$ in $\overline{S}_2$. Lines $\overline{A}\overline{A}'$ and $\overline{B}\overline{B}'$ in $\overline{S}_2$ intersect in $\overline{P}$, the image of P in S_2. Thus, because any point P of S_2 can be projected from line CC' into a point $\overline{P}$ of $\overline{S}_2$, the conjecture is seen to be valid for the case of two projective planes in S_4 with the intersection point self-corresponding.*

10-3. Perspective lines in S_3

It can be shown that if two pro- jective spaces S_k and $\overline{S}_k$ have no points in common they are per- spective. An analytic proof of this fact will be given for the simplest case—that of two skew (noninter- secting) lines in S_3. It will be shown that two given lines in S_3 are per- spective from not only one line in

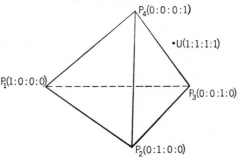

Figure 85

S_3 but from each of an infinite set of lines which lie on a quadric surface.

For the proof of the last statement a tetrahedron of reference is employed (Fig. 85). The analysis used heretofore for configurations in the plane relative

---

* For a more extended treatment, the reader is referred to E. Bertini, *Einführung in die Projektive Geometrie Mehrdimensionaler Räume*, Seidel, Vienna, 1924. (This is a translation by A. Duschek of the second edition in Italian of the work of Bertini, *Geometria proiettiva degli iperspazi*, Giuseppe Principato, Messina, 1923.)

to a triangle of reference extends readily to analysis of configurations in S_3 relative to a reference tetrahedron. The equation $u_i x^i = 0$, with $i = 1, \cdots, 4$, represents a plane in S_3, with the plane coordinates u_i. The equation $u_i x^i = 0$ expresses the incidence of the dual point and plane elements. For fixed x^i and variable u_i the equation represents all the planes of the *bundle* of planes through the point x^i. Observe that the plane coordinates of the faces of the tetrahedron of reference opposite the vertices P_σ, with $\sigma = 1, 2, 3, 4$, may be written as $[\delta_\sigma^i]$ by use of the Kronecker delta. For instance, if $\sigma = 4$, then $\delta_4^i = 0$ unless $i = 4$, so that the plane opposite P_4 has the coordinates $[0:0:0:1]$.

To prove that two skew lines S_1, $\bar{S}_1$ are perspective in S_3, take P_1, P_2 of the reference tetrahedron on S_1, and P_3, P_4 on $\bar{S}_1$ (Fig. 86), with P_1 and P_3 as cor-

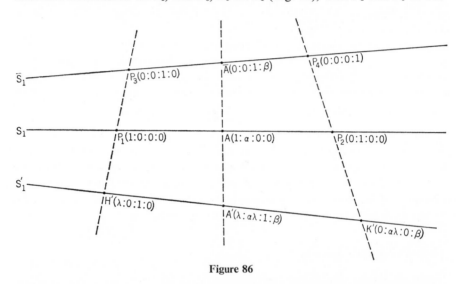

Figure 86

responding points on the two given ranges, and likewise with P_2 and P_4 corresponding. Let A, $\bar{A}$ be a third pair of corresponding points. Because A is on $P_1 P_2$, its coordinates are a linear combination of those of P_1 and P_2. Hence, let $(1:\alpha:0:0)$ represent A, where α is fixed. Similarly, let the coordinates of $\bar{A}$ be $(0:0:1:\beta)$, with β fixed. Now a variable point H' on $P_1 P_3$ has coordinates $(\lambda:0:1:0)$, a variable point K' on $P_2 P_4$ has coordinates $(0:\mu:0:1)$, and a variable point A' on $A\bar{A}$ has coordinates $(\nu:\nu\alpha:1:\beta)$, where λ, μ, ν are parameters. The points H', A', K' are collinear if the matrix

$$\begin{pmatrix} \lambda & 0 & 1 & 0 \\ 0 & \mu & 0 & 1 \\ \nu & \nu\alpha & 1 & \beta \end{pmatrix}$$

has rank two. On demanding that the first row of this matrix be a linear combination of the second and third rows, it is found that $\beta\mu = \alpha\lambda$, $\nu = \lambda$. Hence, the lines S_1 and $\bar{S}_1$ are perspective from the line S_1' containing $H'(\lambda:0:1:0)$,

$A'(\lambda:\alpha\lambda:1:\beta)$, $K'(0:\alpha\lambda:0:\beta)$. This proves the statement that S_1 and $\overline{S}_1$ are perspective in S_3.

Observe next that the line $H'A'K'$ depends upon one parameter λ. Hence, S_1 and $\overline{S}_1$ are perspective from each of an infinite set of lines in S_3. The locus of these lines is the next object of study. If x^i is a point on the line $H'K'$, then

(6)
$$\rho x^1 = r(\lambda) + s(0), \quad \rho x^2 = r(0) + s(\alpha\lambda), \quad \rho x^3 = r(1) + s(0), \quad \rho x^4 = r(0) + s(\beta),$$

in which r and s are parameters. Eliminate r, s, and ρ from (6) to obtain

(7)
$$\alpha x^1 x^4 = \beta x^2 x^3$$

as the equation of the *regulus* of lines in S_3 from each of which S_1 and $\overline{S}_1$ are perspective. Note that if the unit point $U(1:1:1:1)$ is taken on the regulus (7), then $\alpha = \beta$, and the equation reduces to $x^1 x^4 = x^2 x^3$.

A second regulus is next obtained. It is the set of lines joining corresponding points on S_1 and $\overline{S}_1$ (Fig. 86). It is left for the reader (see Exercise 3) to verify that the three points $Q(1:\lambda:0:0)$, $\overline{Q}(0:0:\alpha:\beta\lambda)$, $Q'(\alpha:\alpha\lambda:\alpha:\beta\lambda)$ on the respective lines S_1, $\overline{S}_1$, S_1' are collinear, and that the locus of the lines $Q\overline{Q}$ as λ varies is the regulus with the equation

(8)
$$\alpha x^1 x^4 = \beta x^2 x^3.$$

But this is precisely equation (7). Hence, the quadric surface with equation (7) contains two reguli, which means that the quadric is doubly ruled. From the foregoing development there follows the

THEOREM: *The locus of the lines joining corresponding points of two projective point ranges on two skew lines in S_3 is a quadric surface which also contains the regulus of lines from each of which the two ranges are perspective.*

The case of a projectivity between two nonintersecting planes S_2 and $\overline{S}_2$ is considered next. The projectivity will be shown to be a perspectivity. The two planes must be immersed in S_5 because they are disjoint. Because S_2 is projectively related to $\overline{S}_2$, any point of S_2 maps into a unique point of $\overline{S}_2$. Thus, there are ∞^2 lines in S_5 which join corresponding points in S_2 and $\overline{S}_2$. Select a plane π in S_5 which does not intersect S_2 or $\overline{S}_2$ but which contains a point P' of the line

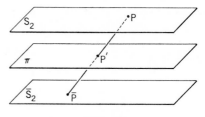

Figure 87

joining P in S_2 with its correspondent $\overline{P}$ in $\overline{S}_2$ (Fig. 87). The space S_3, which is the join of π and point P, contains P and P' and therefore point $\overline{P}$. Hence, the intersection of this S_3 with $\overline{S}_2$ is P. Thus it is seen that the doubly infinite set of S_3 spaces determined by π and the ∞^2 lines $P\overline{P}$ project the points of S_2 into the points of $\overline{S}_2$. Hence, S_2 and $\overline{S}_2$ are perspective in S_5.

EXERCISES

1. Explain why a projectivity from S_k to $\bar{S}_k$ is determined by $k + 2$ pairs of corresponding points.

2. Discuss the degenerate cases of the projectivity (5) when the rank of the matrix (a_j^i) is 1, 2, $\cdots$, k.

3. Obtain the second regulus—that is, the locus of lines joining corresponding points on S_1 and $\bar{S}_1$—by filling in the details leading to equation (8).

4. Show that the line joining two points x_1^i and x_2^i meets the quadric (7) in two points.

5. Show that there is a triply infinite set of lines which intersect a given line in S_3. This set is called a *complex* of lines.

6. Show that a doubly infinite set of lines intersects two given lines in S_3. This set is called a *congruence* of lines.

7. Show that three given lines in S_3 are met by a singly infinite set of lines—that is, by a regulus.

8. Show that four given lines in S_3 are all intersected by *two* lines (which may happen to coincide).

9. Prove that no two generating lines of a regulus intersect, but that any line of one regulus of a quadric meets a given line of the other (complementary) regulus in a single point.

10. Prove that if a line meets a quadric in three points, the line lies entirely on the quadric.

11. Given the three lines $x^1 = 0$, $x^4 = 0$; $x^2 = 0$, $x^3 = 0$; $x^1 + x^2 = 0$, $x^3 + x^4 = 0$, (a) find the quadric which contains them, (b) find the equations of the two lines which intersect the three given lines and also the fourth line given by

$$x^1 + 2x^2 + 3x^3 = 0, \quad 3x^2 + 2x^3 + x^4 = 0.$$

$$\text{Ans. } x^1 - x^4 = 0, \, x^2 - x^3 = 0; \, x^1 + x^4 = 0, \, x^2 + x^3 = 0.$$

12. Find the equation of the quadric which contains the lines $x^2 + cx^4 = 0$, $x^3 - ax^4 = 0$; $x^3 + ax^4 = 0$, $x^1 - bx^4 = 0$; $x^1 + bx^4 = 0$, $x^2 - cx^4 = 0$. *Suggestion:* Any plane through the first line is given by $x^2 + cx^4 + \lambda(x^3 - ax^4) = 0$, and any plane through the second by $x^3 + ax^4 + \mu(x^1 - bx^4) = 0$. The point $(-b:c:\sigma:1)$ generates the third line. The condition for this point to be on the line of intersection of the planes is $b\lambda\mu - a\lambda + c = 0$. Eliminate λ and μ to obtain

$$ax^1x^2 + bx^2x^3 + cx^3x^1 + abc(x^4)^2 = 0.$$

13. Show that, in general, three hyperplanes in S_4 intersect in a line (S_1), and that three hyperplanes in S_5 intersect in a plane (S_2).

14. Show that a line either intersects a hyperplane of S_n in a unique point or lies in the hyperplane.

10-4. The quadric

In the preceding section a quadric in S_3 appeared as the locus of lines joining corresponding points of two projective point ranges on two skew lines. It is instructive to see the quadric defined in other ways. The first is an extension of the conic as defined by Steiner (Section 8-4). A conic in S_2 is the locus of the intersections of corresponding rays of two coplanar projective line pencils with distinct centers. For the extension to S_3 the centers of the pencils become two skew lines, and the rays of a pencil in the plane become planes through a line in S_3—that is, a pencil of planes in S_3. The equation $a_i x^i + \lambda b_i x^i = 0$ represents ∞^1 planes through the line l of intersection of the planes $a_i x^i = 0$ and $b_i x^i = 0$, with $i = 1, \cdots, 4$. Similarly, $c_i x^i + \mu d_i x^i = 0$ is a set of ∞^1 planes through the line $\bar{l}$ of intersection of $c_i x^i = 0$ and $d_i x^i = 0$. The homography $\mu = (\alpha\lambda + \beta)/(\gamma\lambda + \delta)$ establishes a correspondence between pairs of planes in the two pencils. The locus of the lines of intersection of corresponding planes is found by eliminating λ and μ to obtain

$$(9) \qquad [(\alpha a_i - \beta b_i)d_j + (\gamma a_i - \delta b_i)c_j]x^i x^j = 0,$$

which is the equation of a quadric surface.

The Steiner definition will now be used again but with a particular choice of the lines l and $\bar{l}$ as axes of the pencils of planes. Let l, $\bar{l}$ be the lines $P_1 P_3$, $P_2 P_4$ of the tetrahedron of reference (Fig. 85). Any plane through $P_1 P_3$ is given by $x^4 + \lambda x^2 = 0$, and any plane through $P_2 P_4$ by $x^1 + \mu x^3 = 0$. If α and δ in the homography are taken as zero, elimination of λ and μ from $x^4 + \lambda x^2 = 0$, $x^1 + \mu x^3 = 0$, and $\gamma\lambda\mu = \beta$ gives

$$(10) \qquad \gamma x^1 x^4 = \beta x^2 x^3,$$

which is of the form of equation (7) for the quadric locus. One should observe that the axes l, $\bar{l}$ of the projective plane pencils lie on the quadric (10).

In the plane case the conic was defined dually as the envelope of the lines joining corresponding points of two projective ranges. In order to see the dual situation in S_3, recall from Section 4-1 that the point and plane are dual elements in S_3 and that the line is self-dual in S_3. Here, the dual of a pencil of planes through a line is a range of points on a line. The extension to S_3 of the pencil of lines in S_2 incident with a point C is the pencil of planes incident with a line l. Thus, the dual of the statement "the locus of the *lines* of intersection of corresponding *planes* of two projective *planar* pencils in S_3 is a quadric surface" becomes "the locus of the *lines* joining corresponding *points* of two projective *point* ranges in S_3 is a quadric surface." This statement recalls Exercise 2 of Section 1-2, and is equivalent to the definition leading to equation (7).

Polar Correlation

A quadric surface may be defined as the set of points in S_3 which are incident with their corresponding planes in a polar correlation. This will be shown by the following development.

The collineation (5) for S_3 is written as

$$(11) \qquad \rho \bar{x}^i = a_j^i x^j, \qquad |a_j^i| \neq 0, i, j = 1, \cdots, 4.$$

The theory (including classification) of collineations and correlations in S_3 follows closely the development in Chapter 7 for S_2 (with one important difference, which will be noted presently).

Under the collineation (11), points go into points, lines into lines, and planes into planes. The inverse of (11) is given (as in Section 7-1) by

$$(12) \qquad \sigma x^i = A^i_j \bar{x}^j,$$

where A^i_j is the cofactor of a^j_i in the matrix (a^i_j). The incidence relation $u_i x^i = 0$ in S_3, being invariant, becomes $\bar{u}_i \bar{x}^i = 0$ in $\bar{S}_3$. The mapping (11) induces the mapping

$$(13) \qquad k\bar{u}_i = A^j_i u_j$$

on the dual plane coordinates u_i. The inverse of (13) is

$$(14) \qquad r u_i = a^j_i \bar{u}_j.$$

Now consider the mapping (11) of S_3 into itself. As in Section (7-2), the fixed points of S_3 may be investigated. A new feature is that equation (13) of Section 7-2, that is, $|a^i_j - \lambda \delta^i_j| = 0$, is of the fourth degree in λ, so that there are, in general, four fixed points in S_3 under the collineation (11).*

The present object of study is the extension to S_3 of the correlation defined in Section 7-6. The equations

$$(15) \qquad \rho \bar{u}_i = a_{ij} x^j, \qquad |a_{ij}| \neq 0, \, i, j = 1, \cdots, 4,$$

represent a one-to-one correspondence between points of one space S_3 and planes of another space $\bar{S}_3$. The inverse of (15) is

$$(16) \qquad \sigma x^i = A^{ji} \bar{u}_j.$$

The incidence condition $u_i x^i = 0$ of point x^i and plane u_i shows, by use of (16), that

$$u_i x^i = u_i A^{ji} \bar{u}_j = \bar{u}_j \bar{x}^j,$$

from which

$$k\bar{x}^j = A^{ji} u_i,$$

or

$$(17) \qquad k\bar{x}^i = A^{ji} u_j,$$

which equations have the inverse

$$(18) \qquad k' u_i = a_{ji} \bar{x}^j.$$

Next consider the spaces S_3 and $\bar{S}_3$ as coincident, and use the same coordinate system for both. To a *point P* in S_3 corresponds a *plane $\bar{p}$* in $\bar{S}_3$, and to a point

---

* A detailed classification of collineations of S_3 according to the nature of the fixed points will not be given here. The reader may refer to F. S. Woods, *Higher Geometry* (Dover, New York, 1922) or to J. G. Semple and G. T. Kneebone, *Algebraic Projective Geometry* (Oxford University Press, 1952).

$\overline{P}$ in $\overline{S}_3$ corresponds a plane p in S_3. Let points P and $\overline{P}$ coincide, that is, let $k\overline{x}^i = x^i$, and demand that the correspondents p and $\overline{p}$ also coincide. It follows from equations (15) and (18) that $a_{ij}x^j = \lambda a_{ji}x^i$, or

$$(19) \qquad (a_{ij} - \lambda a_{ji})x^j = 0,$$

for which the condition for a nontrivial solution is

$$(20) \qquad |a_{ij} - \lambda a_{ji}| = 0.$$

Because (20) is a quartic in λ, it can be concluded that only four points exist for which the coincidence of P and $\overline{P}$ implies the coincidence of p and $\overline{p}$ under the general collineation (15) of a space S_3 into itself.

Let it be demanded next that the coincidence of P and $\overline{P}$ implies the coincidence of p and $\overline{p}$ for all points of S_3. This requires that equations (19) be identities in the x^i; that is,

$$(21) \qquad a_{ij} - \lambda a_{ji} = 0,$$

for all i and j. Interchange i and j in (21), and multiply by λ to have

$$\lambda a_{ji} - \lambda^2 a_{ij} = 0,$$

which, with (21), shows that $\lambda = \pm 1$. If $\lambda = 1$, equations (21) show that the matrix (a_{ij}) in (15) is symmetric. If $\lambda = -1$, then $a_{ij} = -a_{ji}$, which means that the matrix (a_{ij}) is skew-symmetric. This case, where $\lambda = -1$, was rejected in Section 7-6 because of the fact that the determinant of a skew-symmetric matrix of odd order is zero. In S_2, where (a_{ij}) is of the third order, this would make the correlation singular. However, in S_3, where the matrix (a_{ij}) is of the fourth order, a nonsingular correlation (15) exists for which (a_{ij}) is skew-symmetric. If the bars are deleted in (15) and (16), it is seen (as in the plane case) that the correlation (15) for which (a_{ij}) is symmetric is a *polar correlation*. It establishes a correspondence in S_3 by which to every point P there corresponds a unique plane p called the *polar plane* of P, and to every plane p in S_3 there corresponds a unique point P called the *pole* of p.

Now let it be required to find the set of points in S_3 which are incident with their corresponding polar planes. Use the incidence relation $u_ix^i = 0$ and (15) in the form $\rho u_i = a_{ij}x^j$ to see that

$$u_ix^i = a_{ij}x^jx^i = a_{ij}x^ix^j = 0.$$

Hence, the points incident with their polar planes are on the quadric surface $a_{ij}x^ix^j = 0$. The envelope of the planes of S_3 which are incident with their poles under a polar correlation is the plane quadric $A^{ij}u_iu_j = 0$, in which the A^{ij} are the cofactors of the elements a_{ij} in the matrix (a_{ij}) of the point quadric $a_{ij}x^ix^j = 0$.

The case $\lambda = -1$ gives rise to a new phenomenon in S_3 for which the correspondence $\rho u_i = a_{ij}x^j$, with (a_{ij}) skew-symmetric, is called a *null system*. This is treated further in Section 6.

Conjugate Lines

It should be observed that the quadric Q with equation

$$(22) \qquad\qquad a_{ij}x^ix^j = 0$$

was obtained from a polar correlation, but that any quadric (22) determines a polar correlation. The polar plane of any point y^i with respect to the quadric Q is given by $a_{ij}y^ix^j = 0$. The plane coordinates of this polar plane are given by $\rho u_i = a_{ij}y^i$, which defines the polar correlation.

The polar plane of a point z^i relative to Q has the equation $a_{ij}z^ix^j = 0$. Any point $y^i + \lambda z^i$ on the join l of y^i and z^i has the polar plane relative to Q given by $a_{ij}(y^i + \lambda z^i)x^j = 0$, or, in another form, $a_{ij}y^ix^j + \lambda a_{ij}z^ix^j = 0$. The latter equation shows that as the point $y^i + \lambda z^i$ moves along the line l, its polar plane relative to Q revolves about the intersection $\bar{l}$ of the polar planes of y^i and z^i. The lines l and $\bar{l}$ are called *conjugate lines* (or a polar pair of lines) relative to the quadric.

Let the polar plane $a_{ij}x_1^ix^j = 0$ of a point x_1^i contain a second point x_2^i, so that $a_{ij}x_1^ix_2^j = 0$. It follows from the symmetry of (a_{ij}) that the polar plane of x_2^i contains x_1^i. The join l of x_1^i and x_2^i is conjugate to the intersection $\bar{l}$ of the polars of x_1^i and x_2^i. Choose any point x_3^i on $\bar{l}$. Its polar plane contains l and a unique point x_4^i on $\bar{l}$. The tetrahedron determined by the four points x_σ^i is called a *self-polar* tetrahedron relative to the quadric Q. There are ∞^6 self-polar tetrahedra with respect to a quadric in S_3. (See Exercise 13 on p. 188.) If i and j in the equation $a_{ij}x^ix^j = 0$ have the range $1, \cdots, n + 1$, the equation represents a *hyperquadric* in S_n. It can be shown that there are $\infty^{n(n+1)/2}$ self-polar simplexes relative to a hyperquadric.

Composite Quadrics

The classification of composite conics given in Section 8-3 is now extended to the quadric Q: $a_{ij}x^ix^j = 0$ in S_3, with $a_{ij} = a_{ji}$. Let r denote the rank of the matrix (a_{ij}). If $r = 4$, the point quadric Q is a *proper* quadric, and it follows that the plane quadric Q: $A^{ij}u_iu_j = 0$ is also proper. There is complete duality between proper point and plane quadrics, by which to every theorem concerning a proper point quadric there is a corresponding theorem concerning a proper plane quadric. However, complete duality no longer holds if $r < 4$.

Next, let $r = 3$, and consider the tangent plane to Q at the point y^i on Q. Its equation is $a_{ij}y^ix^j = 0$. Any point y^i for which $a_{ij}y^i = 0$, with $j = 1, \cdots, 4$, is a singular point (vertex) on Q—that is, a point at which the tangent plane to Q is indeterminate. If $r = 3$, the four equations $a_{ij}y^i = 0$ have a unique point as a solution, so Q has one vertex. Any point on the join of y^i and any other point x^i on Q has coordinates $y^i + \lambda x^i$. Because $a_{ij}(y^i + \lambda x^i)x^j = a_{ij}y^ix^j + \lambda a_{ij}x^ix^j = 0 + \lambda 0 = 0$ for all λ, the surface Q is composed of lines through y^i. Thus, Q is a conical surface of the second order. (See Exercise 5.)

Next let $r = 2$. The equations $a_{ij}y^i = 0$ are now satisfied by a line of points, so Q is a pair of planes intersecting in the line of vertices. If $r = 1$, the four equations $a_{ij}y^i = 0$ reduce to a single equation, which shows that a plane of vertices exists. The quadric Q reduces to two coincident planes—the plane of vertices counted twice. The trivial case, where $r = 0$, is that for which Q is indeterminate.

The foregoing discussion can be extended to a classification of composite hyperquadrics given by

(22′) $$H: \qquad a_{ij}x^ix^j = 0, \qquad\qquad i, j = 1, \cdots, n + 1.$$

Any point y^i not on H is conjugate to any point z^i, which lies in the polar hyperplane of y^i relative to H given by

(23) $$a_{ij}y^ix^j = 0.$$

The condition for conjugacy of y^i and z^i is therefore $a_{ij}y^iz^j = 0$, which shows that the polar hyperplane of z^i relative to H contains the point y^i. More generally, let y^i be any point of a space S_k; that is, let

$$y^i = \lambda^\sigma x_\sigma^i, \qquad\qquad \sigma = 1, \cdots, k + 1.$$

The polar hyperplane of the point y^i relative to H is then

$$a_{ij}\lambda^\sigma x_\sigma^i x^j = 0,$$

or

$$\lambda^\sigma(a_{ij}x_\sigma^i x^j) = 0.$$

Because the last equation holds for arbitrary values of λ^σ, it follows that

(24) $$a_{ij}x_\sigma^i x^j = 0, \qquad\qquad \sigma = 1, \cdots, k + 1.$$

The intersection of the $k + 1$ hyperplanes in (24) is a space S_{n-k-1}. The two spaces S_k and S_{n-k-1} are conjugate polar spaces relative to the hyperquadric H. In particular, if $k = 1$ it is seen that a line S_1 has a space S_{n-2} as its polar space. Observe that if $n = 3$ the line is polar to a line. Note also that polar subspaces of the same dimension occur only in the spaces for which n is an odd number.

If the rank r of the matrix (a_{ij}) in (22) is $n + 1$, the equations $a_{ij}y^i = 0$, with $j = 1, \cdots, n + 1$, have only the trivial solution. There is no singular point on the hypersurface, and to every point in space there is a unique polar hyperplane. In particular, for every point y^i on H there is a unique tangent hyperplane. If $r = n$, a unique solution for y^i exists, so there is one vertex on the hyperquadric at which the tangent hyperplane is indeterminate. In this case the hyperquadric consists of ∞^{n-2} lines through the singular point. If $r = n - 1$, there is a line of vertices on H. If $r = n - 2$, H has a plane of vertices. In general, if $r = n - k$, there is a space S_k of vertices on H in S_n. Finally, if $r = 1$, H consists of a hyperplane of vertices counted twice.

EXERCISES

1. Show that nine points (no four coplanar) determine a quadric surface in S_3, and that ∞^1 quadrics contain eight given points.

2. Find the form of the equation of the quadric if the vertices of the reference tetrahedron and the unit point are on it.

3. Find the form of the equation of the quadric in S_3 if the reference tetrahedron is self-polar.

4. (a) Show that $x^1:x^2:x^3:x^4 = \sigma:\sigma\tau:1:\tau$ is a parametric representation of the quadric in the canonical form $x^1x^4 = x^2x^3$. (b) Show that the equation in plane coordinates u_i of the point locus $x^1x^4 = x^2x^3$ is $u_1u_4 = u_2u_3$.

5. Find the planar envelope (plane equation) of the point quadric

$$3[(x^1)^2 + (x^2)^2 + (x^3)^2] + 8(x^2x^3 + x^3x^1 + x^1x^2) = 0.$$

Ans. $u_4^2 = 0$.

6. Use the theorem in Section 8-3 to investigate the composite quadrics in plane coordinates.

7. Find the condition under which the plane $u_ix^i = 0$ is tangent to the quadric $a_{ij}x^ix^j = 0$ in S_3.

8. Denote the cofactor of a_i^τ in the matrix (a_i^τ), with $i, \tau = 1, \cdots, 4$, by A_τ^i. Show that any three planes $a_i^\sigma x^i = 0$, with $\sigma = 1, 2, 3$, not belonging to the same pencil of planes, intersect in the point

$$x^1:x^2:x^3:x^4 = A_4^1:A_4^2:A_4^3:A_4^4.$$

10-5. Linear osculants

Let the $n + 1$ coordinates x^i of a point in S_n be functions of a single parameter t. As t varies from a to b on the real interval $a \le t \le b$, the point $x^i(t)$ describes an arc of a curve C. It is supposed that the correspondence between the values of t on the interval and the points on C is one-to-one, and that the functions $x^i(t)$ possess derivatives at least up to order k for all $a \le t \le b$. Note that the functions $\rho(t)x^i(t)$ determine the same curve C provided that $\rho(t)$ does not vanish on the interval $[a, b]$. According to the usual notation, let

$$x^i, x^{i\prime}, x^{i\prime\prime}, \cdots, x^{i(k)}$$

denote the derivatives of orders $0, 1, 2, \cdots, k$ of the functions x^i. The two points x^i and $x^{i\prime}$ determine a line in S_n which may be called the *linear tangent space* $T^{(1)}$ *of the first order* to the curve C at any point $x^i(t)$. Any point of $T^{(1)}$ has coordinates of the form $x^i + \lambda x^{i\prime}$. But if $\rho(t)x^i(t)$ is used instead of x^i, any point of $T^{(1)}$ is given by

(25) $$\rho x^i + \mu(\rho x^i)' \equiv (\rho + \mu\rho')x^i + (\mu\rho)x^{i\prime}.$$

On comparing this form with $x^i + \lambda x^{i\prime}$ it is evident that the point $x^{i\prime}$ can be made to coincide with any point on $T^{(1)}$ by a proper choice of the function $\rho(t)$. Hence, the point $x^{i\prime}$ has in itself no geometric significance, but the line determined by x^i and $x^{i\prime}$ does have geometric significance.

The first derivative point of ρx^i is $\rho'x^i + \rho x^{i\prime}$, and the second derivative point of ρx^i is

$$\rho''x^i + 2\rho'x^{i\prime} + \rho x^{i\prime\prime},$$

which is a linear combination of x^i, $x^{i\prime}$, $x^{i\prime\prime}$. The linear space $T^{(2)}$ determined by the points x^i, $x^{i\prime}$, $x^{i\prime\prime}$ may be called the linear tangent space of the *second order* to the surve C at any point $x^i(t)$. Any point of $T^{(2)}$ has coordinates of the form $x^i + \lambda_1 x^{i\prime} + \lambda_2 x^{i\prime\prime}$, where λ_1 and λ_2 are parameters. The spaces $T^{(1)}$ and $T^{(2)}$ are also called *linear osculating spaces* of the first and second orders. More generally, a linear osculating space $T^{(k)}$, of order k, to C at x^i is the point set with coordinates

$$x^i + \lambda_1 x^{i\prime} + \lambda_2 x^{i\prime\prime} + \cdots + \lambda_k x^{i(k)},$$

where $\lambda_1, \cdots, \lambda_k$ are parameters. The spaces $T^{(1)}$ and $T^{(2)}$ are referred to more briefly as the tangent line and osculating plane, respectively, to C at the point $x^i(t)$. The coordinates ξ^i of any point in the osculating plane are given by

(26) $$\xi^i = x^i + \lambda_1 x^{i\prime} + \lambda_2 x^{i\prime\prime}, \qquad i = 1, \cdots, n + 1.$$

If $n = 3$, the parameters λ_1, λ_2 may be eliminated from (26) to obtain

(27) $$\begin{vmatrix} \xi^1 & \xi^2 & \xi^3 & \xi^4 \\ x^1 & x^2 & x^3 & x^4 \\ x^{1\prime} & x^{2\prime} & x^{3\prime} & x^{4\prime} \\ x^{1\prime\prime} & x^{2\prime\prime} & x^{3\prime\prime} & x^{4\prime\prime} \end{vmatrix} = 0$$

as the equation of the osculating plane to a curve C at $x^i(t)$ in S_3.

EXAMPLE

Find the equation of the osculating plane to the cubic curve $x^1 = (t)^3$, $x^2 = (t)^2$, $x^3 = t$, $x^4 = 1$ at the point where $t = 1$.

Solution: Calculate $x^{1\prime} = 3t^2$, $x^{2\prime} = 2t$, $x^{3\prime} = 1$, $x^{4\prime} = 0$, and $x^{1\prime\prime} = 6t$, $x^{2\prime\prime} = 2$, $x^{3\prime\prime} = x^{4\prime\prime} = 0$ and use (27) to obtain

$$\begin{vmatrix} \xi^1 & \xi^2 & \xi^3 & \xi^4 \\ t^3 & t^2 & t & 1 \\ 3t^2 & 2t & 1 & 0 \\ 6t & 2 & 0 & 0 \end{vmatrix} = 0,$$

which, on expanding, takes the form

$$\xi^1 - 3t\xi^2 + 3t^2\xi^3 - t^3\xi^4 = 0.$$

With $t = 1$, the required osculating plane has the equation

$$\xi^1 - 3\xi^2 + 3\xi^3 - \xi^4 = 0.$$

If the points x^i, $x^{i\prime}$, $x^{i\prime\prime}$ are independent, they determine the two-osculating space (osculating plane) to C at x^i. However, if these three points are dependent at all points of C, then $x^{i\prime\prime} \equiv \alpha(t)x^i + \beta(t)x^{i\prime}$ for $i = 1, \cdots, n + 1$, and, as a consequence, $x^{i\prime\prime\prime}$ and all higher derivatives of x^i are linear combinations of x^i and $x^{i\prime}$ for all t. This means that the curve C is a straight line. The functions $x^i(t)$ satisfy a differential equation of the type

(28) $$\theta'' + p(t)\theta' + q(t)\theta = 0,$$

which should be compared with equation (28) in Section 3-11 (p. 68). If any particular set of functions $x_1^i(t)$ is known to satisfy (28), then the general solution of (28) is projectively related to $x_1^i(t)$ on the straight line C. It may be said that (28) defines a projectively equivalent class of solutions on a line.

The next case to consider is that for which the points x^i, $x^{i'}$, $x^{i''}$, $x^{i'''}$ are linearly dependent. In this case $x^i(t)$ satisfy a differential equation of the type

$$(29) \qquad\qquad \theta''' + p(t)\theta'' + q(t)\theta' + r(t)\theta = 0,$$

and all points of C lie in the space S_2 determined by the points x^i, $x^{i'}$, $x^{i''}$. If a set of functions $x_1^i(t)$ are integrals (solutions) of equation (29), then the function $\bar{x}_1(t) = a_i x_1^i(t)$, where the a_i are arbitrary constants, is a solution of (29). A set of solutions $\bar{x}_1^i(t)$ of (29) is given by

$$(30) \qquad\qquad \bar{x}_1^i(t) = a_j^i x_1^j(t),$$

which is a projectivity in the osculating plane in which the curve C lies.

In general, if the curve C is in S_n the points x^i, $x^{i'}$, $\cdots$, $(x^i)^{(n+1)}$ must be dependent. Consequently, $x^i(t)$ must satisfy a differential equation of the type

$$(31) \qquad\qquad \theta^{(n+1)} + p_1(t)\theta^{(n)} + \cdots + p_{n+1}(t)\theta = 0,$$

which defines a projectively equivalent class of solutions in S_n. If one curve $x^i(t)$ is a solution of (31), then every projective transform $\bar{x}^i = a_j^i x^j$ of C is also a solution of (31).

If the transformations $\theta(t) = \rho(t)\bar{\theta}(t)$ and $t = t(\tau)$ are effected on equation (31), the curve C is not altered. The form of the transformed equation is

$$(32) \qquad\qquad \bar{\theta}^{(n+1)} + \bar{p}_1(\tau)\bar{\theta}^{(n)} + \cdots + \bar{p}_{n+1}(\tau)\bar{\theta} = 0.$$

If a function $f(p_1, p_2, \cdots, p_{n+1})$ exists which is equal to $f(\bar{p}_1, \bar{p}_2, \cdots, \bar{p}_{n+1})$, then f is a *projective invariant* and the vanishing of f describes a projective property of the curve C.

Surface Osculants

Let the $n + 1$ coordinates x^i of a point in S_n be functions of two independent parameters u and v. As u and v vary over some domain of the uv plane, the point $x^i(u, v)$ generates a surface S. It is assumed that the rank of the matrix

$$\begin{pmatrix} x^1 & \cdots & x^{n+1} \\ \dfrac{\partial x^1}{\partial u} & \cdots & \dfrac{\partial x^{n+1}}{\partial u} \\ \dfrac{\partial x^1}{\partial v} & \cdots & \dfrac{\partial x^{n+1}}{\partial v} \end{pmatrix}$$

is three. The surface is immersed in S_n. A curve C on S is obtained by taking u and v as functions of a parameter t. A tangent line to C at a point $P(x^i[u(t), v(t)])$ is determined by the points x^i and $x^{i'}$, where

$$x^{i\prime} \equiv \frac{dx^i}{dt} = \frac{\partial x^i}{\partial u}\frac{du}{dt} + \frac{\partial x^i}{\partial v}\frac{dv}{dt},$$

so that $x^{i\prime}$ is a linear combination of $\partial x^i/\partial u$ and $\partial x^i/\partial v$. It is evident that all tangent lines to curves on S at P are in the plane of the three points x^i, $\partial x^i/\partial u$, $\partial x^i/\partial v$. This is the tangent plane to S at P.

Consider next the osculating plane to a curve C on S at P. It is determined by the points

$$x^i, \quad x^{i\prime} = x_u^i u' + x_v^i v', \quad x^{i\prime\prime} = x_{uu}^i u'^2 + 2x_{uv}^i u' v' + x_{vv}^i v'^2 + x_u^i u'' + x_v^i v'',$$

where the subscripts denote partial derivatives. If the curve C on S is allowed to vary, the functions $u(t)$ and $v(t)$ are changed, as are also u', v' and u'', v'', in general. However, if u' and v' are held fixed but u'', v'' are allowed to vary, a family of curves through P on S with a common tangent line is obtained. (Only the ratio u'/v' need be constant to determine the fixed tangent.) In this case x^i and $x^{i\prime} = x_u^i u' + x_v^i v'$ are fixed at P but the point $x^{i\prime\prime}$ varies. A point in the osculating plane to C at P is in the space determined by the four points

$$x^i, \quad x_u^i, \quad x_v^i, \quad x_{uu}^i u'^2 + 2x_{uv}^i u' v' + x_{vv}^i v'^2.$$

As is to be expected, the ambient space of all the osculating planes to curves on S through P with a fixed direction is a space of three dimensions. The osculating planes constitute a pencil of planes through the fixed tangent line at P.

Next allow the tangent to curves on S through P to vary; that is, let u' and v' be variable. One seeks the dimensionality of the space containing the osculating planes to variable curves on S as the direction of the curves varies. With u' and v' variable, it is seen that the point $x_{uu}^i u'^2 + 2x_{uv}^i u' v' + x_{vv}^i v'^2$ used above is now a linear combination of the three points x_{uu}^i, x_{uv}^i, x_{vv}^i. Hence, the osculating planes being considered belong to the space determined by the six points

$$x^i, \quad x_u^i, \quad x_v^i, \quad x_{uu}^i, \quad x_{uv}^i, \quad x_{vv}^i,$$

that is, a space S_5, in general. The dimensionality may be reduced under certain conditions. For instance, if it happens that the surface is a plane, then x_{uu}^i, x_{uv}^i, x_{vv}^i are linear combinations of x^i, x_u^i, x_v^i for all values of u and v, and consequently the osculating space is reduced from S_5 to S_2. If the space of the osculating planes is S_3, then two linear equations containing x^i, x_u^i, x_v^i, x_{uu}^i, x_{uv}^i, x_{vv}^i must exist. That is, the $x^i(u, v)$ must satisfy two linear second-order partial differential equations. It can be shown in this case that the surface S is either actually in S_3 and not S_n, or is a *developable surface*, which can be defined metrically as a surface with total curvature zero at every point. (See Section 9-7.) Projectively, a developable surface may be defined as a ruled surface for which the tangent plane does not vary as the point of tangency moves along a ruling.*

---

* For further results in projective differential geometry, the reader is referred to E. P. Lane, *Projective Differential Geometry of Curves and Surfaces* (University of Chicago Press, 1941).

EXERCISES

1. By duality the curve C with point coordinates $x^i(t)$ is determined as the envelope of the osculating planes to C. Let $u_i(t)\xi^i(t) = 0$ represent the osculating plane to C at t. Show that this plane is also given by

$$\begin{vmatrix} \xi^1 & \xi^2 & \xi^3 & \xi^4 \\ x^1 & x^2 & x^3 & x^4 \\ x^{1\prime} & x^{2\prime} & x^{3\prime} & x^{4\prime} \\ x^{1\prime\prime} & x^{2\prime\prime} & x^{3\prime\prime} & x^{4\prime\prime} \end{vmatrix} = 0,$$

so that the plane coordinates u_i are proportional to the cofactors of $x^{1\prime\prime\prime}$, $x^{2\prime\prime\prime}$, $x^{3\prime\prime\prime}$, $x^{4\prime\prime\prime}$ in the determinant

$$D(t) \equiv \begin{vmatrix} x^1 & \cdots & x^4 \\ x^{1\prime} & \cdots & x^{4\prime} \\ x^{1\prime\prime} & \cdots & x^{4\prime\prime} \\ x^{1\prime\prime\prime} & \cdots & x^{4\prime\prime\prime} \end{vmatrix}.$$

2. Show that the u_i in Exercise 1 may be taken as $(\partial/\partial x^{i\prime\prime\prime}) \log D$, and that the sum $x^{i\prime\prime\prime}(\partial/\partial x^{i\prime\prime\prime}) \log D = 1$; that is, $u_i x^{i\prime\prime\prime} = 1$.

3. Show from Exercise 1 that the relations

$$u_i x^i = 0, \quad u_i x^{i\prime} = 0, \quad u_i x^{i\prime\prime} = 0$$

obtain, and that these equations determine the ratios of the $u_i(t)$. (See Exercise 8 on p. 268.)

4. By successive differentiation of the equations in Exercise 3, and by use of the result in Exercise 2, show that the equations

$$u_i x^i = 0, \quad u_i' x^i = 0, \quad u_i'' x^i = 0, \quad u_i''' x^i = -1$$

hold.

   These equations determine x^i as functions of u_i and their derivatives.

   Remark: If the x^i satisfy a given differential equation of the fourth order, the corresponding differential equation which the u_i satisfy can be found. The latter is Lagrange's *adjoint* equation of the given differential equation.

5. Verify that the form of equation (29) is unchanged under a change of parameter $t = \phi(\tau)$ and also under a change of multiplying factor given by $\theta(t) = \rho(t)\psi(t)$.

10-6. The null system

In Section 10-4 it was seen that there are two types of polar correlation in S_3:

$$(33) \qquad\qquad \rho u_i = a_{ij} x^j, \qquad\qquad |a_{ij}| \neq 0.$$

One type (with $\lambda = 1$) has a symmetric matrix (a_{ij}). For this type it was shown that the incidence relation $u_i x^i = 0$ holds only for points on the quadric $a_{ij} x^i x^j = 0$. The other type, with $\lambda = -1$, has a skew-symmetric matrix (a_{ij}). It will be seen that a cubic curve in S_3 plays the role of the quadric for this type.

Multiply both sides of (33) by x^i and sum on i to have

$$(34) \qquad \rho u_i x^i = x^i a_{ij} x^j = a_{ij} x^i x^j \equiv 0.$$

The reader should verify that the sum $a_{ij} x^i x^j$ is identically zero by virtue of the fact that $a_{ij} = -a_{ji}$. It follows that $u_i x^i = 0$ for all points x^i in S_3. Hence, in a polar correlation with a skew-symmetric matrix, every point is incident with its corresponding plane. This type of correlation is called a *null system*, a designation used in the theory of statics as developed by Möbius.

It can be shown that any system of forces acting on a body can be replaced by an equivalent system consisting of a single force and a couple with its axis along the line of the single force (the *central axis* of Poinsot). A line l through a point P of the central axis and perpendicular to the central axis is such that the sum of the moments of all the forces of the system about the line is zero. For this reason the line l is called a null line, and the plane through P perpendicular to the central axis is called a null plane. It can be shown that the correspondence between points of space and their null planes is a correlation with a skew-symmetric matrix.*

Any property of correlations of the first type which does not depend upon the symmetry of the matrix (a_{ij}) is also a property of correlations of the second type. For instance, if a point $P(x^i)$ moves along a line l through the points y^i and z^i, with $x^i = y^i + \lambda z^i$, then its polar plane p is given, from (33), by

$$\rho u_i = a_{ij}(y^i + \lambda z^i),$$

so that, as λ varies, the polar plane p of P turns about the line l' of intersection of the polar planes $a_{ij} y^i x^j = 0$ and $a_{ij} z^i x^j = 0$ of the points y^i and z^i. The lines l and l' are conjugate lines in the null polarity. Note that the polar plane of y^i contains y^i and l', and the polar plane of z^i contains z^i and l'. If l and l' coincide they are called *self-polar*. (See Exercise 2.)

The Cubic Curve in S_3

In Section 10-4 the conic in S_2 was generalized to the quadric in S_3. But, instead of generalizing the conic (a curved space V_1 of one dimension) in S_2 to a quadric (a curved space V_2 of two dimensions) in S_3, it is possible to generalize the conic in S_2 to a cubic curve (V_1) in S_3. This will be done next in order to exhibit the null polarity relative to a cubic curve in S_3.

The conic in S_2 can be determined by specifying the point (or line) coordinates as the ratios of three polynomials of the second degree in a parameter t. By choosing a particular coordinate system it was seen in Section 8-2 that the conic can be represented in the simple form $x^1 : x^2 : x^3 = t^2 : t : 1$. In a similar manner the cubic in S_3 is given by

$$\rho x^i = \phi^i(t), \qquad\qquad i = 1, \cdots, 4,$$

---

* See, for instance, S. L. Loney, *Statics* (Cambridge University Press, 1924), p. 226.

where the $\phi^i(t)$ are cubic polynomials in the parameter t. By a particular choice of coordinates the cubic is represented more simply by

(35) $$x^1:x^2:x^3:x^4 = t^3:t^2:t:1.$$

It follows from (35) that

$$\frac{x^1}{x^2} = \frac{x^2}{x^3} = \frac{x^3}{x^4} = t,$$

so that the cubic (35) lies on each of the three quadric surfaces given by

(36) $$(x^3)^2 = x^2x^4, \quad x^2x^3 = x^1x^4, \quad (x^2)^2 = x^1x^3.$$

Because two quadric surfaces intersect in a quartic curve, the residual intersection of the first two quadrics, for instance, in (36) must be a straight line. Observe that the line of intersection of the planes $x^1 = 0$, $x^2 = 0$ lies entirely on both the second and third quadrics in (36) but has only the point $(0:0:0:1)$ of intersection with the first quadric—that is, the point where $t = 0$ on the cubic curve (35).

In the Example of Section 10-5 the equation of the osculating plane to the cubic (35) at any point t on it was found to be

(37) $$\xi^1 - 3t\xi^2 + 3(t)^2\xi^3 - (t)^3\xi^4 = 0.$$

It is readily shown that the plane (37) intersects the cubic in no other point. If $Q(\xi_1^i)$ is any point in space (not on the cubic curve), substitution of ξ_1^i for ξ^i in (37) yields a cubic equation in t, which shows that through Q there are three osculating planes to the cubic curve. If t_1, t_2, t_3 are the values of the parameter t at these three points P_1, P_2, P_3 of osculation on the cubic, one has

(38) $$\xi_1^1 - 3t_i\xi_1^2 + 3(t_i)^2\xi_1^3 - (t_i)^3\xi_1^4 = 0, \qquad i = 1, 2, 3.$$

The equation of the plane determined by the three points P_i is

(39) $$\begin{vmatrix} \xi^1 & \xi^2 & \xi^3 & \xi^4 \\ t_1^3 & t_1^2 & t_1 & 1 \\ t_2^3 & t_2^2 & t_2 & 1 \\ t_3^3 & t_3^2 & t_3 & 1 \end{vmatrix} = 0.$$

In order to use the conditions (38), multiply the fourth column in (39) by ξ_1^1, and then subtract $3\xi_1^2$ times the third column from the fourth column, add $3\xi_1^3$ times the second column to the fourth column, and, finally, subtract ξ_1^4 times the first column from the fourth column. The equation (39) reduces, by virtue of (38), to the form

(40) $$\xi_1^4\xi^1 - 3\xi_1^3\xi^2 + 3\xi_1^2\xi^3 - \xi_1^1\xi^4 = 0.$$

It is readily verified that the plane (40) through P_1, P_2, P_3 also contains the point $Q(\xi_1^i)$. This proves the

THEOREM: *The plane through the points of contact P_1, P_2, P_3 of the three osculating planes to a cubic curve in S_3 through a point Q not on the curve*

contains the point Q; and the osculating planes to the cubic curve at P_1, P_2, P_3 *intersect in the point Q.*

By virtue of this theorem a null system is established relative to a given cubic curve in S_3. To a plane q there corresponds in q the point Q, which is the intersection of the osculating planes to the cubic at the points P_1, P_2, P_3 where q intersects the cubic. To a point M in space there corresponds the plane m (through M) which is determined by the three points of osculation of the three osculating planes through M to the cubic. In particular, if M is on the cubic, the plane m corresponding to M is the osculating plane to the cubic at M. Thus, just as the quadric is self-conjugate under the polar correlation with symmetric matrix, the cubic in S_3 is self-conjugate under the polar correlation with skew-symmetric matrix. The correlation by which any point ξ_1^i corresponds to the plane (40) with plane coordinates u_i is given by

(41)
$$
\begin{aligned}
\rho u_1 &= \xi_1^4, \\
\rho u_2 &= -3\xi_1^3, \\
\rho u_3 &= 3\xi_1^2, \\
\rho u_4 &= -\xi_1^1,
\end{aligned}
$$

which has the skew-symmetric matrix

$$
\begin{pmatrix}
0 & 0 & 0 & 1 \\
0 & 0 & -3 & 0 \\
0 & 3 & 0 & 0 \\
-1 & 0 & 0 & 0
\end{pmatrix}.
$$

Focal Point Locus

A developable surface may be defined as the envelope of a one-parameter family of planes. If $f(x^1, x^2, x^3; t) = 0$ represents the family of planes, then $f = 0$ and $\partial f/\partial t = 0$ are two planes which intersect in a generator (*characteristic line*) of the developable surface enveloped by the family of planes. [Compare this with the envelope of a line in the plane discussed in Section 4-3 (p. 79) and with Exercise 7 in Section 1-2 (p. 4).] The planes given by $f = 0$, $\partial f/\partial t = 0$, and $\partial^2 f/\partial t^2 = 0$ determine a point (called the *focal point*) on the characteristic line, or generator, of the developable surface. The locus of the focal points as t varies is a curve called the *cuspidal edge* (or *edge of regression*) of the developable surface.

Let it be required to find the cuspidal edge of the developable surface enveloped by the family of planes (37) which osculate the cubic (35). The equations $f = 0$, $\partial f/\partial t = 0$, $\partial^2 f/\partial t^2 = 0$ in this instance are equivalent to

(42)
$$
\begin{aligned}
\xi^1 - 3(t)\xi^2 + 3(t)^2\xi^3 - (t)^3\xi^4 &= 0, \\
\xi^2 - 2(t)\,\xi^3 + (t)^2\xi^4 &= 0, \\
\xi^3 - (t)\,\xi^4 &= 0,
\end{aligned}
$$

the solutions of which are given by

$$\xi^1:\xi^2:\xi^3:\xi^4 = (t)^3:(t)^2:t:1.$$

Hence, the cubic (35), a point locus in S_3, is seen to be the locus of the focal points of the osculating planes to the cubic. The locus of the characteristic lines of the osculating planes can be shown to be the developable surface generated by the tangent lines to the cubic.

10-7. Line coordinates

The coordinates x^i of a point, and the coordinates u_i of a plane have been used in this chapter. The coordinates of a line in S_3 will now be introduced. This can apparently be effected in two ways, because a line is determined either as the join of two points x_1^i, x_2^i or as the intersection of two planes u_i^1, u_i^2. Observe that the matrix

$$(43) \qquad \begin{pmatrix} x_1^1 & x_1^2 & x_1^3 & x_1^4 \\ x_2^1 & x_2^2 & x_2^3 & x_2^4 \end{pmatrix}$$

of the coordinates of $P_1(x_1^i)$ and $P_2(x_2^i)$ in S_3 determines twelve second-order determinants, denoted by

$$(44) \qquad p^{ij} \equiv x_1^i x_2^j - x_1^j x_2^i, \qquad\qquad i, j = 1, \cdots, 4.$$

However, note that because $p^{ij} = -p^{ji}$, the twelve quantities can be reduced to the six coordinates

$$(45) \qquad p^{12}, \quad p^{13}, \quad p^{14}, \quad p^{34}, \quad p^{42}, \quad p^{23}$$

of the line $P_1 P_2$. Plücker called them *ray coordinates*. Given two points P_1 and P_2, the coordinates (45) are determined. However, given six quantities p^{ij}, they may not be coordinates of a line. A line in S_3 depends upon four parameters. Therefore, the six quantities (45), considered as homogeneous coordinates, must satisfy one condition. This can be found as follows. The determinant

$$(46) \qquad \begin{vmatrix} x_1^1 & x_1^2 & x_1^3 & x_1^4 \\ x_2^1 & x_2^2 & x_2^3 & x_2^4 \\ x_1^1 & x_1^2 & x_1^3 & x_1^4 \\ x_2^1 & x_2^2 & x_2^3 & x_2^4 \end{vmatrix}$$

is clearly identically zero. The expansion of (46) by second-order minors yields

$$(47) \qquad \omega(p) \equiv p^{12}p^{34} + p^{13}p^{42} + p^{14}p^{23} = 0,$$

a ubiquitous relation for line coordinates p^{ij} in S_3.

It should be verified that any two distinct points on a line determine line coordinates which are proportional to those obtained for any other choice of two points on the line. To do this, let $x_\tau^{i'} = \alpha_\tau^\sigma x_\sigma^i$, with $\sigma, \tau = 1, 2$, be two distinct points on the join of x_1^i and x_2^i, so that $\delta \equiv |\alpha_\tau^\sigma| \neq 0$. One has, from (44),

$$p^{ij'} = x_1^{i'} x_2^{j'} - x_1^{j'} x_2^{i'} = \alpha_1^\sigma x_\sigma^i \alpha_2^\rho x_\rho^j - \alpha_1^\sigma x_\sigma^j \alpha_2^\rho x_\rho^i$$

$$= (\alpha_1^1 \alpha_2^2 - \alpha_2^1 \alpha_1^2)(x_1^i x_2^j - x_1^j x_2^i) = \delta p^{ij}.$$

Hence, line coordinates are determined up to a nonzero proportionality factor
The matrix (p^{ij}) of the coordinates p^{ij} has the form

$$(48) \qquad (p^{ij}) \equiv \begin{pmatrix} 0 & p^{12} & p^{13} & p^{14} \\ -p^{12} & 0 & p^{23} & p^{24} \\ -p^{13} & -p^{23} & 0 & p^{34} \\ -p^{14} & -p^{24} & -p^{34} & 0 \end{pmatrix},$$

and the determinant $|p^{ij}|$ of the matrix (48) has the value

$$(p^{12}p^{34} + p^{13}p^{42} + p^{14}p^{23})^2 \equiv \omega^2(p).$$

Axis Coordinates

Now consider a line l determined as the intersection of the planes π_1 and π_2 with coordinates u_i^1 and u_i^2. The line coordinates of l (called *axis coordinates* by Plücker) may be taken as the six second-order determinants

$$q_{ij} \equiv u_i^1 u_j^2 - u_j^1 u_i^2$$

from the matrix

$$\begin{pmatrix} u_1^1 & u_2^1 & u_3^1 & u_4^1 \\ u_1^2 & u_2^2 & u_3^2 & u_4^2 \end{pmatrix}.$$

Again, it can be shown that any other two distinct planes through l determine coordinates proportional to q_{ij}. Also, the q_{ij} satisfy the relation (47); that is,

$$(49) \qquad \Omega(q) \equiv q_{12}q_{34} + q_{13}q_{42} + q_{14}q_{23} = 0.$$

Because a line l is determined either by p^{ij} or by q_{ij}, there must be some relation connecting p^{ij} and q_{ij}. In order to discover it, note that the points x_1^i, x_2^i determining l are incident with the planes u_i^1, u_i^2 which determine l. Hence,

$$(50) \qquad u_i^1 x_1^i = 0, \quad u_i^1 x_2^i = 0, \quad u_i^2 x_1^i = 0, \quad u_i^2 x_2^i = 0, \qquad i = 1, \cdots, 4.$$

Multiply the first and third of these equations by u_j^2 and u_j^1, respectively, and then subtract to find $x_1^i q_{ij} = 0$. Similarly, from the second and fourth equations it follows that $x_2^i q_{ij} = 0$. If j is taken as 1, the last two equations give

$$x_1^2 q_{21} + x_1^3 q_{31} + x_1^4 q_{41} = 0,$$
$$x_2^2 q_{21} + x_2^3 q_{31} + x_2^4 q_{41} = 0.$$

Now solve for the ratios of the q's to obtain

$$(51) \qquad q_{12} : q_{13} : q_{14} = p^{34} : p^{42} : p^{23}.$$

It can be shown in a similar way that the complementary indices in (51) can be interchanged. Thus, one finds that

$$(52) \qquad p^{12} : p^{13} : p^{14} : p^{34} : p^{42} : p^{23} = q_{34} : q_{42} : q_{23} : q_{12} : q_{13} : q_{14}.$$

EXAMPLE 1

Find the coordinates of the points A_i, with $i = 1, \cdots, 4$, where the line l with coordinates p^{ij} intersects the faces opposite the vertices P_i in the tetrahedron of reference.

Solution: The given line is the intersection of the planes $u_i^1 x^i = 0$ and $u_i^2 x^i = 0$, and the point A_1 is in the plane $x^1 = 0$. Solve the three equations for the ratios

$$x^1:x^2:x^3:x^4 = 0:q_{34}:q_{42}:q_{23} = 0:p_{12}:p_{13}:p_{14}.$$

Hence, the coordinates of A_1 are given by the entries of the first row of the matrix (p^{ij}) in (48). The coordinates of A_2, A_3, A_4 are found, similarly, to be given by the second, third, and fourth rows, respectively, of the matrix (p^{ij}). (For the dual of this Example, see Exercise 1.)

EXAMPLE 2

Show that the line coordinates of the edges $P_i P_j$ of the tetrahedron of reference are given by $p^{ij} = 1$ with the others all zero.

Solution: Consider the points $P_1(1:0:0:0)$, $P_2(0:1:0:0)$. The only nonvanishing determinant in the matrix

$$\begin{pmatrix} 1 & 0 & 0 & 0 \\ 0 & 1 & 0 & 0 \end{pmatrix}$$

is $p^{12} = 1$. In a similar way, the statement is verified for the remaining edges.

EXAMPLE 3

Show that if the line $l(p^{ij})$ lies in the plane $x^1 = 0$, then $p^{12} = p^{13} = p^{14} = 0$ and the remaining coordinates of l are arbitrary.

Solution: The line l is determined by the points

$$\begin{pmatrix} 0 & x_1^2 & x_1^3 & x_1^4 \\ 0 & x_2^2 & x_2^3 & x_2^4 \end{pmatrix},$$

where the nonzero entries are arbitrary. Hence, $p^{12} = p^{13} = p^{14} = 0$, and the remaining line coordinates are arbitrary. Observe that the line $l(p^{ij})$ lies in the plane with equation $x^\alpha = 0$, with $\alpha = 1, \cdots, 4$, if and only if $p^{\alpha\beta} = 0$, with $\beta = 1, \cdots, 4$. If l lies in both $x^1 = 0$ and $x^2 = 0$, then all of p^{ij} are zero with the exception of p^{34}. The line l is therefore the edge $P_3 P_4$ of the tetrahedron of reference.

It may be noticed in Example 3 above that

$$p^{ij}u_j \equiv p^{i1}u_1 + p^{i2}u_2 + p^{i3}u_3 + p^{i4}u_4$$

reduces to $p^{i1}u_1$ for the plane $x^1 = 0$ with coordinates $[u_1:0:0:0]$. But, since $p^{11} = 0$ and $p^{12} = p^{13} = p^{14} = 0$, the conditions for incidence may be written as $p^{ij}u_j = 0$, with $i = 1, \cdots, 4$. This condition will now be seen to hold for incidence of a line p^{ij} with any plane u_i. Consider the sum on j

$$p^{ij}u_j \equiv (x_1^i x_2^j - x_1^j x_2^i)u_j \equiv x_1^i(u_j x_2^j) - x_2^i(u_j x_1^j).$$

If the points x_1^i and x_2^i of l are in the plane u_i, then $u_j x_1^j = 0$ and $u_j x_2^j = 0$, and consequently $p^{ij}u_j = 0$ for $i = 1, \cdots, 4$. Conversely, if $p^{ij}u_j = 0$, this means that the point coordinates $(p^{i1}, p^{i2}, p^{i3}, p^{i4})$ are incident with the plane $[u_j]$. It may be verified that not all of p^{ij}, with $j = 1, \cdots, 4$, are zero for at least two values of i, so that two points of l do lie in $\pi(u_i)$. Hence, the line $l(p^{ij})$ is incident with the plane u_i if and only if $p^{ij}u_j = 0$ for $i = 1, \cdots, 4$.

A dual argument shows that the line l is incident with the point x^i if and only if $q_{ij}x^j = 0$ for $i = 1, \cdots, 4$.

It is shown next that two lines l and $\bar{l}$ with coordinates p^{ij} and $\bar{p}^{ij}$ intersect if and only if

(53) $\omega(p, \bar{p}) \equiv p^{12}\bar{p}^{34} + p^{13}\bar{p}^{42} + p^{14}\bar{p}^{23} + \bar{p}^{12}p^{34} + \bar{p}^{13}p^{42} + \bar{p}^{14}p^{23} = 0.$

Equation (53) may be expressed by

(54) $$e_{ijkl}p^{ij}\bar{p}^{kl} = 0,$$

where e_{ijkl} is defined to be $+1$ or -1 according as i, j, k, l take on values which are an even or odd permutation of the numbers 1, 2, 3, 4, and e_{ijkl} is zero if any two of the subscripts are equal. Thus, for instance, $e_{2314} = 1$, $e_{3214} = -1$, and $e_{2344} = 0$. It is to be noted that the indicated sum in (54) produces a nonzero factor times $\omega(p, \bar{p})$, but this does not affect the vanishing or nonvanishing of the form in (53).

In order to develop the condition (53) that two lines intersect, suppose that l is determined by x_1^i and x_2^i and $\bar{l}$ by $\bar{x}_1^i$ and $\bar{x}_2^i$. If l and $\bar{l}$ intersect, the four points must be coplanar, the condition for which is the vanishing of the determinant of the four sets of coordinates; that is,

$$e_{ijkl}x_1^i x_2^j \bar{x}_1^k \bar{x}_2^l = 0,$$

which is equivalent to equation (53).

Observe that the condition (47) under which the numbers p^{ij} are coordinates of a line can be written as

(55) $$\omega(p) \equiv e_{ijkl}p^{ij}p^{kl} = 0.$$

Equation (53) may be called the *polarized* form of (55). The alternative form of (55) for the complementary coordinates q_{ij} is

$$\omega(q) \equiv e^{ijkl}q_{ij}q_{kl} = 0,$$

in which the definition of e^{ijkl} is the same as that for e_{ijkl}.

Systems of Lines

Because the six coordinates p^{ij} of a line l in S_3 are homogeneous and satisfy the relation (55), a line in S_3 has four degrees of freedom. Ordinary space is therefore four-dimensional in lines. The lines whose coordinates satisfy an equation given by, say, $f(p^{12}, p^{13}, p^{14}, p^{34}, p^{42}, p^{23}) = 0$, where the function f does not contain the form $\omega(p)$ in (55) as a factor, have three degrees of freedom. The set of lines satisfying $f = 0$ is called a *complex* of lines—a linear complex if f is linear, a quadratic complex if f is of the second degree, etc. The set of lines satisfying two equations $f = 0$, $g = 0$ constitute a *congruence* of lines. The lines of a congruence have two degrees of freedom. Finally, the assemblage of lines which satisfy three conditions $f = 0$, $g = 0$, $h = 0$ is called a *ruled surface*. Its lines have one degree of freedom.

The Linear Complex

The simplest form for a complex is that for which the function f is linear in the coordinates p^{ij}. Let the linear equation of the complex be written as

$$(56) \qquad \omega(c, p) \equiv c_{12}p^{34} + c_{13}p^{42} + c_{14}p^{23} + c_{34}p^{12} + c_{42}p^{13} + c_{23}p^{14} = 0.$$

Two cases arise. The first is the rather special one in which $\omega(c, c) = 0$; this means that the constant coefficients c_{ij} in (56) are themselves coordinates of a line. The further condition $\omega(c, p) = 0$ in (56) means that all lines of the complex intersect the line c. Thus, the configuration of all lines which meet a given line in S_3 is a *special* complex. (See Exercise 5 on p. 262.)

The second case is that for which $\omega(c, c) \neq 0$. Write equation (56) in the form

$$\omega(c, p) \equiv e_{ijkl}c_{ij}p^{kl} = e_{ijkl}c_{ij}(x_1^k x_2^l - x_1^l x_2^k)$$

$$= (e_{ijkl}c_{ij}x_1^k - e_{ijlk}c_{ij}x_1^k)x_2^l = (e_{ijkl}c_{ij} - e_{ijlk}c_{ij})x_1^k x_2^l = 0.$$

This is of the form $(d_{kl}x_1^k)x_2^l = 0$, which can be interpreted to mean that the plane with coordinates $u_l \equiv d_{kl}x_1^k$ contains the point x_2^l. The correspondence $u_l = d_{kl}x_1^k$ with skew-symmetric matrix (d_{kl}) is the null system of Section 10-6.

Line complexes of order higher than the first will not be treated here. Mention is made, however, of two interesting quadratic complexes—the complex of lines tangent to a quadric surface and the tetrahedral complex composed of the lines which meet the faces of a tetrahedron in four points with a constant cross ratio. The determination of the equations of these quadratic complexes is left to the Exercises.

Line Congruences

The totality of lines which depend upon two parameters is a line congruence. It is also called a *rectilinear* congruence to distinguish it from a congruence of curves or other geometric loci. Instances of line congruences are: (1) the intersection of two complexes, (2) the lines of a bundle, (3) all the lines of a plane, (4) the totality of lines meeting two skew lines, and (5) the lines obtained by specifying a direction in space at each point of a surface. Relative to the last instance it is an interesting problem in differential geometry to find the differential equations of the curves on the surface with the property that the osculating plane at every point contains the specified direction at the point. These are the *union curves* on the surface relative to the specified congruence.* In case the congruence of lines is normal to the surface the union curves become the geodesic curves on the surface.

Consider the congruence of lines common to two linear complexes; that is, let the coordinates p^{ij} of a variable line satisfy the two equations

$$(57) \qquad\qquad \omega(a, p) = 0, \quad \omega(b, p) = 0$$

---

* For a discussion of them see the author's *Tensor and Vector Analysis, with Applications to Differential Geometry* (Ronald, New York, 1962).

of the form of equation (56). It is evident that the intersection of the complexes (57) belongs to every complex of the pencil $\omega(a, p) + \lambda\omega(b, p) = 0$, which can be expressed by

$$e_{ijkl}(a^{ij} + \lambda b^{ij})p^{kl} = 0.$$

The values of λ for which the complexes of the pencil are special are the values of λ for which $a^{ij} + \lambda b^{ij}$ are coordinates of a line. The condition for this is

$$e_{ijkl}(a^{ij} + \lambda b^{ij})(a^{kl} + \lambda b^{kl}) = 0,$$

or

$$e_{ijkl}(a^{ij}a^{kl} + 2\lambda a^{ij}b^{kl} + \lambda^2 b^{ij}b^{kl}) = 0,$$

or

(58) $$\omega(a, a) + 2\omega(a, b)\lambda + \omega(b, b)\lambda^2 = 0.$$

If $\omega^2(a, b) - \omega(a, a)\omega(b, b) > 0$ there are two real and distinct values of λ, to each of which there corresponds a special complex of the pencil. If these two complexes are given by (57), one sees that the congruence (57) is the set of lines meeting the axes of two special complexes.

If the quadratic (58) has coincident roots there is only one special complex, with an axis *l*. In this case, the lines of the congruence are the totality of lines which intersect the axis *l* and belong to a second complex.

Linear Combinations of Lines

A novel situation arises from the fact that the numbers p^{ij} must satisfy the quadratic relation $\omega(p) = 0$ if the p^{ij} are to be coordinates of a line *l*. A linear combination of a set of lines may not be a line. To see this, consider first two lines l_1, l_2 with coordinates p_1^{ij}, p_2^{ij}. The linear combination $\bar{p}^{ij} \equiv \lambda^\sigma p_\sigma^{ij}$, with $\sigma = 1, 2$, gives a set of coordinates of a line if and only if $\omega(\bar{p}) = 0$; that is,

$$e_{ijkl}\bar{p}^{ij}\bar{p}^{kl} = 0,$$

or

$$e_{ijkl}\lambda^\sigma p_\sigma^{ij}\lambda^\tau p_\tau^{kl} = 0,$$

which is the quadratic relation in λ^1, λ^2 given by

(59) $$(e_{ijkl}p_\sigma^{ij}p_\tau^{kl})\lambda^\sigma\lambda^\tau = 0.$$

The coefficient of $(\lambda^1)^2$ is zero because the p_1^{ij} are coordinates of a line. Similarly, the coefficient of $(\lambda^2)^2$ is zero. Hence, (57) is satisfied for arbitrary λ^1, λ^2 if and only if

$$e_{ijkl}p_1^{ij}p_2^{kl} = 0,$$

which means that the lines l_1 and l_2 must intersect. Therefore a linear combination of two lines l_1, l_2 is a line if and only if the lines l_1, l_2 intersect. If l_1 and l_2 do not intersect, then λ^1 or λ^2 must be zero. In this case the only lines linearly dependent upon two skew lines are the lines themselves. This sort of discussion can be continued relative to $\bar{p}^{ij} = \lambda^\sigma p_\sigma^{ij}$ with $\sigma > 2$. Further information on configurations of lines in S_3 appears in the next section, where a correspondence between lines of S_3 and points of S_5 is explored.

10-8. The hyperquadric in S_5

Before introducing the principal object of study in this section—the correspondence between ruled three-space and points of a quadratic manifold in S_5—it is well to prepare the way by discussing some similar but less complex correspondences between point sets of one space and certain loci of another space.

Binary Quadratic Forms and a Conic

It was seen in Chapter 3 that the form

(60) $$f(x^1, x^2) \equiv a_{ij}x^i x^j \equiv a_{11}(x^1)^2 + 2a_{12}x^1 x^2 + a_{22}(x^2)^2$$

vanishes for two points P_1, P_2 on a line (S_1). The ratios of the ordered set of coefficients $(a_{11}:a_{12}:a_{22})$ in f determine a point P in a projective space S_2. Thus, one observes that the point P in S_2 is the image of the pair of points P_1, P_2 in S_1. In order to see more of the structure of the correspondence, consider any point Σ on S_1 as given by $x^1 + \sigma x^2 = 0$. If this point is considered as two coincident points, it is represented by $(x^1 + \sigma x^2)^2 = (x^1)^2 + 2\sigma x^1 x^2 + \sigma^2(x^2)^2 = 0$. Hence, the point ξ^i in S_2 to which the double point Σ corresponds is given by

(61) $$\xi^1:\xi^2:\xi^3 = 1:\sigma:(\sigma)^2.$$

There is a set of ∞^1 points on S_1 obtained by letting σ vary. On eliminating σ from (61), one obtains the conic

(62) $$C: \qquad (\xi^2)^2 \equiv \xi^1 \xi^3$$

as the image in S_2 of the variable point $(\sigma:-1)$ on S_1, with each point on S_1 considered as a double point. The conic C in S_2 may be obtained otherwise by considering the totality of forms f (that is, the totality of points in S_2) and asking for the set of points in S_2 which correspond to double points on S_1. All points in S_2 for which $a_{12}^2 - a_{11}a_{22} = 0$ satisfy the condition. This is the conic $(\xi^2)^2 = \xi^1 \xi^3$ in (62). A projectivity which carries pairs of points on S_1 into pairs of points on S_1 effects a projectivity in S_2 which leaves the points of the conic C invariant. Thus the projective geometry of pairs of points on a line S_1 is equivalent to the geometry of a space S_2 under the group of projectivities which leave a conic invariant.

To the pencil of pairs of points on S_1 given by $(a_{ij} + \lambda b_{ij})x^i x^j = 0$, there corresponds in S_2 the line of points determined by the points $F(a_{11}:a_{12}:a_{22})$ and $G(b_{11}:b_{12}:b_{22})$. The line FG meets the conic C in two points R and S, which correspond to double points on S_1. The values of λ corresponding to R and S are roots of the equation

$$(a_{12} + \lambda b_{12})^2 = (a_{11} + \lambda b_{11})(a_{22} + \lambda b_{22}).$$

If R and S coincide, then the line FG is tangent to C. Hence, the line FG is determined in this case by the point F (pair $f = 0$) and one of two double points on C where R and S coincide.

Now let R and S be distinct. Point R corresponds to a double point D on S_1, and S to a different double point E on S_1. The tangents to C at R and S intersect in a point H, which corresponds to the pair D, E on S_1.

This last result can be seen otherwise as follows. Observe that if $(\sigma: -1)$ is a point on S_1 given by $f = 0$, then, from (60),

$$(63) \qquad f(\sigma, -1) = a_{11}\sigma^2 - 2a_{12}\sigma + a_{22} = 0.$$

If a_{11}, a_{12}, a_{22} are written as ξ^1, ξ^2, ξ^3, equation (63) is recognized as the line

$$(64) \qquad \sigma^2\xi^1 - 2\sigma\xi^2 + \xi^3 = 0$$

in S_2 which is determined by the point $(\sigma: -1)$, considered as a double point, and one other point in S_2. The envelope of the line (64) as σ varies is the conic C. Any two tangents of the form of (64) intersect in a point H, which is the image of the pair of double points with each considered singly. It is evident that points inside C correspond to pairs of points with complex coordinates on S_1.

Binary N-ic to a Curve in S_n

The foregoing discussion will now be generalized by considering an ordered set of n points on S_1 instead of a pair of points. The vanishing of the binary n-ic form

$$(65) \qquad f(x^1, x^2) \equiv a_1 x^{1^n} + na_2 x^{1^{n-1}}x^2 + \cdots + a_{n+1}x^{2^n}$$

determines n points (real or complex) on S_1. The coefficients $a_1, a_2, \cdots, a_{n+1}$ (taken without their accompanying binomial coefficients) are considered as coordinates of a point in a projective space S_n. The geometry of the binary n-ic is that of sets of n points on S_1, and this will be seen to be equivalent to the geometry in S_n under a group of projectivities which leave invariant a certain curve C of order n in S_n. Note that two forms f and g with proportional coefficients have the same geometry. The totality of binary n-ic forms corresponds to the totality of points in S_n. As in the case of pairs of points, one may consider each point on S_1 as n coincident points. The form f for such a set of n points can be written as

$$(x^1 + \sigma x^2)^n \equiv x^{1^n} + \sigma n x^{1^{n-1}}x^2 + \cdots + \sigma^n x^{2^n},$$

so that the point $P(\xi^i)$ in S_n has coordinates given by

$$(66) \qquad \xi^1 : \xi^2 : \cdots : \xi^{n+1} = 1 : \sigma : \cdots : \sigma^n.$$

The locus of the image point P in S_n as σ varies on S_1 is the curve C with the parametric equations (66). Thus, a one-to-one correspondence is established between the points of S_1 (considered as coincident sets of n points) and the points of the curve C in S_n. The condition under which a general form f contain the point $(x^1 : x^2) \equiv (\sigma : -1)$ is obtained by requiring that $(\sigma : -1)$ render $f = 0$ in (65). That is,

$$a_1 \sigma^n - n a_2 \sigma^{n-1} + \cdots + (-1)^{n+1} a_{n+1} = 0,$$

or

(67) $$\xi^1 \sigma^n - n \xi^2 \sigma^{n-1} + \cdots + (-1)^{n+1} \xi^{n+1} = 0,$$

with ξ^i written in plane of the a_i. Any hyperplane in S_n has an equation of the form

(68) $$u_i \xi^i = 0,$$

where the u_i are hyperplane coordinates. In general, the hyperplane (68) intersects the curve C in (66) at the n points given by the roots of

(69) $$u_1(1) + u_2(\sigma) + u_3(\sigma)^2 + \cdots + u_{n+1}(\sigma)^n = 0.$$

But equation (67) indicates that the hyperplane (68) has n equal roots at the point $(\sigma : -1)$ on C, so that the hyperplane osculates C at $(\sigma : -1)$. Now take a set F_n of n distinct points on S_1 with images $P_1, \cdots, P_n$ on C (with each of the n points considered to be positions at which n points coincide). The image of the set F_n is the point of intersection of the n osculating hyperplanes to C at the points $P_1, \cdots, P_n$. Here, as in the case of the binary quadratic, a projectivity on the points of S_1 induces a projectivity in S_n under which the curve C maps into itself. Thus, the geometry of S_n under a group of projectivities which leave C invariant is the projective geometry of sets of n points on a line. This sort of correspondence was introduced by Hesse (1811–1874) for binary forms of degree two. The general case of S_n was employed by Deruyts, Castelnuovo, and Comessatti.

Conics as Points in S_5

Another instance in which geometry in a higher space corresponds to and illuminates the geometry of a space of lower dimensionality is afforded by the correspondence between conics in S_2 and points of S_5. The six ordered coefficients

(70) $$(a_{11}, a_{22}, a_{33}, a_{23}, a_{31}, a_{12})$$

in the equation $f \equiv a_{ij} x^i x^j = 0$, with $i, j = 1, 2, 3$, of a conic C in S_2 may be considered as homogeneous coordinates of a point F in S_5. The pencil of conics $f + \lambda g = 0$, or $(a_{ij} + \lambda b_{ij}) x^i x^j = 0$, determined by $f = 0$ and $g \equiv b_{ij} x^i x^j = 0$ in S_2 is a line determined by the corresponding points F, G in S_5. In a similar way, one sees that the *net* of conics given by $f + \lambda g + \mu h = 0$, where $h \equiv c_{ij} x^i x^j$, corresponds to a two-dimensional linear subspace $S_2 \subset S_5$, and that sets of four and five base conics in S_2 determine linear subspaces of dimensionalities three and four, respectively, in S_5. According to the results obtained in the preceding instances of this section, it is to be expected that a general conic in S_2 corresponds to a general point of S_5, but that a composite conic in S_2 is related to a special kind of locus in S_5.

Let the ordered set of coefficients in (70) be written more simply as $(\xi^1, \cdots, \xi^6)$, and let the conic C be two coincident lines with the equation

$$(71) \qquad (\alpha_\sigma x^\sigma)^2 = 0, \qquad \qquad \sigma = 1, 2, 3.$$

The ordered coefficients in (71) are given by

$$(72) \qquad \xi^1 : \xi^2 : \xi^3 : \xi^4 : \xi^5 : \xi^6 = \alpha_1^2 : \alpha_2^2 : \alpha_3^2 : \alpha_2\alpha_3 : \alpha_3\alpha_1 : \alpha_1\alpha_2.$$

Because only two essential parameters are involved, the ξ^i in (72) are coordinates of points on a surface V_2 in S_5. Hence, the totality of double lines in S_2 correspond to a surface (called the Veronese surface) in S_5.

Next, let the conic C be two distinct lines in S_2, given by

$$(73) \qquad (\alpha_\sigma x^\sigma)(\beta_\tau x^\tau) = 0, \qquad \qquad \sigma, \tau = 1, 2, 3.$$

The ordered coefficients in (73) are

$$(74) \quad \xi^1 : \xi^2 : \cdots : \xi^6 = 2\alpha_1\beta_1 : 2\alpha_2\beta_2 : 2\alpha_3\beta_3 : (\alpha_2\beta_3 + \alpha_3\beta_2) : (\alpha_3\beta_1 + \alpha_1\beta_3) : (\alpha_1\beta_2 + \alpha_2\beta_1).$$

It is possible to eliminate the four essential parameters in (74) to obtain the cubic locus

$$\xi^1\xi^2\xi^3 + 2\xi^4\xi^5\xi^6 - \xi^1\xi^{4^2} - \xi^2\xi^{5^2} - \xi^3\xi^{6^2} = 0,$$

which is a cubic hypersurface in S_5. Thus, one has the result that the totality of pairs of intersecting lines in a plane is represented by the totality of points on a cubic hypersurface in S_5.

Line Systems in S_3 to Loci in S_5

A final example is adduced to illustrate again the concept of mapping a set of geometric objects of one space into a subspace (an algebraic *variety* or *manifold*) of a higher-dimensional space. This example is that of the representation of lines in S_3 as points of a hyperquadric in S_5. Let the coordinates

$$(p^{12} : p^{13} : p^{14} : p^{34} : p^{42} : p^{23})$$

of a line in S_3, as defined in (44), be written as $\xi^1 : \cdots : \xi^6$. Then the equation (47) takes the form

$$(75) \qquad \omega(\xi) \equiv \xi^1\xi^4 + \xi^2\xi^5 + \xi^3\xi^6 = 0,$$

which represents a hyperquadric Q in S_5. Thus, a one-to-one correspondence is established between the lines of S_3 and the points of Q in S_5. Because the equation (56) of a linear complex in S_3 takes the form

$$(76) \qquad \omega(c, \xi) \equiv c_i\xi^i = 0, \qquad \qquad i = 1, \cdots, 6,$$

which represents a hyperplane in S_5, it is evident that a linear complex (in which a line has three degrees of freedom) in S_3 corresponds to the three-dimensional intersection of a hyperplane and the hyperquadric in S_5. A linear congruence (two degrees of freedom) in S_3 is represented by the intersection of the hyperquadric Q with the three-dimensional intersection space of the two spaces S_4 and S_4', which correspond to the two linear complexes which contain the congruence in S_3. A ruled surface, being the intersection of three linear complexes in S_3, corresponds in S_5 to the curve in which the intersection space S_2 of three hyperplanes meets the hyperquadric Q. The geometry of configurations of lines in S_3 can be studied as the geometry of point loci of subspaces of the hyperquadric Q in S_5, and conversely.

The hyperquadric Q is nonsingular because the determinant of the matrix of coefficients in (75) is

$$\begin{vmatrix} 0 & 0 & 0 & 1 & 0 & 0 \\ 0 & 0 & 0 & 0 & 1 & 0 \\ 0 & 0 & 0 & 0 & 0 & 1 \\ 1 & 0 & 0 & 0 & 0 & 0 \\ 0 & 1 & 0 & 0 & 0 & 0 \\ 0 & 0 & 1 & 0 & 0 & 0 \end{vmatrix} = -1 \neq 0.$$

The polar space of any point $\bar{\xi}^i$ in S_5 relative to Q is given by

$$(77) \qquad \xi^1 \bar{\xi}^4 + \xi^2 \bar{\xi}^5 + \xi^3 \bar{\xi}^6 + \xi^4 \bar{\xi}^1 + \xi^5 \bar{\xi}^2 + \xi^6 \bar{\xi}^3 = 0,$$

which is a hyperplane S_4. The polar space of a line S_1 relative to Q is the intersection S_3 of two hyperplanes, and the polar space of a plane S_2 in S_5 is another plane—the intersection of three hyperplanes. Any two tangent hyperplanes to Q at points A and B intersect in a space S_3, which is the polar space of the line joining A and B. The ∞^1 tangent hyperplanes to Q at points of the conic in which a plane p intersects Q intersect in the plane S_2, which is the polar space of the plane p with respect to Q. In this generalized correlation between linear spaces and their polar spaces relative to Q, the points on Q (all of which represent lines in S_3) are incident with their corresponding polar (tangent) hyperplanes to Q.

In S_3 there are ∞^5 pencils of lines. This means that Q contains a system of ∞^5 lines. There are ∞^3 bundles of lines in S_3, which indicates that there are ∞^3 corresponding planes on Q. Also, there are ∞^3 planes of lines in S_3, indicating another set of ∞^3 planes on Q. Just as the quadric in S_3 was found to have two sets of line rulings, the hyperquadric Q has two sets of plane generators.

Because two bundles in S_3 always have a line in common (the join of the centers), any two planes of one system of plane generators on Q have a point in common. Likewise, because two planes in S_3 always have a line in common, any two planes of the complementary set of plane generators have a point in common. Whereas on a quadric in S_3 each point is the intersection of a unique line from each regulus, on the hyperquadric Q each line is the intersection of a unique plane from each of the sets of generating planes. Finally, as was stated before, a regulus in S_3 corresponds to the conic of intersection of Q and a plane p. The complementary regulus is then in correspondence with the conic in which the polar plane $\bar{p}$ of p intersects Q. This is true because a point on p and a point on $\bar{p}$ are in polar spaces, and the conjugate relation (77) holds, which is the condition (53) that the corresponding lines in S_3 intersect.

EXERCISES

1. As the dual of Example 1 in Section 10-7, show that the coordinates of the planes through the line l with coordinates q_{ij} and through the vertices P_i, with $i = 1, \cdots, 4$, of the tetrahedron of reference are given by the respective rows of the matrix (q_{ij}).

2. Prove that every line which intersects two distinct conjugate polar lines of a null polarity is self-polar.

3. (a) The points $A(1:0:0:\lambda)$, $B(0:1:\mu:0)$, $C(1:1:\nu:\nu)$ generate three lines α, β, γ in S_3 as λ, μ, ν vary. Find the equation of the plane ABC. (b) Now let α, β, γ be projectively related by the particular projectivities $\mu = \lambda - 1$, $\lambda\nu = 1$, and show that the plane ABC osculates the cubic curve, with the contact locus given by $\rho u_1 = \lambda(1 + \lambda - \lambda^2)$, $\rho u_2 = (\lambda - 1)(\lambda^2 - 1)$, $\rho u_3 = 1 - \lambda^2$, $\rho u_4 = \lambda^2 - \lambda - 1$. (c) Show further that this contact locus lies on the quadric surface with the equation $u_2 u_4 = u_3 u_4 + u_1 u_3$ in plane coordinates.

4. A particle A moves with unit speed on the line $2x = y = 2 - z$ from the point $(0, 0, 2)$ at time $t = 0$, a particle B moves with speed 2 from the point $(0, 0, -2)$ at $t = 0$ on the line $2x = -y = z + 2$, and a third particle C moves with speed $1/t^2$ from the point at infinity on the line $x = z = 0$. Show that the plane ABC through the particles osculates the cubic curve with homogeneous plane coordinates given by

$$\rho u_1 = 18 - 12t^2, \quad \rho u_2 = 8t^3 - 18t^2, \quad \rho u_3 = 8t^3 - 3t, \quad \rho u_4 = 8t^3 - 18t^2.$$

5. (a) Show that a cubic curve in S_3 is the intersection of ∞^2 quadric surfaces. (b) Conversely, if a cubic curve lies on a quadric surface, show that the quadric belongs to a net (two-parameter family) of quadrics.

6. Identify the lines for which (a) $p^{23} = 0$, (b) $p^{23} = p^{42} = 0$, (c) $p^{23} = p^{42} = p^{12} = 0$.

7. Determine the condition under which the line with coordinates p^{ij} contains the unit point $(1:1:1:1)$.

8. (a) Consider three linearly independent concurrent lines p, q, r in S_3. Show that the lines which are linearly dependent on p, q, r belong to the bundle determined by them. (b) State and prove the dual of part (a).

9. Verify that equation (47) of the fundamental hyperquadric Q in S_5 is transformed to

$$(x^1)^2 + x^{2^2} + x^{3^2} + x^{4^2} + x^{5^2} + x^{6^2} = 0$$

by the transformation

$$\rho x^1 = p^{12} + p^{34},$$
$$\rho x^2 = p^{13} + p^{42},$$
$$\rho x^3 = i(p^{13} - p^{42}),$$
$$\rho x^4 = p^{14} + p^{23},$$
$$\rho x^5 = i(p^{12} - p^{34}),$$
$$\rho x^6 = i(p^{14} - p^{23}).$$

(The x^i are called *Klein coordinates*.) What is the condition under which two lines x^i and $\bar{x}^i$ (in Klein coordinates) intersect?

10. Show that in euclidean three-space a special linear complex consists either of all lines intersecting a fixed line or of all lines parallel to a fixed plane. (Think of the two cases in which the axis of the complex is or is not in the plane at infinity.)

11. Take the equation of the quadric in S_3 in the form $a_i(x^i)^2 = 0$, with $i = 1, \cdots, 4$. Find the equation of the quadratic complex of the tangent lines to the quadric. *Suggestion:* Use the fact that a line p is tangent to the quadric if and only if p intersects its polar line $\bar{p}$ with respect to the quadric. Let p be determined by the points x_1^i and x_2^i and find the line coordinates of $\bar{p}$.

12. (a) Find the equation of a tetrahedral complex. *Hint:* Let any line p of the complex be determined by x_1^i and x_2^i. Now find the value of λ for which the variable point $x_1^i + \lambda x_2^i$ on p is in a face of the tetrahedron of reference. (b) Verify that this complex is self-dual by showing that the cross ratio of the intersections of p with the planes of the tetrahedron is equal to the cross ratio of the joins of p with the vertices of the tetrahedron.

13. The cross ratio of four planes of an axial pencil is the cross ratio of the four parametric values which determine the planes. Prove that the cross ratio of the points in which any transversal intersects the planes is equal to the cross ratio of the four planes.

14. The four points $A_1(1:1:1:1)$, $A_2(2:-1:2:3)$, $A_3(3:2:-1:1)$, $A_4(1:2:1:2)$ have the respective polar planes $\alpha_1[2:-1:3:-4]$, $\alpha_2[9:-3:6:-11]$, $\alpha_3[-1:3:2:-1]$, $\alpha_4[3:-2:7:-3]$ under the skew-symmetric correlation

$$
\begin{aligned}
\rho u_1 &= -x^2 + x^3 + 2x^4,\\
\rho u_2 &= x^1 - x^3 - x^4,\\
\rho u_3 &= -x^1 + x^2 + 3x^4,\\
\rho u_4 &= -2x^1 + x^2 - 3x^3.
\end{aligned}
$$

(a) Verify that the α_i are incident with A_i, for $i = 1, \cdots, 4$. (b) Verify that the intersection I_1 of α_2, α_3, α_4 is given by

$$
\begin{bmatrix}
9 & -3 & 6 & -11\\
-1 & 3 & 2 & -1\\
3 & -2 & 7 & -3
\end{bmatrix} \rightarrow I_1(53:29:1:36),
$$

that the join j_1 of A_2, A_3, A_4 is given by

$$
\begin{pmatrix}
2 & -1 & 2 & 3\\
3 & 2 & -1 & 1\\
1 & 2 & 1 & 2
\end{pmatrix} \rightarrow j_1[11:4:21:-20],
$$

and that I_1 and j_1 are incident. Let I_2 be the intersection of α_1, α_3, α_4, and j_2 the join of A_1, A_3, A_4. Then I_2 and j_2 are incident. Also, I_3 and j_3 are incident, as are I_4 and j_4, where I_3, I_4, j_3, j_4 are defined in an obvious manner. (The two tetrahedrons $A_1, \cdots, A_4$ and $\alpha_1, \cdots, \alpha_4$ determine an interesting configuration in S_3 called the configuration of Möbius, who discovered it in 1828. Each tetrahedron is both inscribed and circumscribed to the other. No such analogous configuration exists relative to triangles in S_2.) (c) By the incidence condition in a null polarity in S_3 show that any tetrahedron $A_1A_2A_3A_4$ and its polar tetrahedron $\alpha_1\alpha_2\alpha_3\alpha_4$ is a Möbius configuration.

15. In a manner similar to the development following equation (60) relative to binary quadratic forms, discuss the geometry of binary cubic forms by using loci in S_3.

16. (a) Find canonical equations of a collineation which leaves four points P_1, P_2, P_3, P_4 fixed. (b) Find the collineation for which every point of the line P_1P_2 and every point of the line P_3P_4 is fixed. (c) Find the collineation of the type in part (b) which carries any point P into its harmonic conjugate with respect to the points on P_1P_2 and P_3P_4 which are collinear with P. This involutory collineation is a *skew* involution with the lines P_1P_2 and P_3P_4 as its *axes*.

17. Let the points H, K have orthogonal cartesian coordinates x_1^i, x_2^i, where $x_1^4 = x_2^4 = 1$. Show that the line coordinates of HK can be separated into two sets, with p^{23}, p^{31}, p^{12} giving the components of the cross product of the vectors $\overrightarrow{OH}$ and $\overrightarrow{OK}$, where O is the origin, and p^{14}, p^{24}, p^{34} the components of the vector $\overrightarrow{OH} - \overrightarrow{OK}$. What is the vector form of the quadratic relation $\omega(p) = 0$?

18. Read the paper entitled "On representation of circles by means of points in space of three dimensions" by D. Pedoe in the *Mathematical Gazette*, Vol. 21, 1937, pp. 210–215.

10-9. Affine and euclidean specializations in S_3

The specialization of the projective group in the plane by which one line was required to map into itself produced the subgroup of the projective group called the affine group, or the group of affinities. In a similar way, n-dimensional affine geometry is obtained from projective geometry in S_n by requiring that a single hyperplane map into itself. In S_3 the fixed plane may be represented by $x^4 = 0$. Points of this plane are not in the affine space. Hence, for affine geometry x^4 may always be taken as 1. Under the collineation (5), with $k = 3$, the plane $x^4 = 0$ maps into $\bar{x}^4 = 0$ if and only if $a_1^4 = a_2^4 = a_3^4 = 0$, with $a_4^4 \neq 0$. Therefore, a point with affine coordinates x^i, for $i = 1, 2, 3$, maps into a point $\bar{x}^i$ in the affine space by the collineation

(78) $$\bar{x}^i = a_j^i x^j + b^i, \qquad |a_j^i| \neq 0,\ i, j = 1, 2, 3.$$

The reader may verify that if *every* point $(\lambda:\mu:\nu:0)$ of the plane $x^4 = 0$ is a fixed point under the mapping (5), then the corresponding affine mapping (78) takes the form

(79) $$\bar{x}^i = a x^i + b^i, \qquad i = 1, 2, 3.$$

If $a \neq 1$, there is one fixed point in the affine space given by

$$x^i = a x^i + b^i,$$

but if $a = 1$, there is no fixed point in the affine space. Equations (79) define a similitude if $a \neq 1$, and a *translation* if $a = 1$.

Parallel lines in affine space all contain a single point of the plane $x^4 = 0$, and parallel planes all contain a single line in $x^4 = 0$. Because parallel lines map into parallel lines, and parallel planes into parallel planes, it is seen that parallelism is an invariant. Affine geometry is the study of invariants of configurations under the affine mapping (78).

A quadric surface in affine space can be classified according to the nature of its intersection with the plane $x^4 = 0$. For instance, a real ellipsoid is a quadric with nonreal rulings which does not intersect the plane $x^4 = 0$, but a hyperboloid of two sheets has nonreal rulings and intersects $x^4 = 0$ in a conic. If the quadric has real rulings and intersects $x^4 = 0$ in a conic, it is a hyperboloid of one sheet. The elliptic paraboloids (nonreal rulings) and hyperbolic paraboloids (real rulings) are tangent to the plane $x^4 = 0$. A *center* of an affine quadric is the pole of the plane $x^4 = 0$ relative to the quadric.

The Euclidean Case

A specialization of the affine mapping (78) will now be required in order to achieve the mappings of euclidean space. Let it be demanded that the sum

$$(80) \qquad \sum_{i=1}^{3} (x_1^i - x_2^i)^2 \equiv \delta_{ij}(x_1^i - x_2^i)(x_1^j - x_2^j)$$

be invariant under the mapping (78) for every pair of points x_1^i and x_2^i in the affine space. Observe that each member of (80) is the square of the distance between two points of space for a particular choice of coordinates—namely, orthogonal cartesian coordinates. For a different choice of coordinates the corresponding form of the metric would be required to be invariant. One has from (80), and by use of (78),

$$\delta_{ij}(\bar{x}_1^i - \bar{x}_2^i)(\bar{x}_1^j - \bar{x}_2^j) = \delta_{ij}(a_k^i x_1^k - a_k^i x_2^k)(a_l^j x_1^l - a_l^j x_2^l)$$

$$= \delta_{ij} a_k^i a_l^j (x_1^k - x_2^k)(x_1^l - x_2^l) \equiv \delta_{kl}(x_1^k - x_2^k)(x_1^l - x_2^l),$$

from which

$$(81) \qquad \delta_{ij} a_k^i a_l^j = \delta_{kl}.$$

Equation (81) implies that the sum of the squares of the elements of any row of the matrix (a_j^i) is unity, and that the inner product of any two rows is zero. By taking the determinant of both sides of (81) it appears that

$$|a_j^i|^2 = |\delta_{kl}| = 1,$$

so that

$$(82) \qquad |a_j^i| = \pm 1.$$

The conditions (81) require that (a_j^i) in (78) be an orthogonal matrix. The mapping (78), with (81) satisfied, and with $|a_j^i|$ in (82) equal to $+1$, effects rotations and translations in euclidean space. If $|a_j^i| = -1$, the rotation is followed by a reflection in one of the coordinate planes. Thus, it is evident that the motions in euclidean space form a subgroup of the affinities, which, in turn, constitute a subgroup of the projectivities in S_3.

One method of classifying quadrics metrically is by use of a fundamental sys-

tem composed of four invariants and three covariants of the quadric $a_{ij}x^ix^j = 0$.*
Another method is to employ the *absolute conic* in the plane $x^4 = 0$. (It should
be realized that the plane $x^4 = 0$ is not a part of euclidean three-space. Neverthe-
less, it is a useful adjunct for interpretation and classification of configurations
in euclidean space.) The absolute cone in the plane $x^4 = 0$ is a generalization
of the circular points $I(1:i:0)$ and $J(1:-i:0)$ in the plane. It was shown in
Section 6-5 that all circles in the plane contain the I and J points. Consider the
sphere with equation $x^2 + y^2 + z^2 = R^2$, or

$$(x^1)^2 + (x^2)^2 + x^{3^2} - R^2(x^4)^2 = 0$$

in homogeneous coordinates. The plane $x^4 = 0$ intersects the sphere in the
locus

(83) $$x^4 = 0, \quad (x^1)^2 + (x^2)^2 + (x^3)^2 = 0$$

which is called the *absolute conic* (an appellation appropriate to projective
geometry), or the *circle at infinity* (which has a metric connotation). It can be
shown that all spheres in space contain the locus (83), and also that the absolute conic is invariant under the projectivities which satisfy (81). (See Exercises 1 and 2.)

A complete classification of quadrics in S_3 is not given here. However, the
tetrahedron of reference for a few canonical forms will be described.

The canonical equation of the ellipsoid $a^2x^2 + b^2y^2 + c^2z^2 = 1$ is

$$a^2x^{1^2} + b^2x^{2^2} + c^2x^{3^2} - x^{4^2} = 0$$

in homogeneous coordinates. The plane $x^4 = 0$ intersects the quadric in the
conic

(84) $$x^4 = 0, \quad a^2x^{1^2} + b^2x^{2^2} + c^2x^{3^2} = 0.$$

The conics (83) and (84) determine a pencil of conics which have a unique
common self-polar triangle, the vertices of which may be given the coordinates
$P_1(1:0:0:0)$, $P_2(0:1:0:0)$, $P_3(0:0:1:0)$. The fourth vertex $P_4(0:0:0:1)$ of the
tetrahedron of reference is at the center of the ellipsoid. Note that the center
is the pole of the plane $x^4 = 0$. (The center of any central quadric is defined as
the pole of the plane at infinity.)

Condition for Perpendicularity

In order to complete the description of the self-polar tetrahedron of reference
for the ellipsoid, the condition for orthogonality of two lines in S_3 is needed.
Consider first the *isotropic cone* through the point $F(a^i)$ in S_3. It is defined as
the set of lines through a^i and points of the absolute conic. Let $A(x_0^1:x_0^2:x_0^3:0)$
be a point on the absolute; that is, $(x_0^1)^2 + (x_0^2)^2 + (x_0^3)^2 = 0$. Any point $P(x^i)$
on the join of F and A has coordinates

---

* An explanation of this method was given by L. J. Paradiso, "A classification of second-
degree loci of space," *Am. Math. Monthly*, Vol. 33, 1926, p. 406.

(85) $x^i = a^i + \lambda x_0^i,$ $i = 1, \cdots, 4.$

Eliminate λ by use of the equation of the absolute to obtain

(86) $(x^1 - a^1)^2 + (x^2 - a^2)^2 + (x^3 - a^3)^2 = 0$

as the equation of the isotropic cone with the vertex at a^i. Observe that the
quadric (86) may be interpreted either as a real sphere with radius zero or as
an imaginary cone with real vertex.

Next, notice in equations (85) that the point x_0^i, with $i = 1, 2, 3$, in the plane
at infinity (whether it is on the absolute or not) determines a direction; that is,
the x_0^i are proportional to $x^i - a^i$. The condition that two points l^i and m^i
be conjugate relative to the absolute is that $l^1 m^1 + l^2 m^2 + l^3 m^3 = 0$, but this
is the condition that two lines in S_3 with direction numbers l^i and m^i be perpendicular. (The reader may now show that a line and a plane in S_3 are perpendicular if the point at infinity on the line and the line at infinity on the
plane are pole and polar relative to the absolute; see Exercise 3.)

To return to the ellipsoid, it is readily verified that the directions of the edges
$P_4 P_1$, $P_4 P_2$, $P_4 P_3$ of the tetrahedron of reference are mutually perpendicular.
This is true because these lines meet the plane $x^4 = 0$ in conjugate points relative to the absolute.

Diametral Planes

The direction of a set of parallel chords of the ellipsoid determines a point M
in the plane $x^4 = 0$. The polar plane of M with respect to the ellipsoid is the
locus of the midpoints of the set of parallel chords. This locus is called the
diametral plane of the ellipsoid relative to the direction given by M. Any set of
parallel chords has a diametral plane. Diametral planes that are perpendicular
to the chords which they bisect are called *principal planes* of the quadric. The
three vertices of the unique self-polar triangle relative to (83) and (84) determine
the three principal systems of parallel chords, and therefore the three principal
planes relative to the ellipsoid.

From the foregoing discussion it is evident that the coordinate planes $x^1 = 0$,
$x^2 = 0$, $x^3 = 0$ are three faces of the tetrahedron of reference, and $x^4 = 0$ is
the fourth face. If the canonical form $a^2 x^2 + b^2 y^2 + c^2 z^2 = 1$ is subjected to a
translation and rotation of axes, the planes $x^1 = 0$, $x^2 = 0$, $x^3 = 0$ assume
different forms, but the plane $x^4 = 0$ remains invariant. Conversely, if the
general equation of an ellipsoid is given, the equations of its principal planes
can be found as the polars of the vertices of the self-polar triangle of the absolute and the intersection of the quadric with $x^4 = 0$. Any central quadric
can be treated in the manner described for the ellipsoid.

EXAMPLE

Find the principal planes of the quadric

$$x^2 + y^2 + z^2 - xy + xz - yz - 2y - 2z + 2 = 0.$$

Solution: Introduce powers of w to obtain the homogeneous form

$$x^2 + y^2 + z^2 - xy + xz - yz - 2yw - 2zw + 2w^2 = 0.$$

Solve the latter equation with $w = 0$ to find the conic

$$C: \qquad w = 0, \quad x^2 + y^2 + z^2 - xy + xz - yz = 0,$$

which can be shown to be nonreal. The conic C and the absolute determine the pencil of conics

$$x^2 + y^2 + z^2 + 2\lambda(-xy + xz - yz) = 0, \quad w = 0,$$

and the values of λ which yield the composite conics of the pencil are given by

$$\begin{vmatrix} 1 & -\lambda & \lambda \\ -\lambda & 1 & -\lambda \\ \lambda & -\lambda & 1 \end{vmatrix} = 0,$$

or $2\lambda^3 - 3\lambda^2 + 1 = 0$ which has the roots $1, 1, -\frac{1}{2}$. The composite conics are given by $(x - y + z)^2 = 0$ (counted twice) and by two complex lines which intersect in the point $(1:-1:1:0)$. The vertices of a self-polar triangle relative to the absolute can be taken then as $(1:-1:1:0)$ and any two points on $x - y + z = 0$ which are conjugate relative to the absolute, such as $(1:1:0:0)$ and $(1:-1:-2:0)$. The polar planes of the three vertices of the self-polar triangle in $w = 0$ relative to the given quadric are

$$x - y + z = 0, \quad x + y - 2 = 0, \quad x - y - 2z + 6 = 0,$$

and these are the principal planes of the quadric. Their intersection is the point $(0, 2, 2)$, the center of the quadric.

The quadric is evidently an ellipsoid, the lengths of the axes of which can be found by solving for the intercepts of the principal axes (intersections of the principal planes) with the quadric. These are found to be 1, 4, 4. The equation

$$4\left(\frac{x - y + z}{\sqrt{3}}\right)^2 + \left(\frac{x - y - 2z + 6}{\sqrt{6}}\right)^2 + \left(\frac{x + y - 2}{\sqrt{2}}\right)^2 = 4$$

is another form of the given equation of the ellipsoid.

The Hyperbolic Paraboloid

The surface with the equation

$$a^2x^2 - b^2y^2 + 2z = 0$$

intersects the plane $w = 0$ in the composite conic

$$C: \qquad w = 0, \qquad a^2x^2 - b^2y^2 = 0.$$

The three composite members of the pencil

$$a^2x^2 - b^2y^2 + \lambda(x^2 + y^2 + z^2) = 0$$

are obtained by using $\lambda = 0$, $\lambda = b^2$, $\lambda = -a^2$, and the self-polar triangle of the absolute and the conic C is found to have the vertices $P_1(1:0:0:0)$, $P_2(0:1:0:0)$, $P_3(0:0:1:0)$. The polar plane of P_1 relative to the given hyperbolic paraboloid is $x = 0$, that of P_2 is $y = 0$, that of P_3 is $w = 0$, and that of $P_4(0:0:0:1)$ is

$z = 0$. Hence, the coordinate planes and the plane at infinity constitute the tetrahedron of reference. The surface is tangent to one face of the reference tetrahedron at P_4.

The canonical forms of the remaining types of quadrics can be studied in a similar manner, to determine the relation of the tetrahedron of reference to the surface. Some instances are found in the exercises. A few exercises are supplied to suggest further extensions to three-space of results obtained in previous chapters for the plane.

EXERCISES

1. Show that all spheres in S_3 contain the absolute conic (83).

2. Show by use of the absolute that the principal planes of a sphere are indeterminate.

3. Prove that a line l and a plane p in S_3 are perpendicular if and only if the intersections of l and p with the plane at infinity are pole and polar relative to the absolute.

4. Show that the tetrahedron of reference for the real quadric cone $a^2x^2 + b^2y^2 - c^2z^2 = 0$ has the three coordinate planes and the plane at infinity for its faces.

5. Supply the details to verify the statement following equation (78).

6. The principal planes of a quadric with center at the origin are the opposite faces of the vertices $P_1(1:0:0:0)$, $P_2(0:1:0:0)$, $P_3(0:0:1:0)$ in the tetrahedron of reference. What is the effect of a rotation of the axes about the origin on the given vertices?

7. *Tetrahedra with the property of Desargues.* Prove that if the four lines joining corresponding vertices of two tetrahedra are concurrent, then the corresponding faces intersect in lines which are coplanar.*

8. Generalize Section 8-10 to quadrics and tensors.†

9. Show that the cone $\alpha x^2 + \beta y^2 + \gamma z^2 = 0$ has three mutually perpendicular generators (and therefore a singly infinite set of such), if and only if $\alpha + \beta + \gamma = 0$. (See Exercise 19 on p. 189.) *Suggestion:* The problem reduces to that of finding a condition under which a triangle inscribed in the conic $w = 0$, $\alpha x^2 + \beta y^2 + \gamma z^2 = 0$ is self-polar relative to the absolute $w = 0$, $x^2 + y^2 + z^2 = 0$. For this, use the invariant $A^{ij}b_{ij}$ of Section 8-8.

10. Find a necessary and sufficient condition under which the cone

$$ax^2 + by^2 + cz^2 + 2fyz + 2gzx + 2hxy = 0$$

has three mutually perpendicular generators.

11. Find a geometric meaning of the vanishing of the trace $a_{11} + a_{22} + a_{33}$ of the symmetric matrix (a_{ij}), where $i, j = 1, 2, 3$.

---

* For this and related problems see N. Altshiller-Court, *Modern Pure Solid Geometry* (Macmillan, New York, 1935).

† See D. M. Y. Sommerville, *Analytical Geometry of Three Dimensions* (Cambridge University Press, 1934), Chapter 15.

12. Show that the cone in Exercise 10 has three mutually perpendicular tangent planes if and only if $bc + ca + ab = f^2 + g^2 + h^2$.

13. Find a geometric meaning of the vanishing of the trace of the matrix (A^{ij}) of the cofactors of the symmetric matrix (a_{ij}) in Exercise 11.

Index

DATE DUE

GAYLORD			PRINTED IN U.S.A.